Neurons and Symbols

CHAPMAN & HALL NEURAL COMPUTING SERIES

Series editors: Igor Aleksander, Imperial College, London, UK
Richard Mammone, Rutgers University, New Jersey, USA

Since the beginning of the current revival of interest in Neural Networks, the subject is reaching considerable maturity, while at the same time becoming of interest to people working in an increasing number of disciplines. This series seeks to address some of the specializations that are developing through the contributions of authoritative writers in the field. This series will address both specializations and applications of neural computing techniques to particular areas.

Neurons and Symbols

The stuff that mind is made of

Igor Aleksander
Department of Electrical Engineering
Inperial College of Science, Technology and Medicine
London
UK

and

Helen Morton
Department of Human Sciences
Brunel University
Uxbridge
UK

CHAPMAN & HALL
London · Glasgow · New York · Tokyo · Melbourne · Madras

Published by Chapman & Hall, 2–6 Boundary Row, London SE1 8HN

Chapman & Hall, 2–6 Boundary Row, London SE1 8HN, UK

Blackie Academic & Professional, Wester Cleddens Road, Bishopbriggs, Glasgow G64 2NZ, UK

Chapman & Hall Inc., 29 West 35th Street, New York NY10001, USA

Chapman & Hall Japan, Thomson Publishing Japan, Hirakawacho Nemoto Building, 6F, 1–7–11 Hirakawa-cho, Chiyoda-ku, Tokyo 102, Japan

Chapman & Hall Australia, Thomas Nelson Australia, 102 Dodds Street, South Melbourne, Victoria 3205, Australia

Chapman & Hall India, R. Seshadri, 32 Second Main Road, CIT East, Madras 600 035, India

First edition 1993

© 1993 Igor Aleksander and Helen Morton

Typeset in 10/12 Times by Mews Photosetting, Beckenham
Printed in Great Britain by Hartnolls Ltd, Bodmin, Cornwall

ISBN 0 412 46090 4

A catalogue record for this book is available from the British Library

Library of Congress Cataloging-in-Publication data available

♾ Printed on permanent acid-free text paper, manufactured in accordance with the proposed ANSI/NISO Z 39.48–199X and ANSI Z 39.48–1984

Contents

Preface

The object of this book is to present, from first principles, both old and new models of thinking which do not require specialist knowledge of philosophy, psychology, computer engineering or mathematics, although the discussions in the book contain elements of all of these.

We are interested in the way that connectionism, or the study of artificial neural systems, has affected and is likely to affect some of the existing arguments in cognitive science (the science of thought). The point of view we take is that the addition of neural systems extends older models and that connectionism will redirect the course of cognitive science. To this end we take a somewhat unusual stance in trying to discuss existing cognitive science *and* neural systems from the perspective of the same model – a device we have called the 'Neural State Machine Model' (NSMM). Because a 'state machine' is an element in 'automata theory', or the theory of devices with hidden mechanisms, we include a chapter concerned with basic principles of this body of knowledge. We also cover some of the principles of artificial intelligence, as these have become the cornerstone of symbolic cognitive modelling.

While hoping that the level of first principles which we have selected will hold the interest of the expert without losing the attention of the newcomer, we realize that such an aim cannot be achieved perfectly. Nevertheless, we hope that each can find something of interest, even if it means picking and choosing among the chapters of the book. The book is structured as shown in Figure 0.1. and written so that it can be read at different levels of depth.

Chapter 1 is written to give an overview of the issues covered in the whole book. Each subsequent chapter (X) has an introductory part (X.1) which reviews the issues discussed in the chapter. Also, there are two chapters that are entirely introductory and may be skipped by experts. Cognitive scientists may wish to ignore Chapter 4, while AI specialists could skip Chapter 3. Other chapters, while introductory in nature, contain elements of our own point of view. Chapter 2, for example, is an introduction to connectionism,

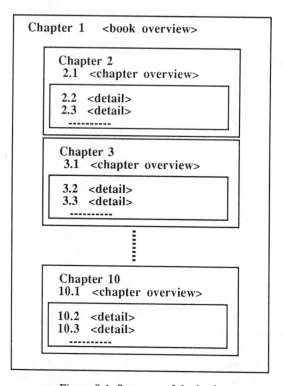

Figure 0.1 *Structure of the book.*

but even experts may wish to read it as we have developed a simplified description which is free of technical detail (such as weight optimization techniques or the headaches of error back-propagation) so as to make it more readily usable in cognitive modelling. Similarly, while Chapter 5 is largely devoted to classical automata theory (and hence well known to some computer scientists and mathematicians), we have looked at this topic with neural systems in mind in a way that the computer formalist may find interesting.

In Chapter 6 we look afresh at the debate that has arisen between 'connectionists' and 'classicists' so that, in Chapter 7, we can outline the 'neural state machine model' leading, in Chapters 8 to 10, to a framework for the study of cognitive science which we think is novel. The basis of this is to seek a rapprochement between the extremes of connectionist methods and artificial intelligence techniques. It also involves the bringing together of language understanding and scene understanding techniques through a mechanism where the two aid one another.

While the approach is blatantly speculative, we hope that it points to new research directions which will benefit from the involvement of cognitive scientists, psychologists, neurophysiologists, philosophers, computing specialists, information engineers and mathematicians.

Igor Aleksander
Helen Morton

1

Introduction: the stuff that mind is made of

Of string, sealing wax, battles, neurons and symbols . . .

1.1 String, sealing wax, neurons and symbols

The central idea is simple. If putting together some bits of string and sealing wax results in a creation that in some sense can be said to have the ability to 'think', not only is this device a thinking machine, but also it explains, albeit in terms of string and sealing wax, what 'thinking' might be. Whether this philosophy appeals or not, it is, in caricature, the approach that is taken in cognitive science. The word 'cognition' for most purposes is the same as the word 'thought' and the bits of string and sealing wax of the present day are neurons and symbols. In particular, artificial neurons are the latest arrivals in the toolbox of the maker of thinking machines. They are also closer to what real brains are made of, so the idea that an explanation of real thinking is being provided becomes increasingly appealing and even quite plausible.

But the story is not so simple. It embraces the well-trodden debates of philosophers, linguists and computer scientists about what are and what are not legitimate explanations of brain, mind and the relationship between the two. The serious consideration of neural networks is a phenomenon of the 1980s, and is in the process of finding a place in the intricate framework of disciplines that make up the modelling of 'thought'. In the chapters that follow, we tell a story normally written in the languages of mathematics, psychology and philosophy. In order not to rely on an intimate knowledge of any of these specialisms, we attempt to look at this tale from first principles.

The issue is whether neural systems increase our understanding of cognition or not (of course artificial neurons may be just as alien to the real mechanisms of brain and mind as string and sealing wax). We begin by stating, in the simplest possible terms, what a neuron is, what a symbol is, what the

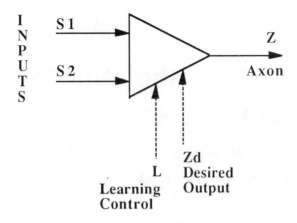

Figure 1.1 *A stripped-down neuron.*

aspirations are for the way that explanations of cognition can be based on these two and what the relationship between them could be.

Put simply, an artificial neuron is an element of information storage, an atom of memory as it were. In Figure 1.1 it is illustrated as having inputs ('synapses' in live neurons) and an output (equivalent to an 'axon'). In general, the neuron generates a signal at the axon which we call Z. It is best to think of this simply as a number. The synapses, S1, S2, . . . receive similar signals from other neurons, or from the senses (ears, eyes etc.). Learning is caused by two further controls: L and Zd. Zd is the desired value of the output, and L is a control which, when energized in some way, causes Zd to be associated with whatever the values of S1, S2, . . . are at the time.

A symbol, on the other hand, is a mathematical device, usually thought to be part of some logical statement such as

'If A is true and B is true then C is true.'

A, B, and C are the symbols in this expression. In this case such symbols are not general numbers: each can only have one of two values – 'true' and 'false'. A study of what can and cannot be expressed by statements of the above kind is the mathematical topic of *logic*.

So the above terse descriptions lay bare the kind of string and sealing wax out of which models of thinking or cognition will have to emerge. The neuron scientist hopes to explain things by looking at assemblies of neurons and finding the characteristics of cognitive events (e.g. the ability to understand language, or recognize images). The logician hopes to explain the same events through the use of assemblies of logical statements. They are both helped by the presence of computer technology. Neural networks can be simulated on computers, or built using much the same silicon technology that goes into conventional computers. A large assembly of logic statements is merely a program for a computer.

In fact, what is now called cognitive science owes much to the existence of computers (Gardner, 1987), and the medium in which cognition is often expressed is that of the 'algorithm' (i.e. a sequence of logical statements involving symbols that could be turned into a computer program). So, at the outset, these two approaches appear to have very different characteristics. The neural approach seems to be set to cast explanations at a level close to some brain mechanism, while the symbolic technique seems to be appropriate to simulations on a computer of the imagined algorithms of cognition.

The points we make in several parts of the book are that these two approaches are not as incompatible as they seem, and that they each have useful properties not possessed by the other. This leads to the notion of bringing the two together in hybrid models of cognition. To give an example we note that the neuron, as simply described above, performs a general logical function:

'If S1, S2, ... then Zd.'

Therefore the difference between the two approaches may occur not in *what* is being done, but more in *how* it is done. The logical approach requires that some designer or programmer works out the logical expressions of some cognitive event, while the neurophile will require that these logical functions be learned. While this immediately conjures up the 'nurture–nature' debate when human minds are being discussed, it is clear that a good model of cognition could contain both approaches – some things are innate and some things are learned. The use of the word 'hybrid' is intended to refer precisely to this collaborative form of arrangement.

Having marked out some of the territory of this book, it is now possible to take a brief anticipatory look at some of the deeper issues that make up the chapters which follow.

1.2 Connectionist euphoria: the return of neurons

The resurgence of interest in artificial neural systems stemmed from the growing realization among researchers that the AI paradigm was deficient in two major respects. Firstly, in concentrating primarily on the end result rather than the process, and thereby largely excluding the consideration both of the mechanisms involved and of human learning, AI models were clearly not addressing the issue of explaining the nature of human thought. Moreover, even the performance of AI models was too poor to marry with the good performance of the human brain. A paper by Hopfield (1982) and the collective writing of the US Parallel Distributed Processing (PDP) group (Rumelhart and McClelland, 1986) were the catalysts that brought like-minded individuals together, and focused attention on the hitherto largely neglected half century of work of those with an interest in the formal description of actual brain mechanisms. There was a powerful upsurge of interest in artificial neural mechanisms and, possibly, some misplaced euphoria.

But connectionism is no longer a novelty. In Chapter 2 we present not only the classical view of connectionist techniques, but concentrate also on those recent developments which are already beginning to make an impact on cognitive science. It was Minsky and Papert's criticisms which put paid to neural system research in the USA in the late 1960s, so it is worth understanding how it was that the multi-layer structures of Rumelhart and his colleagues and the dynamic networks of Hopfield demonstrated that Minksy and Papert's objections were based on a restricted class of neural networks and therefore largely invalid.

One of the points we make in Chapter 7 is that an element missing in both the connectionist way of doing things and in artificial intelligence is some measure of the competence of the structures and algorithms that are being held up as cognitive models. Competence is more than just a question of performance. A chess-playing program may beat the average player simply because it runs on a super-fast microprocessor. Its program, however, could be quite simple minded and be based on exhaustive searching techniques. Some cognitive scientists may accept that this program is a model of the cognition that goes into chess-playing. This would be on the basis that it is better than no model at all and that, since it is symbolic, it is fully explained. But any self-respecting chess players on seeing the details of how the program works would deride the idea that this has anything to do with the way that they and their opponents play chess.

Connectionists too fall into this trap. Right from the start the PDP group has been at pains to argue that PDP systems have some sort of physiological plausibility, and that the group is interested in ' . . . computationally sufficient and psychologically accurate mechanistic accounts of the phenomena of human cognition which have eluded successful explication in conventional computational formalisms . . . ' (Rumelhart and McClelland, 1986, p. 11). Rumelhart and McClelland go on to say that artificial neural networks add the property of learning and parallel processing to the toolbox of the cognitive modeller. However, if a chess-playing program were to be based on a neural net rather than the algorithm mentioned above, this could equally be rejected by the human player as not being a model of his thinking – for reasons which will become clear later. So what is the value of the word 'mechanistic' in the quote above?

The view taken in the descriptions of connectionism in Chapter 2 is that the way in which the brain achieves its competence is important. To illustrate this we relate a demonstration that was carried out during the early development of WISARD-like systems. These systems (which will be described in Chapter 7) are large neural nets that have only one layer and are shown in very broad principle in Figure 1.2. This consists of three groups of neurons.

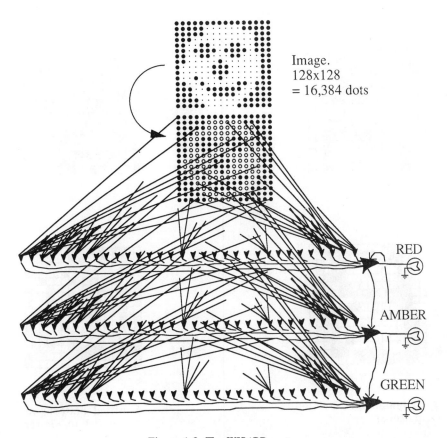

Image.
128x128
= 16,384 dots

Figure 1.2 *The WISARD system.*

Each group is made to sample an image made up of black and white dots (in this case representing a face). Each group controls a light – red, amber or green. The essence of a neural net such as this is that it can be trained to respond to different categories of input images by giving different outputs. In this case, one group of neurons is trained to turn on the green light when it 'sees' a smiling face. Another group is trained to turn on the red light when the face is frowning. The third group turns on the amber light when there is no face present.

The WISARD is also capable of learning to recognize hand-printed characters, and the object of another demonstration was to compare the ability of the artificial system with that of humans. The testing procedure started with a collection of many As and Bs written by different people on a 16×16 grid. However, in order to be able to study learning ability in a fair way, the features of the patterns that are well known to humans were removed, so

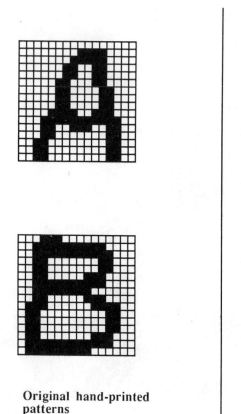

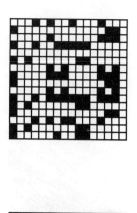

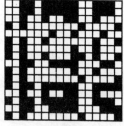

Original hand-printed
patterns

Shuffled patterns as
presented to viewers

Figure 1.3 *Shuffled presentations of As and Bs.*

that they did not look like letters of the alphabet at all. This was done by
shuffling the picture points on a 16×16 grid around, but in the same way
for each image presented. Typical presentations of handwritten As and Bs
are shown in Figure 1.3.

As the connections to the WISARD system are random, the shuffling of
the images seen by the subjects in this demonstration puts them on a par (of
no initial knowledge) with the machine. Both systems were asked to identify
the next image on a list, and the accuracy of a group of about 10 people was
noted, as was the response of the machine. Both are then told the real class
of the image just assessed – this is the training step. Both the machine and
the human subjects exhibit learning curves (accuracy against number of
learning presentations) of roughly the same shape. The size of the neurons

in WISARD was adjusted until the learning curves of humans and the machine matched. This occurred for a relatively modest size – four inputs per first-layer neuron (Aleksander and Fairhurst, 1970). But the main reason for mentioning this experiment here is that any conclusion about the resulting WISARD structure being a model of human powers was invalidated by the following observation.

At the end of a training run the human subjects were able to describe (by drawing) a prototype shuffled image that when unshuffled looked like an A in one case and a B in the other. No such trace could be extracted from the WISARD system, nor could it be found in any neural network model that has purely a feedforward mapping between a sensory area and a recognition of the data. The human clearly uses powers of internal visualization and the ability to refine mental prototypes of sensory events in order to recognize and classify new sensory input. In artificial neural nets such mental prototypes can only be created if the network has some internal feedback connections in which the mental prototypes can reside. These nets are called 'dynamic' (as opposed to 'static' for feedforward systems) or 'recursive'. Such dynamic nets also have the ability of recognizing sequences in time or generating sequences in time and are therefore more 'competent' in many cognitive contexts than static systems. The nature of such cognitive properties is the subject of Chapter 2.

1.3 Artificial intelligence – the house of symbols

Probably the most often quoted definition for artificial intelligence is 'doing on computers that which if done by humans, would be said to require intelligence'. What is not mentioned all that often is why should one do things on computers that are done perfectly well by humans. Traditionally, the answers given range from the need to make computers 'smarter' (whatever that might mean) to providing robots with greater autonomy than they are able to achieve through conventional programming. Some leading commentators (e.g. philosopher and psychologist Margaret Boden, 1977) hold the view that if a computer can be programmed to perform human-like tasks it offers a 'model' of the human activity that is less open to argument than the empirical explanations that are normal in philosophy and psychology. Indeed, in 1978, a colleague of Margaret Boden's at the University of Sussex, philosopher Aaron Sloman, was writing (in Gardner, 1987) that a philosopher who did not acquaint himself with the findings of artificial intelligence could be accused of professional incompetence.

It is these findings which, in our quest to investigate models of thinking, we shall pursue on Chapter 3. In fact, the achievements of artificial intelligence in practical applications are evidently limited and it is the impact that the field has had conceptually in the human sciences that appears to be more lasting in character. But even in this latter sense it is still important to ask how convincing and practical are the AI models of cognition and what the future of this purely symbolic pursuit might be.

While the debate on mechanized thinking is as old as attempts to design computing machines, the roots of practical artificial intelligence could be said to go back to very early attempts to prove that computers are capable of intelligent symbol manipulation as systems that could outwit humans in the playing of games such as chess and draughts (checkers) (Shannon, 1950; Samuel, 1959). This activity is popular as it provides an easy test: beat the human and you are more intelligent than the human (at playing that particular game anyway). While expert humans have proved rather more resilient than at first thought, it is worth asking whether the chess machine that one can now purchase for the price of a couple of novels and which can beat many average players tells us about human chess playing or not.

To debate this point it seems important to have some idea of how a machine works, and that will be explained in Chapter 3. But artificial intelligence is not only concerned with game playing. Curiously, the ability to see seems in humans not to require much intelligence. But in machines this has proved to be a difficult area and AI laboratories have embraced computer vision as a task that requires intelligence at least in some machine sense. In chapter 3 we shall trace the history of machine vision from algorithms that were mainly designed to identify surfaces and simple objects with flat surfaces. The pinnacle of this work is that of David Marr (1982), who sought to develop a complete theory of vision. This starts with the need to define transformations from the sort of data gathered by the cells in the retina to meaningful representations of the objects that create these sensations. At a time when neural approaches were far out of favour, Marr had the courage to make much reference to the operations of the cells in the visual system in the brain. While his work on sketch-like representations received a lot of attention from the research community, his ideas on three-dimensional representations remain largely unexplored, possibly due to his untimely death in 1983.

Another general direction taken by AI researchers is that of the human ability to solve problems. Probably one of the best known descriptions is the General Problem Solver designed by Allen Newell and Herb Simon (1972). This program was based in means–ends analysis and (together with game-playing problems) established that a computer could develop considerable prowess through being able to search very rapidly among many alternative choices. This turns out to be not only the main strength of a computer, but also a focus for questioning the validity of such programming as models of human thinking. Long searches do not seem as competent as the rapid insights that we often appear to have when solving problems. Exclusive reliance on exhaustive searches seems to be a poor basis for a model – we are just not aware of such procedures going on in our heads. Nevertheless, search is central to AI methodology and, in order to assess it properly, it is fully investigated in Chapter 3.

However, the enthusiasm for writing programs that solve problems gave impetus to the most lasting products of artificial intelligence – logic programming and expert systems. Logic programming is based on the use of tenets of symbolic logic as the operators available to the programmer to both state and solve problems: that is, it provides the link between programming and mathematical definitions of reasoning. This could be said to be the focus of the symbolic approach to cognitive models, and therefore deserves considerable attention in this book. Expert systems, while often using the medium of logic programming, provide a way of encapsulating human knowledge of a particular domain in a program and so provide a practical, symbolic way of representing aspects of cognition. These two concepts therefore feature strongly in Chapter 3.

But perhaps the most controversial product of artificial intelligence is the effort of AI scientists to find algorithms for natural language understanding. Clearly this is a key target for models of cognition, as the human ability to use language seems so central to human thinking processes. In Chapter 3 we look at an early proposal by Terry Winograd who, in 1972, developed a program for understanding natural language through which a robot can be instructed to handle a small set of simple objects. Despite the pioneering nature of this work, researchers have found it difficult to extend the method to a broader range of linguistic activities. Indeed, philosopher John Searle (1980) has questioned whether this could ever be done. At the end of Chapter 3, we look at the controversy which has arisen on this point. Searle rejects the idea that a computer could be programmed to understand language, but we ask whether, using a neural system, this feat could be accomplished through learning.

1.4 Cognition: a symbolic science?

In Chapter 4 we provide a commentary of what is now called the field of cognitive science. The term finds a variety of different interpretations, and the task in the context of this book is to highlight the achievements of scientific analysis in this area, and to identify the scope for further advancement in view of the advent of neurally based investigations.

Most will agree that the words 'cognitive science' refer to a relatively recent phenomenon. They began to be used together in the 1970s. There is also general agreement that the existence of the computer, particularly when used to test ideas in artificial intelligence, is a central figure in the expression of ideas in cognitive science. This creates a distinction from fields such as cognitive psychology, but shares with cognitive psychology a concern for the proper acknowledgement of mental states. There is a further degree of agreement between exponents of cognitive science – that the foundations of that which is being modelled are deeply intertwined with philosophy. The concerns of cognitive scientists, though tackled with computing tools of enormous power, are virtually indistinguishable from those of Plato and Aristotle. This consideration has led Gardner (1987) to define cognitive science as 'a contemporary, empirically based effort to answer long-standing epistemological questions – particularly those concerned with the nature of knowledge, its components, its sources, its development and its deployment.

Though the roots of cognitive science may lie in the philosophy of ancient Greece, in Chapter 4 we concentrate on the effect that the more recent phenomenon of computational science has had on this endeavour. This brings together topics enunciated in other parts of the book – artificial intelligence, neuroscience and mathematical linguistics. A central question is, given that computing has a crucial role to play in the modelling of cognitive events, how deeply ingrained is cognitive science in the methods of conventional computing (as contrasted with neural computing)? To answer this we look at two factors – the relationship between conventional and neural computing on the one hand, and the way in which the models of AI became adopted as the basis for cognitive science.

The history of interdisciplinary studies in the area between brain sciences and computing theory probably starts in the meetings between life scientists and mathematicians which took place at the Harvard Medical School and at MIT and are described by Norbert Wiener in his book *Cybernetics* (1948). While cybernetics became defined as the 'science of control and communication in humans and machines', it is clear that both styles of computation were part of the discourse as potential materials for the modelling of the mechanisms possessed by living organisms. This group at times included MIT physiologist Warren McCulloch and logician Walter Pitts, who discussed their work on neuron models in the same frame as John Von Neumann's work on computer structure. The former work is now recognized as the root of neural computing, while the latter is the basis of current conventional computer architectures. So in 1947 there was little or no division between these two approaches in attempts to develop a scientific basis for investigating the faculties of living beings. Gardner (1987) confirms this view by referring to the Hixon symposium which took place at the California Institute of Technology in 1948. Here, too, Warren McCulloch and John Von Neumann presented computational explanations of the way that the brain might process information. But perhaps the most important facet of the Hixon symposium was psychologist Karl Lashley's attack on behaviourism. He argued that behaviourism had ignored the importance of the organization of language. This link between language and mentation is central to the concerns of cognitive science, and, as we shall see in Chapters 6 and 7, is now the battleground between neural and conventional computer modelling styles. However, in 1948 the possibility of finding a new agenda based on the logic of neural models, the computer and the nature of human language was part of the beginning of one single new science – the science of cognition.

The parting of the ways between neural and conventional models of cognition is laid by many at the feet of MIT scientists Marvin Minsky and Seymour Papert (1969). They drew attention to the computational limitations of some configurations of neural networks. Things such as whether two blobs in an image are connected or not turned out to be an impossible task for the networks considered by Minsky and Papert. This was seen as a fatal flaw that would interfere with the programmer's freedom in expressing computational models. It is now clear that Minsky and Papert only considered a limited set of network structures, and the 'multi-layer perceptron', which is a general, albeit somewhat awkward, computing component, overcomes these objections, as later analyses have shown. But Minsky and Papert's influence was quite remarkable in the sense that research in neural modelling virtually ceased in the USA, and neural scientists were squeezed out of the computing arena in the 1970s. But interest in providing computational explanations of cognition was in the ascendant during this time, and it therefore is easy to understand that cognitive science became closely aligned with the artificial intelligence paradigm, relegating neural modelling to the level of the eccentric.

But, as we shall see, the 1980s led to a surprisingly vigorous revival of interest in neural modelling and much of this book is devoted to a survey of the way in which this now interacts with AI to advance cognitive science. But it is interesting to note that the centre of gravity of the contemporary view among the stalwarts of the AI era is (putting extremes aside) one of 'wait and see'. In a recent article, Margaret Boden (1991) refers to the AI effort as GOFAI – Good Old-Fashioned AI – and recognizes that this has common roots with neural models. She also notes that many of the early inspirations of GOFAI have not come to pass, while the range of skills of neural systems remains unproven. She likens the two to a troupe of actors which together put on a good act, but if only one had to be chosen she feels that GOFAI gives a more comprehensive performance. Our own view (mainly in Chapter 7) is that each of the methodologies yields a whole troupe of actors (each an algorithm with some reference to cognition) and that a good play can be put on by taking the best of each bunch.

1.5 Automata: the ghosts of all machines

While the word 'automaton' conjures up the image of a mechanical toy or a soulless organism, in computer science it has a very precise meaning. It refers to all machines whose output behaviour is not a direct consequence of the current input, but of some past history of its inputs. They are characterized as having an internal state which, in a way that we shall see in detail in Chapter 5, is a repository of this past experience. It is evident that there is a parallel between such an inner state, and whatever could be the meaning of the word 'thinking'. The inner state of an automaton is private to the automaton and not available to an external observer. This is surely true of

Figure 1.4 *Representation of a state transition.*

'thinking', and any attempt to understand this process should take note of automata theory. In fact, our attempt to reconcile neurons and symbols later in this book is based on some understanding of the theory of automata, outlined in Chapter 5.

One of the appealing aspects of this theory is that it is extraordinarily simple. It relies on the definition of a set of input events I1, I2, . . . and a set of output events Z1, Z2, . . ., and relates the two through the intervention of a set of internal states, Q1, Q2, ... This intervention takes the following form: every pair of elements, one taken from the set of inputs and the other from the set of internal states, represents a possible combination of a present input and a present state. Such a pair is related to a unique 'next' state. Outputs can be related directly to the internal states. In this way, the system arrives at an internal state through a chain of inputs, different chains leading to different states.

Some examples may help to clarify how the idea of an automaton may be used. Imagine that an operator on a production line is overseeing the production of widgets (W) and gadgets (G). These are produced singly, in sequences of one or two of the same product. So, should a sequence of three familiar objects be produced, the operator must remove the extra objects, as they may be faulty. One very handy aspect of automata, particularly where the set of states is finite (in which case the automaton is called a Finite State Machine), is that the function of the automaton can be represented by a diagram – the state transition diagram. This represents the states as circles and has arrows between the circles to indicate the transitions between states. These arrows are labelled with the input which is causing the transition. The output associated with each state is also shown as a state label.

So, if state Qj and input Ik result in the next state Qm where an output Zn occurs, this may be represented as shown in Figure 1.4.

Going back to our example, the complete description of an automaton that represents the tedious task done by the operator is shown in Figure 1.5. In terms of the description of an automaton given above, the set of states is {S, W1, W2, W3, G1, G2, G3,},
the set of inputs is {G,W} (related to a gadget or a widget being sensed) and the set of outputs is {N,Y} (related to No action being taken and Yes, the object is removed).

What has been said about input–state pairs leading to new states can be seen, for example, from the pair < W1,G > leading to G1 while < W1,W > leads to W2. The state diagram indicates that, starting in state S, an input W can

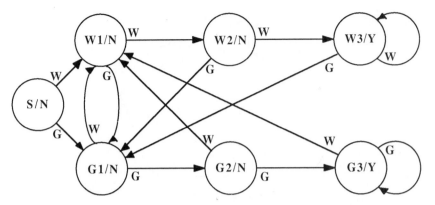

Figure 1.5 *Model of the production line task.*

occur twice before, occurring a third time, it reaches the state W3/Y where the system will remove the object. If at any time a gadget G occurs, the machine will move to state G1 where it will tolerate another G before the gadget is removed. In this way, once all the transitions have been specified, the complete action of what is required is specified. This demonstrates that such automata provide a way of describing fully an outward behaviour which is based in inward states.

In a rather superficial way, this also demonstrates the potential of automata to model some cognitive task. In fact, the example, again in a pretty trivial way, shows that the automaton can recognize sequences of input. It will be shown in Chapter 5 that this ability may be turned towards the recognition of properly formed linguistic sentences. As language, and even linguistic analyses of 'thought', are central tasks in cognitive modelling, Chapter 5 provides a full description of the formal automaton.

But there are other reasons for studying automata which relate to understanding neural networks. Finite state machines are the tools of the trade of the designer of information processing machines. In Chapter 5 we shall see how a specification of an automaton can be turned into hardware. While not wishing to dwell on the engineering of informational machinery, seeing state machines as models of the behaviour of circuits provides the link between the behaviour of a neural net, the structure of that net and the function of its neurons. This can be illustrated by means of a simple example of a network of three neurons, as shown in Figure 1.6.

The neurons are assumed to be binary – they either 'fire' (output a 1) or not (output a 0). Each neuron receives inputs from the other two and we assume that the neurons have learned to perform a simple task: if their two inputs agree (00 or 11), then the neuron does the agreed thing (outputs 0 or 1 respectively). However, if the two disagree, the neuron makes an arbitrary choice of outputting 0 or 1 with equal probability. So, for example, if the

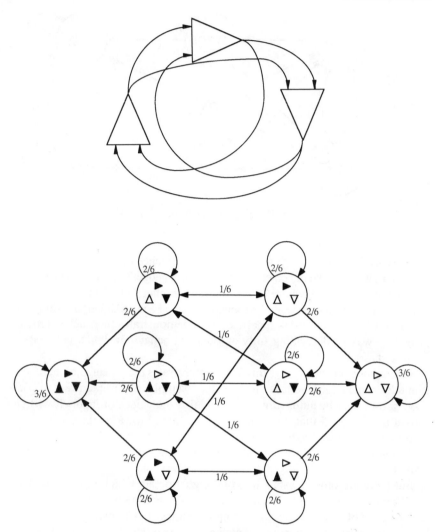

Figure 1.6 *A three-neuron network (top) and what it does.*

neurons are in the 000 state (i.e. all outputting a 0), this state recurs (as does the 111 state). However, if the state is 100 and (conventionally) it is assumed that only one neuron can act at one time (with equal probability of any one of the three neurons acting), the next state will be 000 if the first neuron acts, 100 or 110 with equal probability if the second neuron acts, and 100 or 101 with equal probability if the third neuron acts. Adding up all these probabilities we note that starting with 100 there is a 2/6 probability (about 33%) of returning to 100, 2/6 probability of transition to 000 and 1/6 probability of transition to each of the 110 and 101 states.

The complete behaviour of the system can be shown in the state diagram of Figure 1.6. Several things can be noted. Here there are no external inputs to the system and the transitions are merely labelled in terms of the probability of occurrence, so probabalistic behaviour is easily encompassed within automata theory. Also, the model in Figure 1.6 can be used to give insight into the behaviour of the net, as caused by the learned rules of the neurons (as mentioned above). It can be seen that the system will always settle in state 000 or 111. Also, the probability of starting in any state and ending in each of the two end states can be calculated. This shows that the starting state is more likely to lead to the end stable state to which it is more similar. This is one of the fundamental properties of interconnected neural nets ... but more of this in Chapter 5.

1.6 The great debate

It was Rumelhart's view that PDP theories could extend theories of cognition that started one of the major published debates in the history of cognitive science. (A previous one we have already referred to in Section 1.3 – it related to language understanding and the attack by philosopher John Searle on the ideas of AI researchers.) The view that Rumelhart expressed in the PDP books (quoted in section 1.2 above) gave rise to a skirmish between himself and one of Britain's pioneers in cognitive science, Donald Broadbent (Rumelhart and McClelland, 1985; Broadbent, 1985). Broadbent suggested that connectionism represented behaviour at what could be called an implementational (or physiological) level. He argued that this is an irrelevant way of providing explanations. In computing there are many levels of representation: some are about how the computer is wired (implementational), some are about what a computer can do (computational). A detailed description of the wiring and the content of a register inside a computer says very little about what the computer is actually doing at the time. To Broadbent it appears that concern with the state variations in dynamic neural nets, and with the learning of feedforward nets to recognize patterns, is the same kind of concern as with the operation of a computer register. It is important to know how registers work, and it is also important to know how algorithms work. Unfortunately, Broadbent believes, this will not play a part in a discussion of, say, what distinguishes a declarative program from an imperative one, which is an argument about what the computer is doing. (For those not familiar with computer science terminology, 'imperative' means spelling out the steps of a task for a computer, whereas 'declarative' means giving the computer general functions which it executes, such functions being parts of the whole task). Thus the computational representation is where arguments about these two different programming styles take place.

Perhaps an even stronger statement of this objection is that it would be harder to infer, from an understanding of the behaviour of a register, whether the machine is being used for running a program in computer vision or doing a word processing job. Rumelhart's reply is based on the interrelation between levels of explanation. He believes that there is a match between architecture and algorithm. Some architectures are more 'naturally' suited to some algorithms. In this sense, connectionist architectures, he argues, give rise to algorithms that are natural to those architectures, and if the architectures happen to be related to the structure of the brain then the resulting algorithms have greater value in cognitive science than arbitrary algorithms invented by a programmer. In Chapter 6 we shall look closely at the validity of some of these arguments, leading to the suggestion, in Chapter 7, that the difference between the two methods may be illusory.

The major battle of this war features Paul Smolensky (1988) of the University of Colorado on the side of connectionism and, in the opposing camp, Jerry Fodor of the City of New York Graduate Centre and Zenon Pylyshyn of the University of Western Ontario (1988). Smolensky introduced the concept of the 'subsymbolic' which is based on the notion that concepts in a neural net are represented in a distributed way. So if the state of a net is a symbol, the state of the neural nodes are 'subsymbols'. If a symbol is a concept then the values of the outputs of the neurons in the net are 'subconcepts'. The level of description, he argues, is intermediate between that of the neural circuit and the logical, symbolic, AI level.

The focus of considering connectionism at this subsymbolic level, according to Smolensky, is that neural systems being dynamic have properties that can, from the level of a higher perspective, be described by logical symbolic rules. The key question is whether the whole of cognition should be described from this subsymbolic level and whether any descriptions that are solely symbolic are valid without a subsymbolic underpinning. Smolensky's view is that the rational, cognitive human is best described at the symbolic level, but not every symbolic algorithm is valid as a cognitive model. The subsymbolic is a way of explaining the failures and successes of the symbolic, and in this way does not do away with the symbolic, but becomes an essential partner in the endeavour of defining a complete cognitive science. Smolensky goes further, drawing attention to the paradox of how cognition can, at times, appear to be governed by hard and fast rules, and at others be full of exceptions and contradictions which elude attempts of logical, symbolic modelling. He suggests that the subsymbolic provides a way of resolving the paradox – it has not done so yet, but should not be excluded from the research agenda.

Fodor and Pylyshyn (1988) refuse this outstretched hand, maintaining that 'connectionist and classical theories of mental structure are incompatible'. In other words, they repudiate the notion that connectionism can even provide a lower level of explanation for the existence of laws at the symbolic level. The focus of their argument is that while connectionism has the power of representing mental states it does not have the power of relating these states to one another in the highly structured, syntactic way that logical, symbolic methods have to offer. They see the properties that emerge from the dynamic nature of some connectionist models as merely leading to 'associativism' which, they argue, is not sufficient to represent language-like relationships between mental states. As far as these authors are concerned they see the only role for connectionism as a theory for implementation. So if it were to be the case that a particular parsing algorithm in natural language is best implemented with a specifically structured neural net, so be it. This may be technologically convenient, but, they argue, it adds no more to an understanding of parsing than it would had the system been built of conventional VLSI registers and logic gates.

William Ramsey of the Philosophy Department of the University of Notre Dame and his colleagues (1991) in commenting on the interpretation of connectionist models in the above debate writes ' . . . despite much discussion in the recent literature [the notion of a theoretical explanatory level] is hardly a paradigm of clarity'. In Chapter 6 we attempt to lay out the arguments side by side so as first to extract what clarity there is, and second to expose the lack of clarity where it occurs.

1.7 The illusion in the divide

In Chapter 7 we discuss our own view of the symbolic/subsymbolic divide, which simply argues that there is no divide. The argument relies heavily on the description of state machines formulated in Chapter 5. Here we also begin to describe a model which, at one extreme, can perform conventional computational tasks, while at the other it becomes a dynamic neural net. We call this the Neural State Machine Model (NSMM). It is this model on which we focus the proposed new framework for cognitive neural modelling. The state machine offers a level of representation which suits both the symbolic and the subsymbolic. This is not news to the computer scientist. For example, the syntactic level of language is represented in automata theory as a state machine endowed with some extra memory (the stack). The process of parsing is represented as a dynamic action in the state machine which places and removes the data in the stack. If fact, the stack itself could be seen as a part of the state machine. The very basis of computation as represented by the Turing machine is expressed as a state machine with an infinite tape. Our argument centres on the fact that the state machine is also the appropriate descriptive level for connectionist systems. The dynamism that Smolensky sees as being central to the subsymbolic paradigm is natural to state machines and is represented as a structure of states and state transitions.

The main feature of this style of description is that it clarifies the difference between conventional and connectionist computing. In conventional computing, a programmer is seen as having complete freedom in mapping algorithms into the state machine. The algorithms start in the programmer's head and end as logical prescriptions for the parameters of the state machine through a process of design. The connectionist prefers to take the same state machine and to build up the logical prescriptions for the parameters through learning by exposing the machine to examples of the task it has to perform. These parameters are stored in artificial neurons, which possess powers of extending the learning to other, similar data. So, there is no reason why such a structure should not learn to parse a language by being exposed to suitably labelled sentences in that language: it just may be that such a task is better done by a conventional parser. The main properties of the connectionist state machine are, first, that it has an opportunity of developing sensible behaviour from examples in areas where the programmer fails to find an algorithm (such as in face recognition and in planning) and, second, that it is able to generalize and to provide robust computation beyond the examples that it has learned.

This leads to a state of affairs where connectionist tasks and symbolic algorithms end up in the same representational framework, but get there by very different routes. In Chapter 7 we show examples of the same task (face recognition) as it might be represented through a symbolic approach and a connectionist approach – the difference lies in the nature of the two working algorithms. Some would make much of the fact that connectionist schemes are not easy to understand. We would argue that this is not so much the case as that the algorithm generated by the connectionist approach is not one that the programmer might have thought of in the first place. We also give an example of a learned planning task where the difference between the connectionist and the symbolic lies in the fact that the search for solutions in the neural model occurs at the time of training, while in the symbolic the search has always to be executed at run time.

This raises the question of 'competence', which we define almost in a Turing-test manner. A system is more competent the less it requires the user to change his or her ways from those that would be used if requesting the task to be done by another human. Algorithms stated in symbolic terms and those emerging from neural systems are likely to line up in an interleaved way along this measure of competence.

In Chapter 7 we suggest that a major benefit to cognitive science comes from the ability to introduce a formal study of learning which in normal symbolic work has been partly neglected. Logic methods allow a study of concept formation by building up statements of attribute combinations that go into defining object classes. This is what is called 'machine learning' within the symbolic processing paradigm. However, the state machine model allows a deeper study, which deals with learning of linguistic structures. We give an example of the neural state machine placed in an environment where it has to discover the linguistic responses that lead to rewards. What immediately becomes obvious is that exploratory learning would lead only to the discovery of specific strings rather than the rules of the language. But this is due to a limitation of the way that the data is gathered rather than a limitation of the neural system, and it is shown that the addition of alternative forms of learning, such as from instruction by a knowledge entity, lead to more general results. So, contrary to the concern of connectionists, whose learning theory has to do with low-level representations of altering connection strengths, neural systems have the potential to extend cognitive science to embrace models of the acquisition of cognitive competence.

1.8 Language and neurons

Language in the usual sense of the word (leaving out computer languages and the way that bees communicate by moving their bodies) is a uniquely human property. It is also much of the focus for discussions in artificial intelligence (Chapter 3) and indeed in cognitive science in general. It is at the root of the two major battles in artificial intelligence: the arguments of Searle (1980) against symbolic approaches (only those organisms that have learned to interact with the world to which language refers can 'understand') and the symbolic/subsymbolic argument (discussed in Section 1.6 and in Chapter 6). So, connectionists see language processing and understanding as a rich target.

Indeed, some of the contributors to the PDP publication were concerned with linguistic issues. It is Rumelhart's demonstration that a neural network could learn exceptions to rules in forming past tenses that brought connectionism into the cognitive arena at an early stage (Rumelhart and McClelland, 1986). In Chapter 8 we look at this development, and at several others in which connectionists have sought to explain natural language learning and understanding. In Rumelhart's work, attention was focused on the mistakes that the neural net made in applying rules to that end. These are corrected by training. The impressive part of this demonstration was that these mistakes resembled just those mistakes that children make when learning the same verbs. Rumelhart ends his description by saying, 'We view this work on past-tense morphology as a step toward a revised understanding of language knowledge, language acquisition and linguistic information processing in general'. (It is the confidence with which the claim to a 'revision' is made that set off the debate discussed in Chapter 6).

The PDP books also contain reports of work by McClelland and Kawamoto on the way that the correctness or otherwise of sentences such as

'The boy broke the window with a rock'

or

'The window broke the rock with the boy'

is learned by a neural net.

While these sentences are grammatically correct, the second is recognized as being wrong as 'window' in the given position in the sentence cannot be an Agent and 'boy' in this position in the sentence cannot be an Instrument. The authors show that it is possible for a neural net to act as an acceptor for correct word–attribute combinations and a rejector of incorrect ones. This too fanned the symbolic/neural debate, as the authors make claims that, while such issues are mentioned in theories about 'the language of thought' (Fodor, 1976) they are dismissed as uninteresting exceptions.

Another objective of Chapter 8 is to start flexing the muscles of the NSMM. We demonstrate that, by defining an 'iconic' state in this model, images of events can be built up as words are heard (or read). This shows that appropriate representations may be constructed which identify 'case roles' (i.e. what is doing the doing, with what and so on) as in Rumelhart and Kawamoto's examples mentioned above.

In fact, applying the NSMM in this way leads to a consideration of the role of mental imagery in cognitive tasks. Theories of natural language understanding are usually based on the assumption that such language is fully grammatical. But human beings are very good at forgiving a lack of grammar. Hearing someone shout 'help ... fire ... child ... upstairs' conjures up a vivid mental image which may lead the hearer to say 'there appears to be a child trapped in the upper floor of a house which is on fire'. The role of mental imagery cannot be denied in this form of language understanding – can it be denied in any cognitive theory of language? The fact is that imagery has not featured strongly in current theory, as it escapes formal, symbolic descriptions. The neural state machine, with its ability to build up a state structure, that is, a structure of 'mental' states, is an ideal medium for extending cognitive science in this direction. This is also pursued in Chapter 9.

The last thing we do in Chapter 8 is to acknowledge a need to demonstrate that neural systems used to represent language are capable of 'compositionality'. It is not possible to get rid of grammar altogether in discussions about language. Compositionality is the art of applying commas or brackets to language. For example:

'John loved Mary who hated fish and chips'

is quite clear and unambiguous. Those who attack connectionism express a fear that a connectionist system could confuse this with, for example,

'John hated fish and Mary who loved chips'

To show that this is not true requires that connectionist systems have compositionality. The literature on this topic is reviewed and it is shown that NSMM has this property.

1.9 Seeing and thinking

We feel that the ability of living organisms to process images and understand what they mean holds as important a clue to what thinking is all about as the other major modality – language. It should immediately be said that this does not imply that we regard sightless people as being unable to think. On the contrary, we refer to 'mental imagery' as being capable of operating in any sensual mode. The blind person makes mental images of the auditory and tactile environment, and these are as valid as images based in visual perception. But for the purposes of most of our discussions we shall assume that it is visual information that is involved when we mention an image. Chapter 9 is devoted to all sorts of perceptual processing of images and their relation to cognition. Cognitive scientists and neural network scientists have addressed vision from a variety of angles. We briefly look at these as background before continuing the theme of the importance of mental imagery to cognition.

One of the most influential scientists in the modelling of vision (as mentioned in section 1.2) was the late David Marr (1982). Dare we say it, but it is possible that it will be his philosophy that survives rather than his actual findings. He drew attention to the fact that vision could and should be understood in several different ways. He distinguished between a computational theory of vision (i.e. an abstract definition of a visual task) and its implementation in, say, neural terms. His philosophy was based in saying that such different ways of looking at the same phenomenon were a healthy way of compounding understanding of that phenomenon. He then divided vision into different levels of activity. These include a 'primal sketch', where textural features are grouped and lines or edges may be noted. He linked the theoretical description of this (in mathematical jargon, the 'difference of two Gaussians' – DOG) to what was known of the spatial processing of some cells in the visual cortex. The two matched and Marr's philosophy was satisfied.

As he moves towards an explanation of knowing what an image is, or even naming it, Marr finds it hard to find a suitable computational theory. It is based on 'storing in our heads, somewhere' some highly stylized iconic representations of the world. Linked pipe-cleaner models or shapes made of cylinders are used to describe these prototypes. It is our contention that it is at this level that much still has to be discovered about mental representations. While fully aware of the fact that introspection has its pitfalls, the idea of prototypical representations in terms of pipe-cleaners seems wrong, or perhaps, incompetent within our definition of competence. While it is possible to look at a pipe-cleaner shape and notice that it looks more like a dog than a giraffe or a pig, it seems perhaps dangerous to infer from this that such primitive representations define stored visual knowledge. The mental imagery we use to make sense of the world is immensely rich. We can think of an 'Alsatian' and describe our mental vision of its pointed ears, black shiny nose and so on.

It seems therefore that this richness needs to be explained. But in doing so it is difficult to continue to adopt Marr's symbiosis between computational theory and implementation. The main problem with the visual domain is that images defy mathematical representation. While it is possible to describe a house as some kind of geometrical object, this may be fortuitous, as the same cannot be done with the Alsatian dog or most other things we see and imagine. Also, while it is possible to describe mathematically the boundary between two textures and ascribe rigorous properties to a device which turns these data into (say) a line, the very first of these steps is missing in most things that our eyes dwell on.

We therefore maintain that it is plausible that an alternative to Marr's approach is required, one that puts the data reductions in the early stages of vision to one side and concentrates on the storage of visual material in a framework that is similar to the sensation that is activated at when the material is actually seen. This does not deny the importance of the known signal processing characteristics of the early stages of vision, but it does question the idea that vision is a 'pipeline' process in which the detail of the representation is progressively reduced between the perceptual sensation and its interpretation. In vision the brain is able to search through different levels of stored representational detail. With this requirement in mind we develop the 'iconic' state concept (mentioned in section 1.8 and defined in Chapter 8) and show how a coherent mental image can be built up even if the world is observed with eyes that never stop moving, and taking into account the ability to change the point of view, varying the observation angle and the level of detail that is being observed.

But mental imagery is not an area without controversy in cognitive science. The leading challenge comes from Zenon Pylyshyn (1979), whose commitment to symbolic methods of representation make it difficult for him to deal with images themselves as mental events and only admits symbolic representations. A curious facet of this challenge is that the debate is about the same beliefs that are at stake in the neuron/symbol debate. We review this debate, acknowledging the contribution made in support of mental imagery by Marc Rollins (1989). He suggests that having pictures in one's head explains phenomena that models based solely on language cannot explain. For example, imagine you have been asked 'Do you like the Mona Lisa?'. Those who argue that language is at the root of thought would say that the answer is derived from the stored truth value in your head of the proposition 'I like the Mona Lisa'. This leaves open the possibility of giving the answer without remembering what the picture looks like, or, checking whether it is still liked. Those who believe in mental imagery will argue that the recall of the mental image, and the tests that can be carried out in the head on it, is a more direct way of explaining how the answer to the question is obtained. In Chapter 9 we show that the NSMM goes a long way towards providing just those mechanisms that Rollins' philosophy requires.

1.10 Artificial consciousness: a framework for cognitive science

The claim that 'consciousness' is about to be explained is likely to be interpreted as either trying to do something that is impossible or as a display of naïvety. So it is refreshing to find that Daniel Dennett has recently written a book entitled *Consciousness Explained* (1991). This encourages us to take a look at this wide-ranging term in the closing chapter of this book (Chapter 10). Language, mental imagery, attending, planning, learning and solving problems are all ideas that go into what one calls 'consciousness'. Rather than 'mind', which has a clinical feel and seems to stand apart from the body, consciousness makes a good target for those interested in cognition which includes introspection. Consciousness *is* introspection. In Chapter 10 we bring together some of the ideas that have been raised in the rest of the book. We review and redefine the NSMM and its various modes of learning. We summarize the way that the NSMM enables us to bring together scene understanding, language understanding and mental imagery. Finally, we review the way that this model supports or contradicts Dennett's model of consciousness. The support is greater than the contradiction and the final product is, hopefully, a partial demystification of a traditionally puzzling concept.

Looking into the future, we see concepts such as the NSMM having a liberating effect on cognitive science without denying the success cognitive science has accrued from almost half a century of history largely based on language-like formalisms. It is possible that parts of our brains and their functions are expertly described using mathematical linguistics, but it also may be that other parts and their functions (or the same parts at other times) may be best explained by a neural model that is a vehicle for mental imagery. At least, one thing seems certain – in the future it will become difficult to talk of symbolic models of cognition in a way that makes no reference to artificial neural systems.

2

Artificial neural nets

Bare bones and some cognitive properties

2.1 How to get rid of the frills

The afficionado of connectionism will be disappointed in this chapter. Buzzwords like 'error back-propagation', 'gradient descent' and 'mean value theorem' will, at best, be banished and, at worst, explained only if absolutely necessary. Murmurs of 'you're taking the fun out of neural systems' are likely to be heard.

The plain fact is that the mathematical elegance of some methods of analysis that is implied by the above words has seduced many researchers. It is our belief that such concerns do not impinge on the relevance of neural systems to discussions of cognition. Our approach involves stripping neural systems of such mathematical frills and revealing the bare bones sufficiently to allow us to explain those special emergent properties that make connectionism interesting in the context of cognition. It is this group of properties that the cognitive scientist has to understand in order to decide whether or not neural systems have something to offer. We think of a neuron as a unit that accepts a bunch of numbers, and learns to respond to this by producing a number of its own.

By taking this simple approach we do not wish to imply that the more sophisticated theoretical models have no value; we have merely simplified them to a point that allows us to concentrate on simple, direct explanations of the important properties of neurons. In section 2.2 we first consider the neuron itself. There are two things to be understood – what is meant by 'learning' and what is meant by 'generalization'. The model chosen takes a 'lookup table' view of the neuron, which is unorthodox in the world of connectionism as it does not refer to connection strength variation. We feel that this step allows us to give a pragmatic and accurate description that leads more directly to a discussion of the properties of systems that contain such prototypes than would be possible were one to couch the description in terms of recipes for connection strength adjustment.

In section 2.3 we look at 'multi-layer' networks because one of the most popular neural models of the 1980s is the 'multi-layer perceptron'. The word 'perceptron' was coined by the late Frank Rosenblatt of Cornell University in 1962, who used it to describe a neuron model which he had adapted from an earlier design of McCulloch and Pitts (1943). He used the perceptron in a single layer to perform pattern recognition tasks. It was this single-layer model which, in the late 1960s, was shown by Minsky and Papert to have limited processing capacity, thus suggesting that it was devoid of much potential for 'intelligence'. One of the successes of the 1980s was the proof that the addition of 'hidden' layers of neurons overcomes the objections of Minsky and Papert. These layers are more than a technical frill, as claims are made about some neurons in these layers 'making important discoveries' about the data on which the systems are being trained – this is a cognitive matter, and we explain the sense in which such claims are valid. Also, it is the existence of these hidden units that leads to the needs for learning by 'error back-propagation', a topic which has received much attention. We also consider the difference between localized and distributed representations (i.e. does an idea such as 'cat' lead to activity in one neuron or many?). This last issue is central to some of the arguments in the 'great debate' on the value of connectionism to cognition discussed later, in Chapter 6.

While the networks mentioned above have powers of recognition, cognition is more than that – it has to do with the build-up of experience and with relating perception to that experience. In section 2.4, we introduce the dynamic neural network in which neurons act one upon another. It is this feedback between neurons that gives such networks the ability to sustain 'internal representations' of experienced events. It is precisely the set of internal feedback connections that becomes the residing place of these internal or (why not?) 'mental' representations. These are the representations that not only allow the recall of experience as mental images, but also endow the net with the ability to be sensitive to sequences of incoming symbols (a prerequisite for language understanding) and with the ability to generate outgoing sequences of symbols (a prerequisite for the generation of language-like output).

One of the problems of connectionism on first meeting is that one finds a variety of seemingly competing alternative networks. There are the models of Hopfield, Kohonen, Grossberg and Smolensky to name but a few. There are systems such as Boltzmann machines, ARTs, WISARDs, BAMs, CMACs; so many, in fact, that it is not worth referencing them in detail. Which of these should be picked in order to express some of the notions that cognition demands? Another difficulty for the cognitive scientist is that most of these models are couched in terms of deep mathematical detail, and it is not immediately clear whether an understanding of this is necessary in order to make progress. To get over these problems, we define in section 2.5 a General Neural Unit (GNU) which contains the major properties that are common to all neural models and which is expressed with the minimum of reliance on mathematical formulation. In fact, the rest of this chapter is devoted to a closer discussion of these broad common properties. The GNU has only two variables. One is the balance between the amount of information that the neurons get from outside of a cluster and the amount they get from within – this 'feedback factor' is responsible for how well the net remembers and retrieves experience. The second variable is the nature of training, which will be explained for each of the examples in this chapter.

Section 2.6 is devoted to the act of mental retrieval and section 2.7 to the sequence sensitivity of this process. For example, if the input were to be the letters C-H-A-I-R the evoked mental image would be very different from that generated by a similar but shorter string H-A-I-R. The differentiating cues can come at any time (e.g. C-A-R-T and C-A-R-E) In section 2.8 we look at the opposite problem – the generation of such sequences in response to the input of appropriate images (e.g. a picture of a cat causes the GNU to 'say' C-A-T).

We conclude this chapter in section 2.9 with what may seem a flight of fancy. We regard the GNU as an animate object and interpret some of its properties in cognitive terms. For example, in the function of the neuron we find the repository for long-term memory, which is altered by the training process. The retention of images on the feedback loop is then the site for short-term memory. The switch between one short-term memory state and another is seen as an act of shifting attention. The way in which these cognitive properties depend on the GNU parameters is an obvious target for discussion.

2.2 The minimal neuron

As anticipated earlier, our aim is to define a minimal form of neuron which gives a clear view of the essential properties the device requires in order to be of value in a network. Real neurons are likely to possess these rudimentary properties and many more. In respect of the many artificial models, our device represents some kind of a common denominator. We call our model the s-neuron to remind ourselves that it is simple. An s-neuron has a number (say n) of input connections through which it receives information from other neurons or some sensing devices (light or sound sensors, for example). It also has one output through which it can deliver information to other s-neurons or to 'actuators'. In living brains, actuators are muscles, the contraction of which is controlled by the output information of the neuron. In artificial systems, such actuators are things like screen displays, voice synthesizers or motors that control (say) the arm of a robot. The output information can be thought of as being some sort of assessment of the total input information.

We have used the term 'information' without saying what this is. Here we make our first major simplification and describe a very simple, general form of coding. In s-neuron systems, information will consist of three numbers: $-1, 0$ and $+1$. Broadly, this refers to 'no', 'don't know' and 'yes',

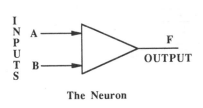

The Neuron

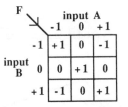

The Truth Table -
the output F is shown for each
combination of inputs

Figure 2.1 *An s-neuron.*

respectively. An engineer might at this stage enquire how such integers are coded. This is not important for the purpose of our narrative.

Now for what the neuron does. We have said that it has n channels. So at any instant these channels carry a set of n digits. A little bit of arithmetic shows that if n were 1 then only the three input messages discussed above would be possible. If n were 2 then all combinations of 3 possible messages in the first input and 3 possible messages in the second could be legitimate input messages. In this case the tally is 9 (i.e. 3^2). Figure 2.1 illustrates one such two-input s-neuron. What a neuron does can be described by a truth table and this particular neuron says yes ($+1$) when the two inputs agree, no (-1) when one input says yes and the other no and don't know (0) when just one of the inputs is don't know (0). In general, the number of distinct messages that an s-neuron with n inputs can receive is 3^n and this too is the size of the truth table which describes what an s-neuron is doing at any time.

Now the neuron must learn some task. Figure 2.2 shows a neuron connected to a 3×3 grid. This grid could be thought of as a 'retina' of some simple animal or a robot. The task here is to distinguish the three possible vertical bars from the three horizontal bars shown in the figure. We'll ask the neuron to say 'yes' to all vertical bars and 'no' to all horizontal ones.

It is worth pondering here on the size of the truth table for this s-neuron. There are 9^3 ($=729$) possible entries into this truth table. We assume that before learning takes place, they all contain the 0 entry. The simplest way for the neuron to learn this or any other task is for it to be given the ability to act as some kind of lookup table into which the desired output for each of the six patterns may be written and then retrieved at some future point. So the best way of thinking of the learning function of a neuron is as the ability to write desired outputs into slots in a truth table selected by given examples of input. (This is not a difficult electronic task – see Chapter 5 of Aleksander and Morton (1990) for a full description.) The procedure is referred to as "training".

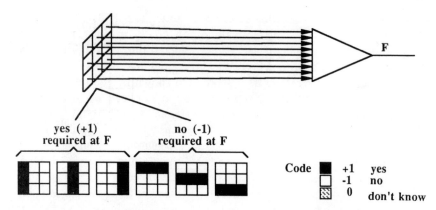

Figure 2.2 *A larger s-neuron connected to a 'retina'.*

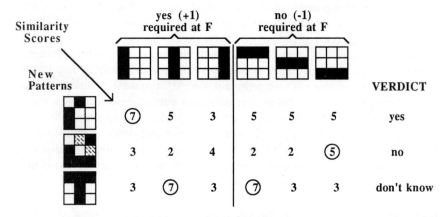

Figure 2.3 *What is meant by similarity?*

It is worth noting that most connections would not describe the function of the neuron in this way – they would refer to the strengthening or weakening of some input 'weight' of the neuron. However, we have chosen to go down the lookup table route, as it is simpler to understand, completely general and, as has been argued elsewhere, it includes systems in which learning is represented by weight changes (Aleksander, 1991).

Another useful facet of this approach is that it separates the two major properties of the neuron: learning and generalization. So far, we have seen learning as entering values into a lookup table and retrieving those entries later. The question raised under the heading of generalization is how the neuron should best respond to input messages that have not occurred during train-ing. In our lookup table model this is the same question as how the spaces in the table not encountered during training should be handled. We suggest a very simple way of answering this question.

The similarity of any input pattern encountered during training may be calculated simply by scoring a point for each of the nine inputs in which the two agree. Some patterns and their scores are shown in Figure 2.3. Now, in order to decide how these new patterns are to be classified, we take the maximum score and see whether it is unique to one or more training patterns in the same (yes or no) class. If it is, it is given the same classification as the appropriate class. If the maximum occurs for both classes, the pattern is left in the 'don't know' state. The third pattern in Figure 2.3 is of this kind.

For our s-neuron, we assume that when training is complete a mechanism exists that causes all the entries in the lookup table to be affected appropriately by the training set so that the neuron acts exactly according to the generalization scheme described above. The electronics enthusiast will find a description of how this could be done in the literature. (In Aleksander (1991), a device called the G-RAM is the electronic version of our s-neuron.) In conventional connectionism the adjustment of connection strengths (weights) at the input of an artificial neuron brings about a generalization which approximates our 'ideal' scheme, while in real neurons the nature of the generalization is not precisely known. However, it must be something like our description. The difference should not be sufficient to detract from the application to real brains of arguments about cognition based on our artificial neural systems applying to real brains.

2.3 Multi-layer networks

Much of the 1980s revival of interest in neural networks was based on the discovery that networks consisting of several layers of neurons have considerable flexibility. As mentioned in section 2.1, this is a technical matter and would not have been of interest in a discussion on cognition except for one fact. As we shall see in Chapter 6, the 'great debate' on whether or not connectionism has anything to offer to a study of cognition centres on the way information may be represented in specific layers of a network.

Figure 2.4 helps to illustrate some of the concepts involved in this discussion. There are three layers in this network. The retina, as in the previous section, is where the raw sensory information is turned into patterns of yes/no signals. We assume that pictures of objects are sensed at this layer. Cats, owls, penguins and pheasants constitute the menagerie for this demonstration. One factor that we gloss over for the time being is that the number of points in the retina may be large, but we assume that each of the neurons in the second layer is connected to all these points. In fact, neither in artificial systems nor in real brains do neurons get such a good view of images, and the consequences of this need to be taken into account. However, this is not the place to examine these consequences – we shall assume for now that the second layer neurons can learn and generalize for complete input patterns.

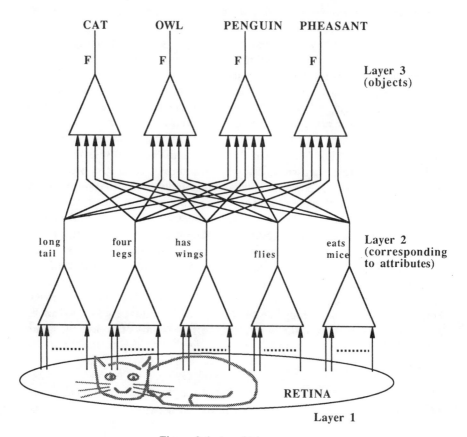

Figure 2.4 *A multi-layer net.*

For the time being we shall assume that the second layer is given, by a trainer, some arbitrary attributes of these animals, as shown in Figure 2.4, while the third layer is devoted to the final recognition of the objects themselves. This is a plausible scheme, and there are no difficulties with training the network provided that the second layer is trained with appropriate information at the same time as the third layer. So, for all examples of cats, the second layer would be trained to say 'yes' to 'long tail', 'four legs' and 'eats mice', with 'no' at 'wings' and 'flies'. (In case the reader is disturbed by the non-visual nature of some of these attributes it should be remembered that these are chosen by the trainer rather than necessarily being visible in the picture of the object.)

The second layer generates what are known as 'attribute codes' with each attribute code leading to a single neuron saying 'yes' in the third layer. So, from left to right the attribute vector for a cat is

object	long tail	four legs	has wings	flies	eats mice
cat:	yes	yes	no	no	yes

$\longleftarrow$ ———————————— vector ———————————— $\longrightarrow$

The attribute codes for the other creatures are:

owl:	no	no	yes	yes	yes
penguin:	no	no	yes	no	no
pheasant:	yes	no	yes	yes	no

It would be possible to have much more general neurons in the third layer; one, for example, for 'bird' would say 'yes' to the attribute vectors which trigger off 'owl' and 'penguin'. Tacitly this solves a problem that exists with logic systems which would use rules such as 'a bird has wings and flies'. The penguin, despite being a bird, fails this test, requiring the writing of a special rule. The neural system, given enough neurons, will accept experience as it comes, whereas rule-based systems need to distinguish between major rules and exceptions. Of course this points to the fact that the net could be trained so that at the third layer more than one neuron says yes in response to an input pattern (for example, yes at both 'owl' and 'bird').

There is much discussion on the difference between the original one-yes-only representation and the one where more than one neuron can say 'yes'. The original one-yes-only representation at the third level is localized: one neuron per object where the objects are distinct and mutually exclusive. At the second level each neuron represents a different attribute, but several attributes can coexist in response to an input pattern. However, each combination of attributes ('attribute vector') at the second layer fully defines the objects at the third, so this is a distributed rather than a localized representation. So 'cat', by being associated with a single neuron, can be called a 'symbol' and the third level representation 'symbolic', while representation at the second level is via attribute vectors, which are also a complete description of a 'cat', and is called 'subsymbolic'. Smolensky makes much of the cognitive properties of this distributed method of representation in neural nets (see Chapter 6).

In general, intermediate layers in a network are needed for technical reasons either related to the limited learning capability of conventional neuron models (owing to the use of weights, not all slots in the truth can be filled independently – the details of this may be found in Aleksander and Morton (1990)), or as a result of neurons not being completely connected to their input layer (so the information that they generate is partial, and other neurons are needed to bring together some of these partial assessments). Whether the output is localized or not, error back-propagation is needed when the exact coding required for the intermediate layers is not known and has to be derived from the errors made at the output layers. In brief, error back-propagation is a process where errors that are detected at the outputs of a multi-layer net lead to calculations which determine where, in the previous layer, the errors may have come from. This is then repeated to cater for the layer before that, and so on. Once all these calculations are complete, each neuron has been assessed in terms of how much it might be contributing to the output errors. This is useful statistical knowledge which does not require detailed knowledge of what the intermediate neurons are meant to be doing. This statistical knowledge is used to make adjustments to the neuron functions in a way that is calculated as being most effective at removing the output errors (see Aleksander and Morton, (1990), Chapter 8 for full details).

The general question that concerns us here is, given the structure in Figure 2.4 with the labels on the output neurons fixed, and given a method of propagating errors backwards, will the appropriate attribute units be 'discovered' at the second layer? It is often hinted in the literature that such discoveries by 'hidden' units are part of the 'intelligence' of the connectionist approach. It is easy to show that the discovery of the precise attributes (e.g. 'has four legs') used in the example in Figure 2.4 is unlikely. In the case of learning from errors in the output layer, the role of the second layer is merely one of finding a distinct set of codes which does not confuse any two of the creatures. There is a vast number of such codes – here is an arbitrarily chosen example (in which the second layer of neurons no longer has the labels used in Figure 2.4):

cat:	yes	no	yes	no	yes
owl:	no	no	no	yes	yes
penguin:	no	yes	yes	no	no
pheasant:	yes	yes	yes	yes	no

These codes would work perfectly well, even though it would be hard to argue that the second intermediate layer neurons have discovered meaningful features. So, we would argue that if intermediate layers are to represent meaningful features the training procedure must tell these layers what to do.

2.4 Feedback: the mechanism of the inner image

We are pessimistic about the degree of relevance of feedforward only systems, as just described, to an understanding of cognition. Humans who recognize patterns are also capable of describing them when they are not actually looking at them. This requires some method of sustaining the images that a neural system has learned. We would suggest that feedback is the key physical ingredient which provides a site for this type of inner activity related to previous experience.

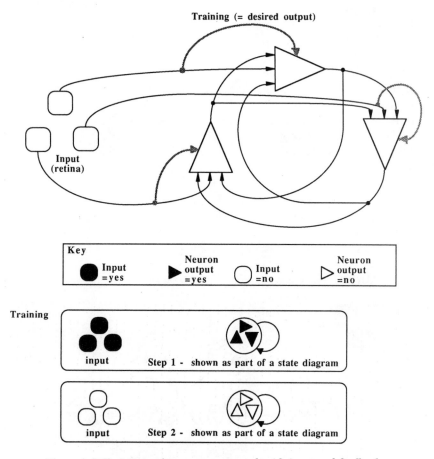

Figure 2.5 *Training a three-neuron network with input and feedback.*

In Figure 2.5 we recall the three neuron network already seen in Figure 1.6. We now add some sophistication – inputs from a very simple three-sensor input 'retina' and the ability to learn and generalize. It should be noted that now each s-neuron has three inputs, two from the other two s-neurons and one from the sensors. To understand training, notice that the 'desired output' connection, which tells the neuron what to do, receives its input directly (refer to Figure 1.1). Not shown is the learning control line (L in Figure 1.1).

It is assumed that the trainer is capable of setting the output of the neurons (we now drop the s in s-neuron) to be the same as the current content of the retina, and when the learning control is activated each output value is linked to the pattern of current inputs of its respective neuron. In this way the network is made to learn to recognize and respond to two input patterns – three yeses (blacks) and three nos (whites). Learning, in this case, is making the outputs

Input (a)

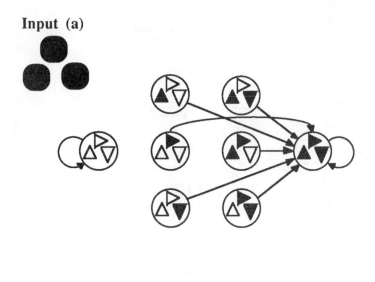

Input (b)

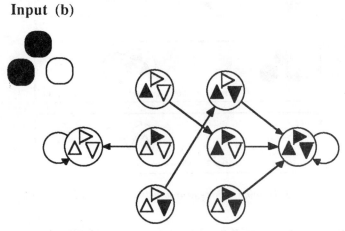

Figure 2.6 *State diagrams for the three-neuron net in response to inputs.*

of the neurons have the same value as the input. So the learned state is the pattern of neuron outputs which, in this case, is three yeses or three nos. A state diagram is used to describe what goes on. The first step creates a replication of the all-black pattern at the neurons and this does not change as long as the all-black pattern remains at the input. This is shown as a state (circle showing the firing pattern of the neurons) leading back to itself. A similar step is taken with the all-white input. But the network could have eight possible states, and we have so far only looked at two of these. It is important to understand what happens in the remaining states. Figure 2.6 illustrates this. It is assumed that there is synchronism – at a given moment (dictated by the arrival of some kind of clocking pulse) all the neurons assess their inputs and decide what their output should be. The generalization of the neurons is such that if two or three inputs are white, the output will be white. So for the network in Figure 2.5 with the all-black input (a), any state that already has at least one black neuron will feed this to the other two, each of which will then have two input black values, and the subsequent state will be the all-black state. There are no further changes with time.

An anthropomorphic description of what is going on is that the all-black input is recognized when the network enters its 'internal representation' of the all-black pattern. Looking at the complete state diagram in Figure 2.6, however, it is evident that there is one condition under which the input is not recognized by the network entering the all-black state – when the three neurons are all in the white state. We assess this situation by assuming that when the network is asked to do its recognition, whatever it was doing before would have left it, with equal probability, in any one of the possible states. So, when the all-black input is presented, the probability of it being recognized by a proper elicitation of the internal representation is 7/8.

Perhaps more interesting, however, is a reaction of the net to an input it has not seen during training. This is input (b) in Figure 2.6. It is noted that the only two stable states are still the all-black and all-white states. The input is more similar to the all-black state and the neural net reacts to this by entering the appropriate internal state, albeit with a probability of 6/8 (75%) with a 25% possibility of getting it wrong by entering the other learned state. A similar behaviour occurs when the input is all-white or 2/3 white, only this time the probability is 7/8 and 6/8 respectively for the system to enter the all-white state.

The possible 'failures' of this net are also worth noting. The central one is the fact that once the net enters one of its recognition states it cannot be shifted from this state by a change of input alone. The only way in which the above recognition probabilities can be achieved is if the net is somehow 'shaken up' before it is asked to make a decision. An engineer would refer to this as 'injecting noise' into the net. That is, the outputs of the neurons are disrupted by some electronic means to put the net into an arbitrarily chosen state before asking it to make a decision about the nature of its inputs. These are the sort of results that neuroanatomists may wish to know about, as it suggests they should look for sources of noise in areas of the brain where there is much feedback.

But the aim of this section is to illustrate the effect of feedback in a net, not to present a marketable recognition gadget or to provide a lesson in neuroanatomy. This effect is to create internal states that can be recalled by the net given an appropriate stimulus. Trained in the way described, these internal states become representations of the sensory input. We take the view that this is the mechanism whereby a neural network can build experience of a world it senses through its sensors. Now we shall look at a more flexible model of nets with feedback which, owing to their ability to change state with time, are said to be 'dynamic' (sometimes the word 'recursive' is used).

2.5 A General Neural Unit

A general difficulty with the science of neural nets is that it contains a proliferation of different models of neurons and structures that use them. This is certainly true of dynamic neural networks. The intention now is to present a general system which, like the model of the single neuron outlined in section 2.2, has the basic properties of most dynamic models and contains the minimum of complexity necessary to understand those properties that may be important in a study of cognition. Figure 2.7 is the focus of attention. As this looks somewhat daunting we shall explain its features one at a time.

First, the network consists of a number of neurons. In the figure, the number is 64, of which only three are shown. The neurons learn and generalize in the same way as was described in the earlier parts of this chapter. Also, as in Figure 2.6, the 'yes/no' outputs of the neurons taken together as an image form the state of the system. For convenience we have shown this state as

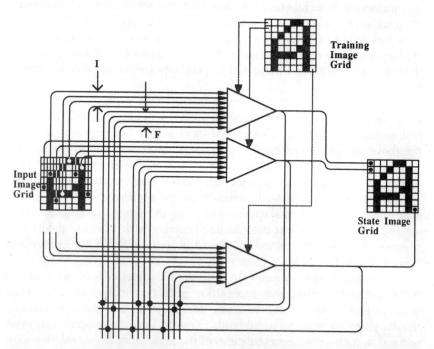

Figure 2.7 *A General Neural Unit, having 64 eight-input neurons connected in a single layer with feedback.*

a grid of 8×8 boxes in which a 'yes' is indicated by a black square and a 'no' by a white one. Some version of a letter 'A' appears as a state on this grid. We shall return to this later.

There is a similar grid which represents the input to the network. Here too we shall see the letter 'A' and again we shall return to the meaning of this later. The most important thing to note in the way that the neurons are connected is that each device receives some of its inputs from the outputs of the neurons (that is from the state of the network) and some from the input image. In the figure we have assumed that each neuron has exactly eight inputs, of which half came from the state and half from the input. We have previously shown that this half and half split leads to a good performance (Aleksander and Morton, 1991) and we shall return to the reasons for this in the next section. For now, it is important to note that the feedback connections and the input connections are made in an arbitrary manner.

Now let us consider the training procedure for this system. Here we note the existence of yet another grid in the figure, labelled the training image grid. This is connected to the 'desired output' terminals of the neurons and, as the net is trained, this image determines the content of the state grid. All this is exactly the same as the procedure we saw for the three-neuron net in Figure 2.6. Three chunks of information are involved in this process – the current state (S) which is present on the state image grid, the input present on the input image grid (I) and the next state present at the desired output (training image) grid (S'). When the learning mechanism is activated, the neurons will cause the combination of the current state and input (S,I) to produce the next state (S'). Another way of putting this is that the 'transition' between state S and state S' for input has been learned.

In principle, it is possible to build up any state diagram through training this system. But there is a snag. Because any individual neuron does get a view of the entire (S,I) input, it could happen in training that for two training steps one neuron is required to respond differently to the same input. This is called a contradiction. Often, what is done with contradictions is to set the response to the 'unknown' value, which causes the neuron to output yes and no arbitrarily but with equal probability (like tossing a coin).

There is a rule of thumb that can be used to avoid contradictions. Ntourntoufis (1991) calculated that if the neuron has the same number of inputs as trained states, the probability of a contradiction occurring is about 13%. So, say that the GNU contains neurons with eight-inputs each: only about eight transitions can safely be trained, but even then there is a very strong likelihood of one being disrupted by a contradiction. What this means is that one transition that was thought to have been learned will provide the right next state in all its binary points except one. This point will vacillate between yes and no. It will be assumed in what follows that the rule of thumb of fewer

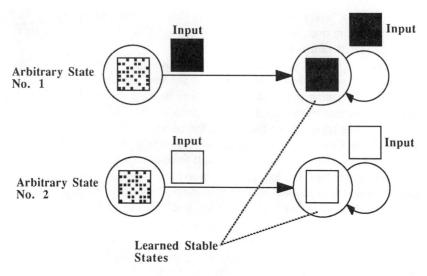

Figure 2.8 *Learning the all-black and all-white patterns.*

transitions than inputs per neuron is always observed and that the effect of contradictions being negligible can be ignored.

On the other side of the coin of limited training due to contradictions, the generalization properties of the neuron define many more transitions than those that have been trained. This effect has already been seen in Figure 1.6 and is exactly the same in GNUs. We shall illustrate the effect of this generalization further in the rest of this chapter when discussing some emergent properties of the GNU.

So, what we have seen in this section is a general system which is neurally inspired (in the sense that layers of neurons can be found in the brain each with its characteristic amount of feedback – often zero feedback), theoretically general and not too difficult to bear in mind.

2.6 The simple retrieval of internal states

The specific objective of this section is to examine the question of generalization in a GNU with a particular task in mind – the retrieval of states that have been made stable by training. Take a GNU with the structure shown in Figure 2.7. Let the number of inputs for each neuron be eight: four from the state and four from the input image (as in the figure). We aim to show that the net can build up internal states that are representations of input images and retrieve these even for distorted inputs. It will be realized that this is important

in models of cognition, as the transfer of 'sensory' data from input to internal
state is a prerequisite for having internal representations of the world through
the senses.

Imagine that the initial state is some arbitrary condition with roughly
half of the neurons being black and half white. We will teach the system
the all-black image first and then the all-white image. It is assumed that
the input and the teaching grids receive their inputs through the senses
and that, in the first case, they receive the all-black image. The learning
mechanism is now activated, which means that the neurons each receive
an arbitrary input on four terminals and all-black on the other four terminals;
this is made to output black. The procedure is repeated once the state
image has gone black, forcing the all-black state to be stable with an
all-black input.

Now it is assumed that the state is made arbitrary again before repeating
exactly the same procedure with the all-white pattern. The state diagram that
results from the learning so far is shown in Figure 2.8.

Table 2.1

Training step number	Input	State	Output
1	1111	1010	1
2	1111	1111	1
3	0000	1100	0
4	0000	0000	0

To begin to understand how this device retrieves patterns, imagine that
one particular neuron has been trained as in Table 2.1 (remembering that two
training steps have taken place for each output – one for an arbitrary state
and the other for the state transferred from the input). Now, given an input
such as the all-black input and some arbitrary state not used before, say that
the input to this neuron is 1111 0001. Recalling the generalization rule of
the neuron, its output will be the same as the output of the closest input message
on which the neuron was trained. To work out 'closest' we simply count
the total number of differences between the current value of inputs and
those in the training pattern to which it is being compared. So in this
example, there are

    3 differences from training pattern 1
    3 differences from training pattern 2
    7 differences from training pattern 3
    5 differences from training pattern 4

So the current input message to the neuron is equally 'closest' to pattern 1 and to pattern 2. But as both these patterns require the 1 output there is no disagreement, and the neuron will output a 1. In fact, with the all-1 input pattern and the all-0 input pattern no arbitrary state will do other than output the learned value. The effect of this is that the network has learned to transfer the appropriate image to the state.

The rigorously minded reader will notice that it might just be possible for a situation to arise where the training patterns are such as to allow an arbitrary pattern to cause the neuron to be in the 'don't know' state where it will output 0 or 1 arbitrarily. This line of reasoning also leads to the conclusion that this is an unlikely occurrence – happening in a small number of neurons in a large net. Hence, starting in an arbitrary state the next state may have few departures from the appropriate prototype, but the state after that will have a much smaller number and so on. For the purposes of cognitive modelling it is possible to assume that the input pattern will be transferred to the state in one or very few steps.

So far, only the effect of transferring one of the prototypes from input to state has been considered, but what if the input pattern is not identical to one of the prototypes, but similar to it? Here we give an intuitive account of what might happen (for the full probabilistic theory see Aleksander and Morton (1991)). So, instead of having all 1s in the input pattern, say that

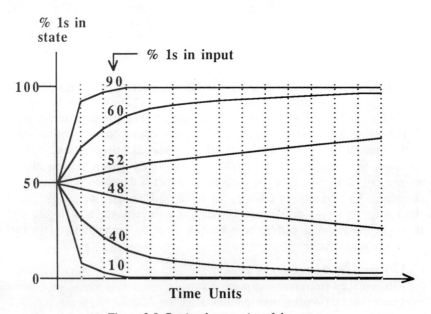

Figure 2.9 *Retrieval properties of the net.*

there are three 0s among the 64 1s. As the neurons are connected at random to the input image, the chances are that these occur at the input of three different neurons. In fact, a statistician will tell us that the chances against this are about one in ten. Say, then, that the total input to one of these three neurons is 0111 0000 (The last four 0s come from an arbitrary starting state). The effect of this situation is that for such neurons the probability of being in a don't know condition is increased. In this case the number of differences from training patterns 1 and 4 is 3. As these require different outputs the neuron will output 0s and 1s at random.

Looking at the remaining neurons leads us to the conclusion that even though the initial internal state of the net is arbitrary, the next state is much more like the appropriate prototype, and with time the state ends up with a reproduction of a training prototype even if the input remains defective. This is illustrated in Figure 2.9.

A slightly more picturesque example is shown in Figure 2.10 (taken from Aleksander and Morton (1991), where the system has been trained in three prototypes: a 'church', a 'tree' and a 'house'. Here the possibility of training patterns interfering slightly with one another is noted, as the retrieval is not perfect. But, as we have begun to see above, the generalization of the neurons stacks the statistics for the net towards finding the internal state, among those for which it has been trained, which most resembles the current input.

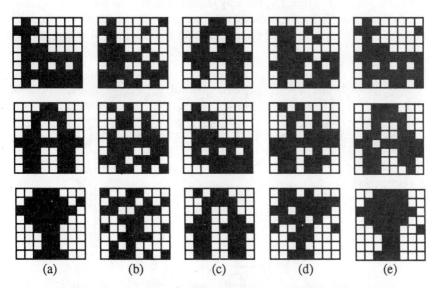

(a)   (b)   (c)   (d)   (e)

Figure 2.10 *Reconstruction of patterns using a General Neural Unit: (a) training patterns; (b) noisy test patterns; (c) too much feedback (seven feedback lines to one input): typical retrieval errors; (d) no feedback: the output remains distorted (slight improvement); (e) optimal 50% feedback.*

In sum, and in a looser form of wording, the net is capable of learning images by tranferring them to its internal state, and the result of this acquisition is that it will always try to 'make sense' of new input images by relating them to learned ones.

2.7 Input sequences – the beginnings of language

Image retrieval as seen in the last section is but one of the ways in which the simple GNU made of neurons can store and retrieve information. In this section we look at the way that sequences of input images can lead to a retrieval of experience. The environment of a cognitive system is not likely to be static. This makes it extremely important for the system to be able to make sense of a changing input image. Moreover language can be seen as a series of input sequences (of symbols of sounds) that needs to be understood. So, again, making sense of sequences is essential if such systems are ever to provide models for linguistic abilities or to have such abilities.

In this explanation we shall assume that the input images have an opportunity of changing all at once at regular time clicks (engineers call them clock pulses). It is known in engineering circles that this assumption does not reduce the modelling power of such 'clocked' systems. In short, the clicks can be made to follow one another in very rapid succession giving the illusion of continuity (as in a cine film, or on the television).

Looking back at Figure 2.7, the only requirement for this scheme to become sequence sensitive is that there should be a time delay of a single click associated with the state memory. For example, during training, say that the state is

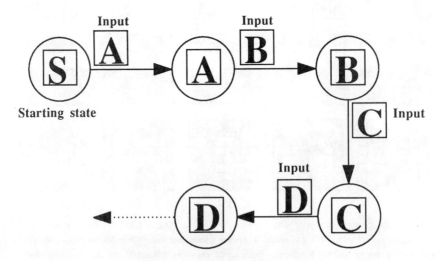

Figure 2.11 *Sequence learning.*

S (arbitrary). Then the input A occurs and the usual manner of training creates the transition between S and the newly learned state A for input A. Now, before another click occurs, say that the input changes to B, then the learning at the next click will be a transition from state A to the new state B for input B. This is shown in Figure 2.11. Should the sequence be A, B, C, D, ... then the learned state diagram is also shown in Figure 2.11.

Now let us look at some experimental results that can be obtained with the GNU in Figure 2.7. The first has to do with demonstrating that the system trained in three symbols in endless rotation will reject the same symbols if presented in the opposite rotation.

The symbols in Figure 2.12 are three positions of a vertical bar shown as the training set. Starting in an arbitrary state, it is seen that as the learned sequence is input (test sequence 1) the state mimics it. Note that the state at click X combines with the input at clock X+1. This eventually predicts the input at click X+1. However, if the three new bars are presented in inverse order, although every now and then the state attempts a prediction, this is destroyed by the non-arrival of the predicted input.

So far, recognition has been presented as the ability to predict input symbols, that is, to generate an internal state sequence which is synchronized to the input. This is an extension of the case of image retrieval, where the static

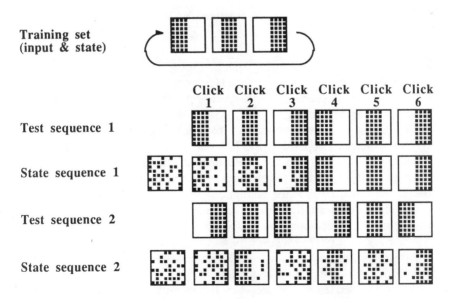

Figure 2.12 *What is meant by sequence recognition.*

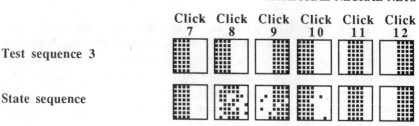

Test sequence 3

State sequence

Figure 2.13 *Recovery from a transposed symbol.*

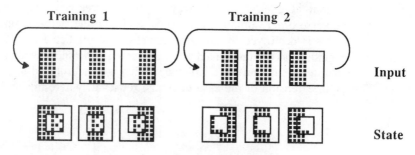

Figure 2.14 *Sequence identification.*

internal state is a replica of the input. However, the generalization of the net has the property of recovering this synchrony, even if the input is disrupted, as is shown in Figure 2.13.

In this figure it is assumed that by click 5 the system has achieved synchrony and the input at click 7 is out of sequence. While this causes considerable distortion to the prediction, it still bears a resemblance to the missing input, just on the strength of the memory of the previous state. By click 10 all is well – the disruption has been overcome.

The third demonstration goes a little further by causing the net to signal an identity of the recognized sequence. Here we train on both sequences, but with the addition of the inclusion of an identity in the training image. This is shown in Figure 2.14 as the letter R for the sequence that goes to the right and L for the one that goes to the left.

In the test sequence it is seen that the identity of the sequence itself is recovered for the two sequences. Despite its simplicity, this little demonstration shows a deep and important principle. The state part of the neural net can be subdivided and trained to do different things at the same time. This is a particularly useful feature when a neural network is used to do some planning – part of it can keep track of a planning goal, another part of a present state, while a third part 'visualizes' the next best action. We shall return to this in Chapter 7.

2.8 Learning to act

So far we have concentrated on showing that the GNU is capable of learning to react appropriately to inputs, whether these be static or varying with time. We shall see that one of the most important features of a cognitive system is that it can take appropriate actions in response to static or changing inputs. However, that is not the end of it, and in this section we shall hint at the way in which the GNU can generate descriptive sequences of some part of its state, thus not only learning to act, but, in an embryonic way, learning to 'speak'. Again, we shall proceed with a description of demonstrations that can be performed with a structure like the GNU of Figure 2.7.

The simplest form of output activity is for the net to generate decriptive sequences of its input. Figure 2.15 shows a training sequence that makes the GNU spell out the shape of the input image.

Three features of this demonstration might be noted. The first is that, once again, the state, and, in this case, the state sequence, of the net, is not heavily affected by the distortions in the input. The second is not so obvious. The demonstration represents rather a large number of training steps, twelve to

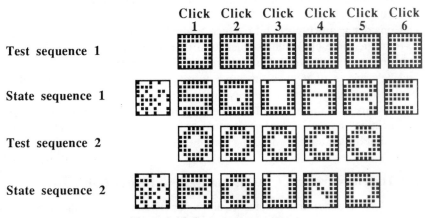

Figure 2.15 *Sequence generation.*

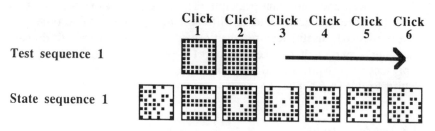

Figure 2.16 *Fading memory.*

be precise. As discussed in section 2.5, the avoidance of contradictions requires that more than 12 inputs per neuron be used. In fact, 16 are required for this experiment. Some of the disruptions in the state patterns are in fact still due to a tendency for contradictions to occur, rather than to the distortion of the input. The third feature is that we have used a 'neural' state from which the net starts and finishes. This is within the possibilities of training and may be quite a convenient way of ensuring a known starting point for the system. In fact, some neutral input could also be used, for which the neutral state can be trained to be stable.

A further demonstration in shown in Figure 2.16. Here the output is returned to the neutral image while the net is in the middle of an output sequence. The result is that the net continues its sequence by 'fading' into the neutral state rather than getting to it abruptly. This is a typical 'short-term memory' effect – the feedback retains a trace of the learned sequence for a few time clicks.

It is this ability to generate sequences that is seen as the basis for learning and generating grammatically correct sequences of symbols. We shall return to this topic in Chapter 7. For the time being we look at yet another possibility in which the 'split state' technique seen in Figure 2.14 is used.

Consider again Figure 2.14. Once trained as shown it is quite possible to train the three-click state sequence further to carry on in the presence of a neutral input. In this case the net becomes both reactive to the input sequence and descriptive of it once the input is returned to neutral. An intriguing possibility is that if one were to view only the top line of the state image, the movement of the bar would convey, by means of a sequence, the content of an 'inner' unviewed part of the state. Metaphorically, the net is using a very simple language to describe its inner state.

2.9 The cognitive properties of the General Neural Unit

In this last section of this chapter we allow ourselves some latitude to interpret the properties of the GNU in an anthropomorphic fashion. In this we partly anticipate the discourse in cognition which will take place in Chapter 4. Here we go from GNU to cognition while Chapter 4 will concentrate on cognition itself.

First, we note that in the GNU there is a well-defined relationship between long-term and short-term memory. The long-term memory is due to the behaviours of the neurons themselves, which are fixed by training. By 'behaviour' here we refer to the fact that the relationship of the outputs of a neuron and some specific inputs is fixed during training. This input/output relationship is extended to other inputs by generalization. The short-term memory, on the other hand, is the state activity itself. For example, the inner patterns (columns b, c, d and e) in Figure 2.10 are the short-term memories of a house or a tree that has just been seen by the net as they persist even if the input is replaced by a meaningless pattern. In this case, the inner pattern will persist until a meaningful input, 'known' by the net, is applied, when the attention of the net switches to the retrieval of the new inner state, related to the new input. But perhaps, as mentioned earlier, an even more anthropomorphic example of short-term memory is that of the fading sequences of Figure 2.16.

Attention was mentioned in the last paragraph. As we shall see, this is a much-studied component of cognition. But the attention we have touched on above is only part of the whole component. For example, Colin Cherry (1953) pioneered experiments in which a subject was simultaneously fed two auditory streams of information and was shown to be able to switch attention from one stream to the other at will and through mental effort alone. While what we have said so far explains that the state can lock into an input stream of information (and this can happen even in the presence of a second stream) there is nothing in the GNU that enables it to switch attention 'at will' between the two sources of information. In fact, while saving the discussion on this juicy topic for Chapter 9, we anticipate here that several GNUs are necessary to model this phenomenon.

Figures 2.11–2.14 have much cognitive significance in the sense that being able to recall and label sequences of 'perceived' events is not only a part of cognition that enables us to survive in a world that doesn't stand still, but also suggests that neural schemes have a potential for using a highly sequential tool such as language. This idea is complemented in Figures 2.15 and 2.16, where there is a suggestion that the simple GNU can learn to use 'language-like' sequences not only as a way of responding to a static input but also as a means for 'describing' the inner state of a system. This not only relates to cognition but (to push the flight of fancy to its extremes) suggests that in neural systems one may find explanations of consciousness, a topic largely ignored by cognitive psychologists and cognitive scientists alike. The properties of consciousness not only include the existence of an 'inner world' that bears a relationship to perception and to what can be learned through perception, but also the property of being able to describe (albeit partly –

there is the possibility of a subconscious which is there but cannot be described) and control this inner world.

Of course, here we have not provided a rigorous argument that a GNU can do all these things. Indeed, we have suggested that more than one GNU will have to be brought into descriptions of concepts such as attention. All we have done is to hint at the appropriateness of the neural medium as a carrier of discussions about cognition. In the rest of this book we carry this thought on to greater depth and compare the medium to other methodologies that currently predominate in cognitive psychology and cognitive science.

3

Artificial intelligence
Of symbols and algorithms

3.1 The fairground machine

> Roll up, roll up. See the amazing intelligent machine. It dances, sings, speaks, answers questions, gives advice and beats you at chess. Only sixpence ...

The building of artificially intelligent machines is not only a dream for the fairground entertainer but an ancient intellectual puzzle – a topic of discussion at salons, learned societies and in the small hours of the night among students. But the history books (e.g. Gardner, 1987) pinpoint 1956 as probably the most significant time in moving the idea of the intelligent machine from the fairground into scientific enquiry. A meeting at Dartmouth College in the USA brought together a group of young scientists interested in computation who later were to become some of the leaders of a newly defined science – artificial intelligence. The digital computer appeared to provide, for the first time in the history of science, a machine on which models of what might constitute 'intelligence' could be tested.

The group included John McCarthy, Marvin Minsky, Allen Newell and Herb Simon. They decided to apply to the Rockefeller Foundation to sponsor a modest study on the possibility of using computers for tasks other than calculations – tasks, which if done by their work would require programs which use *symbols* rather than numbers for any aspect of intelligence that they were going to consider. It is from this early emphasis that the paradigm termed 'symbolic' takes its name. This early preoccupation with precision and definite specification suggested that the object of the research was not to produce the ultimate fairground machine, but to model intelligent acts in a more precise way than had ever been done before. Clearly, the possibility of building a machine that did clever things sugared the pill, but the possibility of encapsulating intelligence in precise symbolic formulae seemed to be a prize that glittered sufficiently on its own.

The influence of Turing's work on computability (1936) was very much in the air. To be computable, processes must be stated as precise formulae (or programs – there is little theoretical difference between the two). So the prospect of programs which could do things that seem intelligent in some human sense, it was argued, would imply the discovery of formulae which define intelligence.

One of the objectives of this book is to take a closer look at this symbolic philosophy, since one aspect of it may be defective. Suppose that the entire set of the world's programmers decide to tackle some aspect X of human intelligence yet fail to come up with a suitable program. Do we then (a) assume that X cannot exist, (b) suggest the programmers must keep on trying because if X exists they will eventually find the formula or (c) argue that not all aspects of intelligence can be captured by formulae that programmers know about?

The existence of neural systems is couched heavily in choice (c) since it creates the opportunity to consider machines that can learn from examples and then reproduce the intelligent behaviour. Clearly such machines can be 'ripped open' (in a theoretical sense) and the formula for what they are doing can be extracted from them. But the key point is that this formula may not have been available to programmers in the first place and without neural nets a model for X might never have been found.

But we do not intend to get any deeper into this argument here. The purpose of this chapter is to give a simple explanation of the significance of these symbolic formulae and to raise the question of whether they really capture and explain intelligent acts. We do this by looking at the work that was initiated by the approach taken by the Dartmouth group.

While the Dartmouth meeting originated coordinated work on machine intelligence, the possibility of this had already been raised by Turing in 1950. His interest in computability of processes led him to being haunted by the notion that intelligence might be seen as a computation. In section 3.2 we present Turing's thesis through his 'imitation game' and include his commentary on objections to this thesis. This is done bearing in mind the possible difference between symbolic and neural computing.

Interestingly, an early stab at machine intelligence was being formulated at the same time as Turing was suggesting the possibility of the idea. This came from Claude Shannon in 1950, who designed one of the first programs to play chess. We look at this method in section 3.3, not so much because playing games is a central facet of cognition, but because Shannon's algorithms are typical of the sort of precision that has to go into a model of something which is clearly a human mental act. In fact, descendants of Shannon's method may now be found in inexpensive chess machines that provide a challenge for many, but can be beaten by experts. The same could be said of many *human* chess players, and so the attention is focused on the difference between human and algorithm. In passing, we shall look at the work of Arthur Samuel on playing draughts (checkers in the USA), which allowed the possibility for the system to improve its performance through learning. In contemporary terms his ideas would unashamedly be seen as being neural.

Herb Simon, one of the Dartmouth group, with colleagues Allen Newell and Cliff Shaw, turned to a broader aspect of human activity: general problem solving. In a sense this work, described in section 3.4, was the forerunner of what has more recently been called the 'expert system' (explained in section 3.7). But Simon's work is significant because it further fuelled the idea that important areas of cognition may be modelled by computable formulae. Another approach to problem solving came from work at MIT on artificial intelligence. This concerned the way in which a robot may go about solving problems in a more narrowly defined world than Simon's. The program, called STRIPS, would enable a robot to work out, among other things, how to re-stack a group of coloured blocks with a given target 'in mind'.

But perhaps the greatest challenge for the believer in artificial intelligence is the human ability to communicate through the use of natural language. In sections 3.5 and 3.6 we look at two contrasting approaches. The first is that of Terry Winograd (1972), who suggests that meaning can be extracted from sentence by concentrating on the sets of objects to which words refer. For example the phrase 'flying pigs' would be classed as impossible as the set of objects in the world implied by 'flying' and the set implied by 'pigs' have no objects in common. The second approach is that of Roger Schank (Schank and Ableson, 1977), who believed that words, phrase forms and even entire scenarios of common events in life (which he called 'scripts') could be categorized in order to facilitate the computer's task of searching for a meaning. Our perspective on these algorithms is to ask whether the cognitive activities of human beings could be described by these neat ideas, or whether the ideas only make sense for computers.

In section 3.7 we look at how some of the notions raised above have found their way into current work on expert systems and models of reasoning, while in section 3.8 we consider computer vision by looking briefly at the work of Max Clowes on line diagrams of simple objects. We also explain the philosophy of David Marr, who is seen as a most influential contributor to artificial intelligence through his interest in vision. This is a curious subject in the framework of philosophical debate about intelligence, as it may be argued that seeing in humans is not an intelligent act – a blind person can be every bit as intelligent as a sighted one. And yet, seeing is an extremely difficult problem for computers and this highlights the notion that certain simple human acts may be very hard to translate into computable formulae through the intervention of a programmer/mathematician.

Armed now with the central ideas of the technology produced by AI devotees, it seems time to look, in section 3.9, at some powerful criticisms. The first is that of James Lighthill of the UK who was asked to investigate whether funds spent on AI in the UK were likely to lead to practical results. The second is John Searle's discourse on the inability of inanimate machinery to act as a model of the animate kind. These issues have been argued *ad nauseam* in the literature, but our aim is to highlight the difference that the advent of neural systems might make to the discussion.

3.2 The Turing legacy

Much has been written about Turing's fascination with the possibility of an intelligent machine. It is interesting that his thinking contains arguments that have not only been taken as the axioms of AI but, at the same time, left dynamite on a long fuse under the credence one can place on the idea of AI being important to explanations of cognition. The conflict, as we shall see, comes from his concern for 'computability' in the first place, and his 'imitation game' in the second.

In a highly simplified sense, things are computable if some program or formula can be found for causing a computer, unconstrained by practicalities such as speed or memory capacity, to do the job. Turing had in mind what later became known as the Turing machine. This is a mathematical device which defined the very nature of computation before the first practical computer had been built. Put less circularly, Turing proved that conceptually there exists a general machine that could perform any task that can be specified in unambiguous terms. This creates a difficulty for thinking about intelligent machines: there is no guarantee that many things which living things do that could be said to require intelligence can unfailingly be specified in unambiguous terms. Simple things like 'writing a sonnet and being proud of it' or 'being creative' seem not to lend themselves to precise definitions.

Thinking about such matters led Turing to invent the 'imitation game'. This is often (wrongly) expressed as the question: 'would you be able to work out if you are having a conversation (using a keyboard and screen) with a human or a computer imitating a human?'. Of course, assuming that both human and machine are honest, the issue is easily resolved by a direct question – 'are you a computer?'. But what if the human is honest and the machine lies? Turing disallows this possibility on the grounds that a machine is not a good 'copy' of a human if it is different in such an important respect. So we must consider the possibility that both the machine and the human may lie on occasions and Turing's imitation game allows for just this.

At the start there is no talk of computers. The main player sits at the keyboard and has two lines. One is connected to an honest woman who tries to help the player, while the other is connected to a man who tries to hinder the player by giving dishonest replies whenever he cares to do so. The initial question is whether the player can discover which is which. The machine enters the scene with Turing asking whether it could replace the man. Framing the game in this way allows the machine to dissemble and to be obstructive. This gets around many objections about machines lacking certain abilities like creativity and emotions. When asked whether it had ever written a sonnet it was proud of the machine could say 'yes' without anyone being the wiser. When asked to produce the sonnet it could pretend not to remember it. Other objections such as the machine not being capable of carrying on a conversation unless it had conscious knowledge of the world could be countered by making the machine defensive and act like a somewhat unknowledgeable human being. A 'Who is . . .?' type of question could be rebutted with a 'don't know' answer.

Two of Turing's defences against anticipated criticism are of interest from a perspective of neural systems. The first is what he called 'Lady Lovelace's objection' – a computer cannot be creative, it cannot originate what it was not given by a programmer. If told that a new way of describing the sky was required, the machine would be stuck only with old ways. A human being might be tempted to be original by being somewhat implausible and might say something like – 'it's like the sea only upside down'. An inability to come up with ideas like that might give the game away. As a counter to this, Turing suggested that a machine could be made of neuron models which acquire experience and can produce juxtapositions of learned information. This is perhaps a surprising view for Turing to have held, as he was generally against devices that were not precisely defined. However, he may have just been saying learning about the world is a program like any other and the regurgitation of what has been learned is again open to the inclusion of rule-driven arbitrariness which would make it pass for a creative human being.

A second interesting argument is that there is a certain informality of thinking in humans, the lack of which may show through the imitation game. That is, human thinking seems to be carefree and not heavily controlled by rules. How does a programmer achieve this freedom? It is here that Turing admits that it may not be in the gift of the machine builder to be able to dream up rules that emulate this informality. This potential programming failure is often held up by neural system scientists as the *raison d'être* for an interest in neural systems. Where do the neural systems in the living brain get their informality of thinking from? While the answer is not easily found, the fact that the neural net retrieves information in a way that is only loosely (in the logical sense) related to perceived events at least allows for a framework in which the sought-after informality may be a possibility.

Curiously, the imitation game has received its strongest criticism not through very clever programs failing the test, but through the ease with which a program can be written that might pass for being human. Joseph Weizenbaum entered AI history with his Eliza program. Eliza is a simple system that looks for certain key words in a user's natural language input, and finds appropriate pre-recorded responses. The setting is that of a computer acting as a (Rogerian) therapist. A human input such as 'I am worried about my mother' might be answered by 'Tell me more about your parents'. A further input such as 'Well . . . my father has been dead for some time, but it's my mother who seems to be going batty' may be given the response 'Are you afraid of death?'

(triggered by the word 'died'). In other words the discourse could go on for some time in a completely mechanical way, and remain undetected for the simple reason that humans in the appropriate setting could plausibly react in this way. However, a cursory glance at Weizenbaum's algorithm would quickly reveal that no 'intelligence' was involved – just mindless lookup of prepacked phrases and a few translation rules (e.g. 'my' to 'your').

3.3 Intelligence and the playing of games

The motivation of most early developers of AI programs was to demonstrate that computers were not only calculating engines, but could also perform other feats of 'intelligence' associated with humans. What could be better than finding an arena where the machine could actually pit its wits against those of a human? Playing board games would be an obvious place to start. Claude Shannon, who earlier in his professional life had made enormous contributions to the use of logic in switching circuit design and the development of a statistical theory of communication, was one of the first to write a chess-playing program. With this, the AI endeavour moved from abstract discussion to a real test, and from imitation to competition.

Shannon's idea was simple: use the speed and brutal computing power of the computer to best advantage – never mind trying to simulate human processes. Having said this, however, it was thought that a chess program, chess being a game played by humans, will be *some* kind of a model of the thinking that a human uses when playing the game. In fact Shannon's major algorithm (1950) is based on the human idea of looking as far ahead through the development of a game as possible, evaluating all contingencies as you go along.

So the first problem for the machine is to evaluate the state of the game as indicated by the position of the pieces on the board. Shannon assumed that someone with a good knowledge of the game could always do this, and that a programmer could translate such knowledge into a recipe for a computer. So Shannon assumed that every board position could be given a value and concentrated on finding the best move among the choices available at a particular state of the game. To this end, Shannon developed an algorithm called 'mini-max' which takes into account the fact that an opponent is trying to manipulate the board to leave the player in a board position with the minimum value, while the player is trying to find a position with the maximum value. This process is illustrated in Figure 3.1.

The designer of the search program must decide how far ahead the program is going to look. In Figure 3.1, an impression of looking three levels ahead is given. The elegance of this method comes from the fact that only the board positions at the furthest level need to be evaluated. The player does not yet know where in level three the best move might be, but what he or she does know is that the most valuable move available should always be chosen.

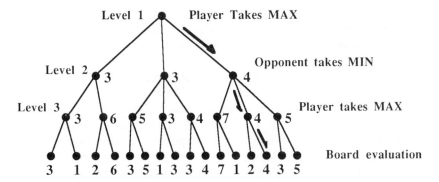

Figure 3.1 *Shannon's minimax algorithm.*

So the nodes of the search tree in level 3 are labelled by the maximum of the values that are available to the player from that node. These become known as the 'backed-up' values at level 3. The opponent is in charge of level 2. It is necessary to assume the worst, that is that the opponent will choose the best move, which is the least valuable move for the player. So the backed up values at level 2 are the minima that are available to each node of the search tree. At this point, the player can decide which is going to be his or her actual next move: the highest backed-up value of all the level 2 nodes.

Clearly this laborious process (with the addition of a few other labour saving frills) pays off, and for the price of a pair of shoes it is now possible to buy a chess machine that beats most average players. Shannon certainly vindicated this brute force policy. However, at master level the human is still capable of beating most machines. So we still are left with the interesting question: why can humans, with their technologically weak hardware, do better than a powerful, speedy computer? The point is important in the neuron–symbol debate, because the neuron seems to have a performance edge over the symbol.

The fact is that while a human is well advised to anticipate happenings in the game as many steps ahead as possible, he or she will not, as a matter of course, develop a complete *n*th level set of evaluations. There are too many of them for a start, even for a low number of lookahead levels. When a player looks at the chess board, attention is focused on very few successor moves. Chess games shown on television are most revealing in this sense. The players are asked to provide a commentary of their thinking and it goes a bit like:

If I do A he'll almost certainly reply with B: that's good for me in the short term as I can win a piece, but it'll put me in a corner in the long term . . .

It is not necessary to know how to play chess to realize that rather than doing an exhaustive search a few moves ahead the player deploys experience in looking down a likely chain of events – a long way down. In thoughts like 'it'll put me in a corner in the long term . . .' the player may be looking a dozen or so moves ahead, which in the brute force method would take forever. But where does this ability come from?

The answer is obvious: from the experience of playing chess. Experienced players, knowing that they are playing other experienced players, have associated in their minds only one or two possible successors to every move. Learning, and the prodigious capacity of remembering the likelihood of development of a current situation, is what makes humans so competent, not only at chess but at the whole business of living. Kelly (1955), a clinical psychologist, emphasizes the importance of prediction, and explains differences in personality between humans on the basis of the ways in which they predict events.

So, learning is important, and indeed very early in the history of game-playing programs Samuel introduced a learning procedure in his draughts (checkers) program. He developed something remarkably like a neural perceptron that was used to learn the value of board states. This was done once the board state was reduced to a set of features (such as forks, capture possibilities, king-making etc.) But it is important to point out the quantitative difference between learning to evaluate board states, and learning to predict events. It's the latter that can be said still to leave game-playing in the front line of interest for those who wish to know more about cognition. Predicting events is the stuff that behaviour is made of (certainly if the theories of Kelly are to be taken seriously). So learning to play board games is a nicely scaled-down version of learning to think under any condition.

3.4 Mechanical problem solving

While the playing of games is a good pastime and can provide an arena for matching humans against machines, it is not all that useful. In fact it is an example of the much more general human ability of problem solving. Life is all about problem solving: what to do if a train is cancelled, how to improve one's income, how to buy that car that can't quite be afforded.

The philosophical question is whether all these differing activities can be tackled by one mechanism, or whether a different mechanism has to be invented for each problem that has to be solved. Herb Simon and his colleagues Alan Newell and Cliff Shaw clearly believed in the former of these possibilities – they developed a problem solving program which made claims to generality. They called it GPS – the General Problem Solver. This works on the basis that the characteristics of problem solving are always the same: there is a current state (e.g. me at home), a goal (me at Edinburgh University), a complete set of subgoals (e.g. me at Edinburgh station or Edinburgh

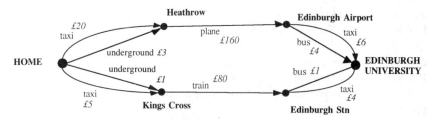

Figure 3.2 *A travelling problem.*

airport or London Airport etc.), and a set of connections between the subgoals (e.g. a taxi will get me from home to London airport). Each of these connections has a value (e.g. 1/(cost of travel)) associated with it. The computational task is one of getting from the current state to the goal in the most valuable way. Figure 3.2 illustrates this example.

So the 'engine' that the computer has to provide is to enable its user to formulate the problem in the form of subgoal nodes, and evaluated links between them. The process of problem solving then becomes an automatic search to find the most valuable path that links the existing state to the goal. Again, the main weapon of the computer programmer stands out prominently: the ability to search through several alternatives in a short period of time. The success of the program depends again on exhaustive searching, albeit constrained by the cost function of the links. There are many computational principles that take these cost functions into account to reduce the size of the search. But again, introspection suggests that this exhaustive search is not what we as humans do when solving problems. We tend to 'see' solutions without consciously seeing all the avenues that we reject. The next example makes this even more explicit.

An exercise of introspection might help to illustrate this. Think of three labelled blocks stacked one on top of the other. C is at the bottom, B in the middle, A on top. Now someone says that A should move to the middle, C should be on top with B at the bottom. As we solve the problem in our heads, we realize that the top block needs to be removed, then the middle one should be removed and put down on the surface. At this point A is put on B, and C is placed on top. In fact, in our 'mind's eye' we see the path to solution much more quickly than it takes to describe the moves. Another noticeable facet is that combinations of blocks that are not on the path to the solution are never envisaged.

Now, how do AI programmers approach this problem? Yet again they use the power of the computer to carry out a complete search of all possibilities until the solution is found. Figure 3.3 illustrates all the possible ways in which three blocks can be stacked and unstacked.

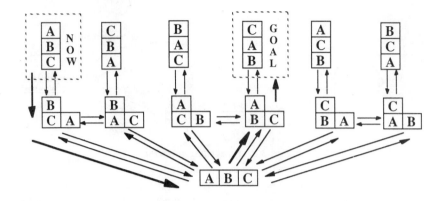

Figure 3.3 *A stacking problem.*

The first thing a programmer would do is to define a set of rules once and for all for the computer to do its searching. Assuming that the whole process takes place on the surface of a table, any block with nothing on top of it can be picked up and put on another block or the table. Another rule is to keep track of the previous configurations and avoid recreating them. Armed with a number of rules of this type the program can do an exhaustive search to find the final configuration given some starting configuration. Say that the blocks start in the configuration shown. After three steps the system foresees all the configurations shown in Figure 3.3. It has to keep them in memory in order to match them up to some goal. It may be lucky, but if not it takes the next step on all configurations that can be taken further. The key thing that is stressed here is that the system carries in memory all unresolved configurations which 'could' lead to a solution.

It is precisely this 'carrying in memory' that causes the cognitive modeller to close one eye to the fact that a human may not report this intermediate experience when solving the same problem. Also, the approach tends to 'explode' as the number of blocks is increased, and even the programmed approach becomes unworkable in a reasonable period of time. This performance criterion is often derided by those who like to believe that computing is a good model for cognition. 'Given the rapid advance of technology', they say, 'computers will get fast enough, so it's the principle that counts'. But even allowing for the parallelism of the brain, its machinery is slow, and the fact that a human sees the solution to a problem very rapidly suggests that some mechanism different from the blind following of rules is at work. Clearly we shall need to return to this question when considering whether a neural model matches experience any better.

3.5 Logic and the meaning of sentences

A clear favourite for the fairground of artificially intelligent automata is the faithful servant-robot who responds unquestioningly to its owner's commands. The owner, of course, will have nothing to do with a computing language, and wants the commands to be in natural language. The owner is prepared to step down to a pidgin version of the language, and is even happy to restrict the discourse to just those things that the robot needs to know about – making tea, doing the washing up and so on. In fact, in the early 1970s, Terry Winograd (1972) at MIT asked precisely this question – whether a robot could be made to understand a simplified natural language relating to a 'toy world' of blocks, spheres and pyramids that have to be moved about.

Winograd's method is based on logic and the notion that words point to sets of things in the world. A phrase such as 'Green ideas sleep furiously' is grammatically correct, but has no meaning. Taking just 'green ideas' requires the listeners to think of the common objects of all those things in the world they know could be green with all those things that could be labelled as ideas. Unless we take green to mean 'ecologically valid' or some such, there are no common elements, as there might have been had the phrase been 'green apples'. But replacing 'ideas' by 'apples' in the original phrase still doesn't make sense, as the set of green apples has no element in common with things that are capable of sleeping. And, what is more, things that sleep have no member of their set in common with things that can be done furiously. The key to this form of meaning extraction requires that the sets of objects related to each of the words that are going to be used in the sentences must all be held in easily available memory.

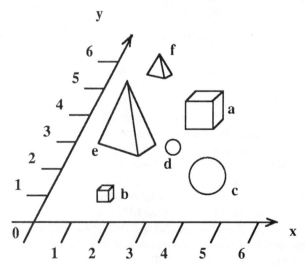

Figure 3.4 *A toy world of simple objects.*

Figure 3.4 shows the type of 'toy world' in which Winograd's robot (called SHRDLU) could perform its feats of language understanding.

It is assumed that the robot is endowed with a vision system that recognizes these objects and lists them in a database, as in Table 3.1. The labels are arbitrary and merely help to refer to things easily.

Table 3.1 *Database for the toy world*

Label	Type	Size	X-position	Y-position
a	Box	Large	3	4
b	Box	Small	2	2
c	Ball	Large	4	2
d	Ball	Small	3	3
e	Pyramid	Large	2	3
f	Pyramid	Small	2	6

Now say that the sentence to be analysed is

'Pick up the ball to the right of the small box'

As might have been gathered earlier, the key to all this is using the sets of things that refer to objects. These may be obtained directly from the database and are (for a set, the objects that make up that set are shown in {} brackets):

the set for the word LARGE: {a,c,e}
the set for the word SMALL: {b,d,f}
the set for the word BOX: {a,b}
the set for the word BALL: {c,d}
the set for the word PYRAMID: {e,f}

It is interesting that sets may be derived for relative statements such as 'to the right of the small box' – it is precisely the set of all objects that have the X position greater than that of the small box. In this case the set is {a,c,d}. The same can be done for words such as ABOVE or (in more elaborate situations, not this one) LARGER THAN, and so on. The captivating thing in this system of understanding is that all utterances become instructions for accessing the database. The machine no longer needs to 'see' the toy world once it is securely tucked away in the database.

The 'understanding' program then develops as follows. First, the words 'pick up' must be identified as an instruction for the robot and looked up in a dictionary. The programmer puts a list of useful instructions such as PICK UP X into this dictionary. Others may be PUT DOWN X, MOVE X FROM A TO B, PUT X ON Y and so on. So the first thing the programmer does is to make the computer scan the recorded sentence for a known instruction. In this case the program will discover PICK UP and expect to have to discover the object X by finding the one that satisfies all the constraints contained in the sentence. The first clue calls for BALL, and the system extracts set {c,d} from the database. 'To the right of the small box' as has been seen, relates to set {a,c,d}. Now, however, the objects that are in both of these sets are {c,d} where only one object is implied by PICK UP X. The programmer has a canny way of dealing with this: the computer is simply preprogrammed to ask the user an appropriate question when ambiguities of this kind take place.

The appropriate question in this case is 'Which one?', to which the answer might be 'the large one'. This brings the set {a,c,e} out of the database which, when compared with the set {c,d} now shows that the only object they have in common is {c} and the robot can go about its business. Its business, in this case is to retrieve from the database the X–Y coordinates of the desired object (X=4 and Y=2, as it turns out here) and take its grasping mechanism there to pick up the object.

To an external observer, the robot's performance is impressive. The language used is a sort of English, the conversation goes both ways (the robot asks for clarifications), and the robot has clearly 'understood' the command since it obeys it. So, could it be said that here is a model that will do as an explanation of language understanding? Alas, the answer is probably negative, in the sense that the method depends on having to deal only with relatively small sets. Also, even if the brute force of a computer allows it to deal with larger sets, it is what the computer is doing that doesn't ring true. If the phrase 'a large grey mammal' were to be understood, the computer would find the set of all grey things, all large things, and all mammals in order to discover a common element. Again, as in game playing and problem solving, the human would probably immediately think of something like an elephant or a dolphin without arrays of other beasts and objects going through the mind.

Some commentators, however, find Winograd's work interesting, as it contains a kind of 'machine mentation' (Dennett, 1991) which may be something like that which goes on in one's head when language is being understood – not in the detail of the computation, but in the fact that an internal process is going on. Others, on the other hand, of whom John Searle is probably the most prominent, argue that in order to understand anything, the organism needs to have first-hand experience of that thing. We shall return to this debate in section 3.10, and then, in Chapter 8, argue that neural approaches mediate between these extremes.

3.6 Scripts in one's head

While extracting meaning from language in highly restricted contexts seems to be feasible for a computer, the ability of humans to do this for what seems to be a vast amount of experience is still a source of some wonder for specialists in artificial intelligence.

Schank and Abelson (1977) considered this problem by focusing on sentences such as:

'He went into the Ritz, was seated at a table, asked for the set menu, was well satisfied and left a tip before leaving.'

Most, on reading this story would be able to answer the question 'What is the Ritz?' as 'Some kind of a restaurant' purely from the nature of the story, and without this being explicitly said. This is made possible by the features of the story that conjure up an unmistakable restaurant scenario. Also, a seemingly central question such as 'What did he do at the Ritz?' could be answered by something like: 'He ate a meal'. In other words, the main point of going into a restaurant is to eat something. This is so much part of what the story expects its listener to know that it does not have to be explicitly stated.

So Schank looked at the possibility of storing story-like 'scripts' in a computer in order to see if this could lead to the understanding of natural language in a manner less constrained than the method suggested by Winograd. In a sense, Schank attempted to have discourses with his robot in one of many toy worlds where Winograd concentrated on just one. This meant facing the problem of storing these scripts in a way that accommodated more than the limited database used by Winograd and could hold a large variety of discourses about the same topic. Also, the framework or script needs to be stored in a very general way, so that the missing bits of a partial story given to the system could still be included in the answers to questions about the story.

The first step Schank took was to cope with the fact that the same thing can be said in many ways by finding one description for these variations. The word 'ate' in 'he ate a hamburger' could be replaced by 'chewed' 'swallowed' 'had' and so on. So it is important to classify verbs into groups. Schank called these SEMANTIC PRIMITIVES examples of which are ATRANS: transfer of possession (e.g. give, lend, buy, sell); PTRANS: physical self-propelled transfer (e.g. enter); MTRANS: transfer of mental data (e.g. tell, inform, teach) MBUILD: build mental store (e.g. listen, learn); ATTEND: focus awareness (e.g. listen, hear, see); PROPEL: cause inertial motion (e.g. throw, launch); INGEST: take into body through mouth (e.g. eat, devour) and so on. We note that some verbs (e.g. listen) can be classified in several ways.

Secondly, Schank suggested that a verb in a particular classification would have some expectations of other words that go with it. He called these structures CASE FRAMES. For example the verb 'give' could have the following case frames:

give → Actor (human/animals); Act (MTRANS); Object (physical); direction (from human/animal to human/animal). As in: 'George gave the dog a bone' or

give → Actor (human); Act (ATRANS); Object (mental); direction (from human to human). As in 'George gave Mary some advice'

So, a computer, on seeing the verb 'give' or one of its derivatives (gave) will set up two hypotheses and try to check them. It will look for the object and try to discover if it is physical. In this case this clinches the matter, and the computer will be able to assign ATRANS to 'gave' in the first example and MTRANS to it in the second.

Schank developed his method in this detailed way (including a way of cutting out irrelevant phrases through what he called 'conceptual dependency'). To continue the account at too detailed a level would not serve our purpose. We need, however, to say something of the final concept in Schank's method: the SCRIPT. It is here that the general form of context was structured so that it could be stored in the computer. For example, the 'restaurant' script may go as follows:

PTRANS (human goes into a restaurant)
ATTEND (look for table, or waiter)

. . .

INGEST (food)

. . .

ATRANS (money to waiter)

So the system would work as follows. The given story would be translated into its semantic primitives. These would then be used as a template and a best match found in the database of a computer that held various scripts. So even if the story above had left out the INGEST part of the script, it would have been retrieved in the script, and 'He ate there' would have been available to the question 'What did he do?'.

Here too the performance of the computer seems impressive. Indeed, Kenneth Colby, a colleague of Roger Schank's at Yale University, used the method to write a 'paranoid' script. This, when interrogated by experts, was indeed reported as being like a paranoid patient. But do scripts ring true in our own awareness of the business of language understanding? In some ways they do. Consider a story such as: 'He went into the Ritz, ordered a set meal and when the race was over, collected his winnings'. This feels like a confusion between two scripts: the restaurant and the races. What does not ring true is the process of a search through all our scripts (how many might one wonder?). Somehow or other, the correct script comes into mind without reference to all the others. As we shall see in Chapter 8, connectionists have an answer to that.

3.7 The wisdom of experts

One of the palpable practical successes of artificial intelligence has been the 'expert system' (or 'knowledge-based system'). This is a method of transferring well-defined human knowledge into a computer so that it could be used by someone else. An obvious area is that of diagnostics ranging from fault-finding in motor cars to the identification of diseases in humans. The method which underpins most expert systems follows the rules of logic, on top of which is overlaid the domain of specialism.

A commonplace method is to give the computer a 'shell' program such as:

IF <observation a1> and <observation b1>.. THEN <conclusion z1>
IF <observation a2> and <observation b2>.. THEN <conclusion z2>

Then if the knowledge domain is the repair of motor vehicles, the observations may be:

a1: the car does not start
a2: the car does not start
b1: the light dims when the ignition is turned on
b2: the engine turns over but does not fire
c1: the engine barely turns or doesn't at all

The conclusions might be:

z1: the battery needs recharging or replacing

z2: petrol is not getting to the carburettor

Then, when used, the machine might ask 'does the car start?'. If the answer is no, both the given rules apply and the programmer decides beforehand which one is going to be checked first. He or she has chosen the first one, so the next question will be 'do the lights dim when the ignition is turned on with the engine hardly turning over?'. If the answer is yes, then z2 is output.

Clearly, any set of diagnostic rules as may be found in a maintenance manual can be represented in the machine by a list of logical rules, and the machine can happily deliver this stored knowledge to a user of the system who does not possess the knowledge. This is a very effective use of a computer, but has disappointing consequences if the expert system is to be thought of as a model of cognition. If, indeed, cognition were a matter of simply regurgitating something that has been absorbed from a repair manual, it could be argued that the written manual is just as cognitive as the expert system. The usual answer to this is that it is the logical mechanism with which the computer sorts out the given rules which is where the cognition of the system takes place.

For example, if the system were given the rules:

IF (A and B) OR (A and not B) THEN the conclusion is Z

the rule (according to the laws of logic) could be simplified to

IF A THEN the conclusion is Z

and this is independent of the knowledge domain.

An example of this is

> 'if the car does not start and the tyres are flat, or the car does not start and the tyres are not flat, check the battery'

is the same as saying

> 'if the car does not start, check the battery'

So the laws of logic allow one to correct badly formulated laws. They also do a lot more, but this is beyond the scope of this brief discussion, and there are some excellent texts available on the subject (e.g. Kowalski, 1979). But having written off the content of the logic program and concentrated on its mechanism, leads us to the inescapable conclusion that the mechanisms of cognition are somehow aligned with the laws of logic. In fact this point is made most strongly by Fodor (1976), almost to the extent of suggesting that logic is an innate bedrock for cognition. In Chapters 6 and 7 we shall look both at the debate that rages on this point and at the way that it may be resolved.

Suffice it to say here that a cognitive organism clearly operates to some extent in a logical way. The question as to whether this is innate or learned is left open for the time being. Clearly there is a trace of Socrates' Meno (the slave who at first cannot work out the size of the side of the square, but by merely being guided by his master, realizes the answer without being given it explicitly) in the belief that logic is dormant in our minds, becoming kindled as the logic of the world is experienced.

The view we take in this book is that there are things that need to be learned (for example, the difference between a mushroom and a toadstool) and that the learning process may suck the 'logic of the world' in with it. So at the end of the learning process, a human being might be indistinguishable from an expert system, but the route taken to get into that state is quite different from the preprogrammed route of the expert system. In other words, the problem with models of cognition based on pure, innate logic, where learning is seen just as a 'slot-filling' exercise (as in the example of the motor car, above) is that it trivializes learning rather than seeing it as the foundation of cognition. Needless to say, our view favours neural models.

3.8 The artificial art of seeing

One of the authors (IA) had just given a lecture to young people on the topic of 'Will Robots Ever See?'. This stressed how difficult a task robot vision is and showed some examples of faltering attempts at seeing in the vision machines of the day. During question time, a girl of about 6 stood up and firmly said, 'Your robots can't be very smart if they can't see. I've been seeing since I was a baby, but, sometimes, I don't get my sums right. If your robot could do my sums then I'd really think that he was smart!'.

How right she was. If artificial intelligence is about 'doing on computers that which is done by humans would require intelligence', why is artificial vision on the AI agenda at all, since vision is so effortless when done by humans? Seeing things would never be included as part of an intelligence test. The shallow answer may be 'because it would be useful to an industrial robot'. The better answer is that making sense of perception is undoubtedly an aspect of thinking or cognition and therefore of concern to cognitive scientists. A related question is whether the methods developed by AI workers are relevant to an explanation of how living creatures do it. To start assessing this, here we shall look at two, distinct, but typical approaches that form part of the AI paradigm.

The first is due to the late Max Clowes of Sussex University and concerns the extraction of meaning from line-drawing representation scenes containing simple straight-edged objects such as boxes and wedges (Clowes, 1971). A typical example is shown in Figure 3.5. Here, (a) is the scene as it might appear, held in the memory of a computer. In (b) the first part of the algorithm is indicated: the discovery of surfaces A, B, C, D and E. The program identifies these by noting areas that are completely surrounded by lines. Anything else is background. Also in (b) are seen typical features of line drawings which are telling in identifying the objects and their relative positions. Specifically: 'y' is the feature of the corner of a cube; 'f' is a 'fork' feature of a corner seen from another angle: '1' is the third way in which a corner could appear and 't' is typical of an object being in front of another.

In (c) the program draws a line diagram (or a 'graph' as it is known in topology) where a circle is used for each surface and a continuous line is drawn between them if a feature is common to two surfaces. Each line bears

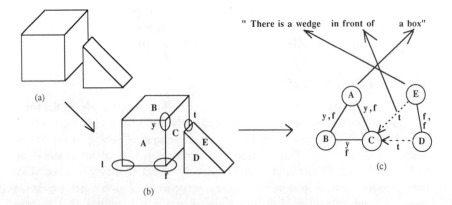

Figure 3.5 *A simple scene with a box and a wedge.*

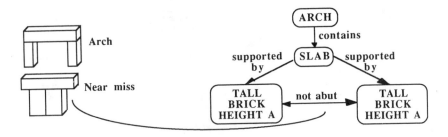

Figure 3.6 *Winston's use of semantic networks.*

the label of the common feature. 't' features are shown differently, as dotted arrows. It turns out that a triangle such as A, B, C is typical of a 'box'. (There are two other possibilities: where only two faces or one face of the cube are visible – they too have their typical graphs). The two-circle graph is typical of a wedge (there are other possibilities), and the 't' features indicate that D and E are in front of the box. This method is robust enough to be able to work out that a box is a box even if one of the corners is hidden. The end result is that the computation is capable of pronouncing: 'there is a wedge in front of a box'.

Clowes was not the only person to have adopted the 'feature-graph' approach; Guzman (1968), Huffmann (1971) and Waltz (1975) have also been major contributors to the development of this topic. Further, Winston's (1975) way of describing complex objects (such as an arch for a table) made of box-like structures, is interesting as it made good use of 'semantic' networks, as illustrated in Figure 3.6.

The line image of an 'arch' made of three slabs is shown on the left and the related semantic network on the right. Winston made good use of 'near misses' in the sense that the semantic network could carry information about the fact that the two supporting slabs should not abut, as this 'near miss' is not an arch.

But a radically different approach is that due to the late David Marr (1982), an émigrée from the Medical Research Council in the UK to MIT, where he developed a much quoted AI philosophy before his premature death in 1983. His first observation was that vision was not just one process. He defined three major categories of operations which may lie between the raw acquisition of the image of a three-dimensional object and its identification. These are illustrated in Figure 3.7.

The first of these is simply the representation of the object as set of picture points, each representing an intensity. The second process is the 'primal sketch', where boundaries are drawn between areas of different intensities or textures. In the third process, knowledge of the way surfaces glint image   primal sketch   2.5-D model   3-D model

Figure 3.7 *Four vision processes.*

in the light is introduced, and the local orientation of the surfaces of the object are calculated. This is called the two-and-a-half-dimensional sketch. The final step is to reduce this somehow to the combination of a set of simple objects, such as cylinders, in order to compare this to a catalogue of such objects stored in memory and so discover what the object really is. This is the three-dimensional model which, in the case of the example of the object in Figure 3.7, would be listed as a 'vase'.

While this approach was highly influential on the work of AI engineers of the 1980s it is Marr's underlying philosophy which has provided those who wish to 'understand' living information processing systems with a long-lasting framework. He suggested that there are three levels at which such processes might be understood: the computational theory level, the algorithmic level and the mechanistic level.

By 'computational theory', Marr refers to what could be computed. For example, in Clowes' work the computational theory rests on the idea that the feature/surface graphs represent the objects uniquely. The 'algorithmic level' then, in the Clowes example, relates to the detailed algorithms that are used to generate the graphs and the method of searching the computer memory in order to obtain the description of the scene. The final, mechanistic level, actually refers loosely to 'brainwave' that performs an operation. In Clowes' case this level does not exist. But in Marr's four-part model of vision, the primal sketch is based on receptors that are known to exist in the living visual system. Some cells only respond when their field of view on the retina of the eye contains changes in image density.

Marr does not suggest that explanations that do not contain all three levels of understanding are in any way flawed. Indeed, his 2.5D (two-and-a-half dimensional) sketch and 3D sketch operations only exist at the theoretical and algorithmic levels, with no mechanical, neural explanation. However, what this classification into theoretical, algorithmic and mechanistic levels does (and this is important to the central argument about symbols and neurons) is to encourage us to distinguish between processes that are plausible as cognitive mechanisms and those that relate only to doing things on computers.

'Most of artificial intelligence and much of cognitive science stops short of looking for the third neural/mechanistic, level of explanation of an intelligent process. By Marr's standards this does not invalidate these ideas as representations of these processes; it merely keeps the door open for theories that have plausibility at this third level, and which would be of greater relevance as representations of cognition than those that are merely deployed at the first two.

3.9 Criticisms

So far this chapter has provided a much simplified but technical account of the highlights of the basic developments in artificial intelligence up to the late 1970s. Let us now turn to the questions of where AI has got to now. The answer to the question, in the context of this book, is that AI has made a fundamental and indelible impact on cognitive science (this is addressed in the next chapter), but that the intrinsic value of the topic has always been a subject of considerable controversy. Now we shall look at a part of this debate in order to develop a perspective from which to approach the controversies that have arisen in the neuron/symbol debate.

Much of the difficulty around AI has arisen from the fact that enthusiastic AI workers, perhaps out of a need to heighten public awareness for their science, or just from sheer enthusiasm for the impressive ways in which the power of the computer could be used, made what now seem outrageous claims for the future of AI. In the late 1970s Marvin Minsky has been quoted as having predicted that as a result of advances in the development of computer power 'within five years, computers would, in every way, have equalled or even surpassed the abilities of humans ...'. Not even the development of massively parallel machines such as the Connection Machine (nothing to do with connectionism – see Hillis (1985)) has brought about spectacular progress in tasks like visual scene understanding and natural language processing. On the theoretical side, 'strong' AI believers (of which there are now probably very few) were putting forward the view that the computer which plays chess or understands stories IS a mind and can be said literally to experience cognitive states. It is not surprising that such views should become the subject of severe criticism.

An early attack came from Hubert Dreyfus (1972), who reacted to the suggestion that reasoning and intelligence could be captured by a heap of logical rules. He drew attention to the fact that human intelligence cannot be isolated from other aspects of consciousness, which include emotions, impressions, and a tolerance for, and an understanding of, an imprecisely defined external world. A more practical, but nevertheless effective, objection came in the UK from Sir James Lighthill (1972), who drew attention to the limited scope of what had actually been achieved in 1972 and contrasted it with the exaggerated promises made by AI workers over the previous ten years. He pointed to an information explosion that lay in wait in the future of methods that were rooted in exhaustive searches (such as game playing and problem solving discussed in this chapter). While these methods looked reasonable in highly constrained worlds, the size of the computation 'explodes' with the complexity of the problem. The effect of the publication of Lighthill's report to the UK Science Research Council was to stem the flow of funding for research in this area.

Another considered attack came from the pen of Joseph Weizenbaum (1976), the designer of the ELIZA conversational program described in section 3.2. ELIZA employed exceedingly simple rules in order to have seemingly intelligent conversations with its users (in the domain of psychotherapy), but patently had no intelligence at all. And yet it came close to the requirements set down by the Turing imitation game. Weizenbaum used this fact to make the point that humans are only too ready to attribute intelligence to unintelligent devices. He saw a danger in this, as people might hand over matters that require human judgement (e.g. complex medical diagnosis) to AI programs that were simplistic and inadequate, and oversold by their designers.

But the most controversial attack, particularly on the pronouncements of 'strong' AI believers, came from philosopher John Searle (1980) with his celebrated 'Chinese Room' example. This refers to the 'understanding' power of a computer when dealing with natural language. The strong AI view is that if a computer, having been told a story, can subsequently answer questions about the story correctly, this is adequate proof that the machine understands the story as well as a human being. We shall give a simple example of Searle's objection to this view. Say that English is the programming language of our machine and (where Searle imagines a story told in Chinese) we shall tell our story in Robotese.

The Robotese story is represented by three symbol strings:

bpee sbok sbee
sbee suok bpee
bbal srok sbee kai bpee

The above sits in a database. The question answering program starts as follows (we use the notation **program**):

**

Check that the question is of the form
    Itke <xxx>?
    It <xxx><yyy><zzz>
where <xxx> and <zzz> could be any two of 'bpee', 'sbee', 'bbal', 'spee', 'bbee', 'sbal' and <yyy> is 'sbok', 'suok', 'srok', 'ssok', 'saok', and 'slok' (yes, some of these do not actually appear in the story strings)

If it has any other form, answer
    'Go on capo so harampa'
**

(We can translate this last statement immediately for our purposes as 'I don't understand the question' – the machine 'knows' nothing of such a translation.)

The program goes on:

**

If the question has the form

    Itke <www>

answer

    'Dik itke'

if and only if <www> is one of the odd (first, third or fifth) symbols in the story.

Otherwise answer

    'Nik itke'

If the question is of the form . . .

**

We could go on with this seemingly pointless exercise and guarantee that the program written in 'English' causes the questions in Robotese to be properly answered. Searle's point is that, not being able to relate the story or the questions to anything at all (in the same way as those who have just read it now must find it incomprehensible), it would be stretching the point to the limit to say that the machine 'understands' the story, even though it answers the questions without faltering. In fact, we can now reveal the nature of that story by providing a translation (actually it refers to a scaled-down version of Figure 3.5, with only three objects in it):

bpee = the big pyramid
sbee = the small box
bbal = the big ball
spee = the small pyramid
sbal = the small ball
sbok = is bigger than
suok = is under
srok = is to the right of
saok = is above
ssok = is smaller than
slok = is to the left of
kai = and

So the story reads: 'The big pyramid is bigger than the small box; the small box is under the big pyramid; the big ball is to the right of the small box and the big pyramid'.

The questions are of the form 'is there <xxx>in the story?' to which the answers could be 'Yes there is' or 'No there is not', or 'is <xxx> <yyy> <zzz>?', to which the answer might be (say) 'yes, the big pyramid is bigger than the small box', etc.

Searle's point of view is often called the 'intentional stance', in the sense that a symbol represents an intention on the part of the user, and this intention comes from the user's experience of what the object addressed by the symbol does or how it may be used. It would be unfair to suggest that all AI researchers are blind to the force of Searle's objection. Indeed, Winograd in 1980 wrote that language understanding cannot entirely be captured by deductive logic because of the intentional nature of the way people use language. His own research programme included modelling the role of language in human action and interaction based on the idea of 'speech acts' (Searle, 1969) which commit the speaker and hearer to some action or transaction. A later publication by Winograd and Flores (1986) pointed out that modelling such intentional behaviour would be enormously difficult, as the computer would have to develop a 'continuous sense of being' which it could share with its interlocutor. Some of the difficulty comes from the fact that artificial intelligence does not have within its repertoire good rules that permit learning with the sophistication that may be needed to capture the 'sense of being'. It may be that connectionism makes this more feasible.

So in summary, it may be important to couple the more violent objections to artificial intelligence with the more absurd claims that had been made for it – they may neutralize each other. The fact remains that the logical, rule-based techniques developed within AI offer rich design tools for improving the performance of computers in a way that suits the intelligence of their human users.

3.10 A neural perspective on AI

As connectionism gained popularity in the mid 1980s, it became fashionable to point first at the theoretical weakness of AI as being merely a metaphor for intelligent behaviour rather than a model of it and, second, at its paucity of practical achievement in areas of language understanding and visual scene analysis. The opportunity made available through connectionism is now seen as compensating for the inability of a programmer to model the processes required in these domains. There has been a tendency for connectionists to display optimism along the lines that connectionism is now the 'true artificial intelligence' and that the symbolic methodology of classical or Good Old-Fashioned AI (GOFAI) was an aberration of computational science and absurdly overrated. But this would be tantamount to counteracting sin with sin. The computational competence of GOFAI is now known, but that of connectionism remains to be established, and its explanatory powers in cognitive science may be only marginally less metaphorical than those of GOFAI. (We shall return to this point in Chapter 7.)

But there is a way in which connectionism might ultimately turn out to have a somewhat unexpected effect on the understanding of congition, a way that was never the aim of artificial intelligence. Clearly, cognition is not one process but many. One of the aims of connectionism is not only to understand the emergent cognitive/computational properties of a given network, but also to understand how such properties could become specialized in different tasks for distinct networks, and how networks with individual capabilities could be made to interact in order to obtain greater sophistication and flexibility from the emergent properties of these assemblies. In other words, the fact that connectionist systems provide a three-way engineering bridge between structure, experience acquisition and behaviour may shed new light on fundamental philosophical issues by acting as analogies for brain, learning and mind. This is a sparse area of knowledge where even metaphors are welcome and where connectionism has an entry which it is not evident that artificial intelligence has.

4

Cognitive science
A symbolic enterprise

4.1 How new is the mind's new science?

The mind's new science: a history of the cognitive revolution is the title of
a most authoritative text on the history of cognitive science written by Howard
Gardner in 1985 with an epilogue written in 1987. The reader who wishes
to discover the fascinating, multi-faceted nature of the subject, would do well
to refer to this comprehensive book. Our task here is to highlight those issues
from the field that impinge on the neuron/symbol debate. Some immediate
questions arise as a result of Gardner's opinion (1987) that 'Cognitive science
is unlikely to have arisen when it did, or taken the form that it has, without
the emergence of the computer in our time'. If connectionism spells out an
alternative way of doing computations, what does this do to the close tie
between cognitive science and conventional computation? What does it do
to cognitive science itself?

Gardner's mention of 'the computer' is generic in the sense that it refers
to the precise, mathematical nature in which things must be specified in order
to be complete and consistent so that they could be confirmed by running
on a computer. There is nothing wrong with this precision, and one of the
objectives of this chapter is to concentrate on this computational attitude in
order to see how far it gets towards answering 'long-standing epistemological
questions, particularly those concerned with the nature of knowledge, its
sources, its development and its deployment' (Gardner, 1987, p. 6). At the
back of our minds will be the notion that, through a study of neural systems,
computation has been extended into areas where systems can acquire and deploy
knowledge in ways that are not common in conventional computing and where
these systems have a rigour of their own.

This is not to say (as is sometimes said by those who have not looked very
closely at connectionism) that the connectionist approach is not as
'mathematical' or 'precise' as the computational methods that are based in
logic. Gardner, in fact, sides with those who see connectionism as occurring

at a 'lower level' than conventional cognitive science. We differ from this point of view, so our survey of cognitive science in this chapter 'keeps its eyes open' for the shortcomings of the conventional logic approach, and stresses areas where there may be opportunities for the neural approach. While cognitive science is said to have a development that is supported by computational theory, its foundation lies in philosophy, psychology and possibly social anthropology. This helps in assessing precisely what questions this science is trying to address. We tackle such fundamental matters in section 4.2, and address issues such as the mind–body problem and the nature of consciousness which arise initially from philosophy.

In section 4.3 we stress the psychological underpinnings of the science, as the aims of cognitive science are more closely aligned with the pursuits of cognitive psychology than the grander horizons of philosophy. A science of thinking (i.e. cognition) must, as a central pillar have something to say about the 'inner' world. This is only available first-hand through introspection, and introspection, as we shall see, has had a chequered career in psychology. But since the 1940s, psychology, under the influence of developments in engineering, has taken much notice of the principle of information processing. Since much of the development of connectionism can be seen as having occurred at the technological level, the relationship between it and psychology can be seen as a continuation of the influence which was earlier due first to information theory and subsequently to the development of computer science.

Much has already been made of the close links between cognitive science and artificial intelligence. In section 4.4 we take a closer look at what cognitive scientists, as distinct from AI engineers, make of this. The distinction comes from the fact that a cognitive scientist is looking for a 'theoretical psychology' (Longuet-Higgins, 1981) where the AI engineer is trying to get computers to do things that may be useful. Some of the issues reviewed in Chapter 3 are revisited in a little more depth to see how well they contribute to a 'theoretical psychology'.

Top of this agenda is the problem of knowledge representation. We devote section 4.5 to this difficult and multi-faceted topic. Cognitive scientists have adopted highly computational models for this (such as frames and semantic networks), and an attempt is made to represent world knowledge explicitly through structures that are made up of statements such as

A dog is a mammal
Mammals feed their young
A dog has four legs
Dog types are <Alsatians, Boxers, . . . >
Alsations have pointed ears . . .

We also hint here at some ways that knowledge might be represented in connectionist systems, though this is considered in more detail in later parts of the book.

While the earlier sections are dominated by what could only be described as a symbolic way of thinking, in section 4.6 we look at the work of Philip Johnson-Laird (1983), which, in some sense is a refreshing break from the AI tradition. His work concerns mental models and stems from the notion that living creatures build models of how the world works 'in their heads' and then refer to them to develop their actions. From the notion of mental models we go on to look at more static (but nonetheless interesting) properties of human memory and related models (section 4.7). Not only are the feats of recall of interest, but also the failures. Just supposing that a neural basis (theoretical or neurophysiological) for both the successes and the failures can be found; then this would be a clear point to the neuron in the neuron/ symbol game, as symbolic representations of memory tend to be trivial. To take, as an example, the fact that a human can only remember about seven entries on a list (Miller, 1956) results in an almost trivial symbolic model (some kind of a limited list where an entry of a new item causes another item to fall off). But why should it be seven? What does this say about the structure of the brain? These are questions that may be answered in the neural domain, but are not tractable in the rule-based domain.

In the last chapter we discussed problem solving purely from Newell and Simon's early symbolic perspective (1972). In this chapter (section 4.8) we look at Herbert Simon's later (1979) review of his approach, which is seen as fundamental in cognitive science. In 1979, Simon considered the behaviour of humans when faced with puzzles which would not necessarily fit in with earlier ideas of goals, subgoals and cost factors. Information-gathering strategies feature strongly in his more recent point of view.

Finally, in section 4.9, we draw together this work and speculate on why it is that theories in cognitive science have shunned the neural domain. If it appears as though we have left out some important topics such as the cognitive approach to language understanding and both seen and imagined images, this is not truly the case. On the contrary, we feel that these topics are sufficiently important to devote separate chapters (8 and 9) specifically to these issues.

4.2 The philosophy of cognition

The legitimacy of cognitive science depends primarily on the belief that a very private act, thinking, lends itself to formal analysis and, more specifically, to being modelled on computers. This is an ancient pursuit which really does not need computers at all and it is high on the list of topics that together make up the notion of 'philosophy'. The clarity with which we, for ourselves, all seem to visualize a private, mental world makes us feel that it should be equally possible to investigate this as physicists and chemists investigate the material world. Yet its privacy for the individual makes it an unreliable material for the experimenter (as we shall see in the next section where the implications of this characteristic for psychologists will be considered).

We shall put aside the ideas of Greek philosophers, ideas which largely centred on the notion that knowledge was innate and could be revealed by 'living and discourse with others'. This notion is easy to discard – it has held sway from a time several centuries before Christ right to the Middle Ages, and it has formed the basis of most modern religions. We are encouraged by Gardner to consider René Descartes as the first explorer of cognitive science. Descartes faced squarely his own mind and his own consciousness and was so certain of its individuality, palpability and reliability that he came to the conclusion that it had an existence of its own, independent of the body. In truth, he suggested a tenuous link between the two: the pineal gland. In his view the body is a lifeless automaton: the mind controls it through this little organ. Perhaps from the standpoint of current wisdom, this seventeenth century view seems a poor explanation of what mind is, but the influence of this 'dualism' should not be underestimated. The average person will find comfort in the notion that thoughts, planning and understanding take place in our own private theatres where 'we ourselves are the unchallenged producers, directors and stage designers. Daniel Dennett (1991) calls this the 'Cartesian Theatre'. This is where, when asked a simple question such as 'What would you like to do on Sunday afternoon?', we rapidly produce alternative scenarios of going to the country, playing tennis, or cutting the lawn before making a decision or telling our interlocutor that we 'cannot make up our minds'.

It is only in the last fifty years that dualism has been severely attacked. The effort was led by British philosopher Gilbert Ryle, who suggested that the concept of 'mind' belonged to the same category as the world of mechanical happenings in living beings. The invention of a place called 'mind' was thus a 'category mistake' and led to what he defined 'the dogma of the ghost in the machine'. However Ryle's view, despite its prominent place in the history of philosophy, does not have a great deal of immediate appeal since it seems to deny the existence of that private world we all experience – the mind.

So the more recent discussion of mind and consciousness have concentrated on how phenomena that are deeply rooted in the material world, that is, the fabric of the brain, give rise to the personal experience of the mind. A comprehensive discussion may be found in *Consciousness Explained* written by Daniel Dennett (1991). This makes significant points which unintentionally impinge on the neuron/symbol discussion. Dennett forcefully rejects the independent existence of a mental theatre (the Cartesian Theatre) in which the owner of that mind acts as an audience of one, as well as the wholly omnipotent director who is constantly controlling the development of what happens on the stage. Dennett sees the fabric of the brain as a machine on which consciousness runs as a special program. He calls this program a 'virtual machine', borrowing the jargon from computer scientists who use it to describe a complex suite of programs that together form a usable package. For example, a word processing package (let us invent its tradename – SMARTWORD) could be made to run on different makes of machine.

But the user of such a system is only aware of the mechanics of the SMART-WORD virtual machine and not the mechanics of the machine on which it runs. Our virtual machines of consciousness 'got there' not as the creation of some divine programmer (SMARTWORD is the product of some non-divine programmer), but through a complex process of evolution. This evolution served both to make the wiring of the brain adapted so that it could 'do good tricks' and to create a pool of ideas (called 'memes') which are distributed around in the minds of humans and also held in human society's mechanical information stores (books, computers etc.). The virtual mind machine itself, Dennett suggests, consists of a vast number of specialist 'homunculi' that are continually revising their view of reality on the basis of what is being received by the 'sense'. So consciousness is like a draft of an article that is constantly being revised by a vast editorial board that comprises a virtual machine which runs on the neurons of the brain. It will not take long to realize that Dennett deals in symbols, not neurons. The neurons are there just as carriers of symbolic operators.

But this approach is open to criticism in the sense that all known virtual machines have been programmed by somebody. We would not go so far as to say that the thought that as complex a virtual machine as any that has ever been programmed by man might come together through a process of evolution is incredible, but would merely draw attention to the fact that it does require an act of belief. Where such an argument requires faith, for a neural scientist, the gap may be plugged by appealing to the emergent properties of the neural nets of the brain. (This will be discussed further in Chapters 5, 7 and 10.)

This selective glance at the vast corpus of body–mind philosophy that needs to be appreciated by anyone who wishes to contribute to the explanation of what 'thinking' might be is merely intended as confirmation that cognitive science is not a single, isolated subject, but one intimately entangled not only in the philosophy and science of ages, but possibly also in contemporary computational science.

4.3 Psychology as science

In 1890, William James, in *The Principles of Psychology*, defined psychology as 'The science of mental life, both of its phenomena and its conditions'. So if there is an intellectual focus for a science of thinking, it surely should be psychology. But a science based on anything mental was bound to run into trouble: can reliable theory and experimentation be applied to something as inaccessible as another person's mind? Towards the end of the last century the dominant figure in the science of introspection was Wilhelm Wundt. Wundt was appointed as professor of 'psychology' in Leipzig in 1875, and there founded the first laboratory dedicated to conducting experiments that illuminated questions of perception. He worked with subjects who were thoroughly trained in reporting their inner perceptions, and introspection was the central technique in his experiments. Described as being neither a dualist nor a reductionist, Wundt did not deny the existence of mind nor the importance of neural mechanism. In much of his writing he showed extensive concern for the way in which the introspective experimental method could be related to the cultural and philosophical concerns of the day.

And then from the USA came the reaction to 'mind' being a suitable topic for psychological investigation. In 1919, John Watson launched an attack on introspection, claiming that the reports of even highly trained subjects cannot be corroborated, owing to their intrinsic privacy. This movement became known as behaviourism, and was devoted to studying the outward response, and *only* the output response to well-defined stimuli. Much of the appeal and long-lasting influence of behaviourism was due to Watson's persuasiveness that behaviourist theories take psychology out of the laboratory and allow the experimenter to study behaviour associated with ongoing daily life. Discussion about mind and thought were put on the back burner, with interest turning to the kind of conditioning earlier discovered by Pavlov. A dog salivates on seeing food, but if a light is turned on consistently before the food is presented the dog begins to salivate when the light is turned on. After Watson, B.F. Skinner became the leading proponent of behaviourism in the 1930s and beyond (Skinner, 1974).

Skinner encouraged experimenters to discover the laws that govern conditioning. The experimental arrangement where a small animal could, say, press a lever which would deliver food, became known as 'the Skinner box' (despite Skinner's objections to this). Skinner defended the 'outward' character of behaviourism by regarding purpose and intention as a repetition of behaviour that had been successful in the past. He saw the concept of a mental world as being unnecessary, since it is inferred from behaviour and is not directly observable. When the smell of a rose is said to 'remind' us of (bring to mind) the rose, this is interpreted as us behaving when stimulated by the odour in the same way as we would have behaved had we been stimulated by the image of the rose. Abstraction and reasoning, in Skinner's terms, are seen merely as complex arrangements of associations with stimuli. The hardest thing to explain in this way is the acquisition of language. Followers of Skinner see language as having been 'wired-in' to the brain by evolution, explaining some of the superiority of the human race over animals.

But behaviourism, too, was destined to have its reaction. A return to seeing mental events as a 'proper' topic for scientific investigation was (according to Gardner) initiated by George Miller's discovery that human memory seemed limited to the recall of only about seven items on a list (Miller, 1956). This seemed to be an 'informational' block and coincided with the development in engineering of highly illuminating theories about the nature of information and information-driven machines, such as computers. So, cognition was back on the agenda, this time looked at from the perspective of information processing. As designers of information processing machines have no problems with the existence of internal states, memory and (computing) languages, cognitive psychologists found in this the scientific background that behaviourists saw as missing in the earlier psychology based on introspection.

This link with science and engineering broadened the range of people who contributed to cognitive psychology. A British engineer, Colin Cherry, an expert in information systems, studied mechanisms of attention. He called this the 'Cocktail Party Problem'. At a crowded gathering, it appears possible to be following one conversation, while another is going on in the background. Cherry showed that while the second conversation may not be 'getting into the listener's mind' to the extent that it could be recalled, the listener is sufficiently aware of it to be able to switch attention to it, if something 'of interest' is noticed in it (Cherry, 1953).

It was another British engineer, Donald Broadbent, who used an information processing model to suggest a mechanism for this human capability (Broadbent, 1958)*. The elements of this model contained information processing machinery – a short-term store, a limited capacity transmission line, a selective filter and so on. From the point of view of the neuron/symbol argument, it is important to realize that Broadbent's model represents the way in which an engineer might construct a machine that can switch attention from one conversation to another. This therefore is an engineering metaphor, and heralded what we see as the metaphoric style – a style that still pervades much of cognitive research. The word 'metaphoric' is used in the sense that the behaviour under study is approximated by a mechanism that is known to be different from the mechanism which gives rise to the behaviour in the first place. In this case, the original mechanism is neural, whereas the model is one of engineering components.

In fact, this metaphoric style was apparent in the work of Kenneth Craik, a British psychologist who is sometimes described as the father of cognitive psychology. He likened the brain to a computer that models the external world and makes sense of stimuli. The remarkable aspect of this description is that it was written in 1943, when computers were not commonplace. (The Von Neumann proposal for the first stored-program computer was made in 1947.) So cognitive psychology made legitimate the use of mechanical metaphors, a style that was central to the next development in cognitive modelling: cognitive science.

4.4 Cognitive science – logical metaphors

In one sense, almost everything in this chapter could be called 'cognitive science'. But some commentators see cognitive science as being restricted to logical, clear descriptions of behaviour. The purists in cognitive science are concerned primarily about 'levels' at which representations could be

---

* We were saddened to hear of the death of Donald Broadbent in April 1993 and wish to acknowledge his helpful comments on the manuscript of this book.

discussed. For example, there is the neural level, but, while most would agree that whatever thought is, it takes place in the central nervous system, cognitive scientists would traditionally not accept that the firing and not firing of neurons is the 'correct' level of representation. Alternatively, there is the phenomenological level, where mental events are inferred from behaviour (common, for example, in everyday conversations: 'He bought a ring, so he must have made up his mind to marry her'). This is the level at which 'mind' may be represented in literature or as a non-technical idea used to discuss the notion in conversation as illustrated. The cognitive scientist sees both these levels as being inadequate in the enterprise of modelling human thought, preferring to think in terms of abstract but clear logical formulations. Concern for the appropriateness of levels may be understood by analogy with the car driver who prefers to describe the performance of a car in terms of the power of the engine, acceleration etc., rather than at the level of the number of molecules present in the cylinder as a function of time, or of the attractiveness of the advertising.

But this leaves open the question of what is the appropriate level for representing the mechanisms of thought? We could think that the neurons are the molecules, but what are the ears, engines and systems of the human mind? It is hardly surprising that the seekers of clean descriptions would show an interest in the work of artificial intelligence experts. Their fairground machines (see Chapter 3) contain systems that play chess, solve problems, maybe understand language and sometimes describe visual scenes. So the level of AI computation naturally seems a direct and relevant way of discussing what is involved in solving problems or playing chess. Margaret Boden, a British philosopher, has been instrumental in bringing AI to the attention of those interested in psychology and philosophy on the premiss that its models of thought are clearer than those of previous theories and they are patently correct, as they can be demonstrated to operate on a computer (Boden, 1981).

An example of this precision applied in psychology is the work of Colby (1975) (already touched on in Chapter 3). His objective was to use rules similar to those of Weizenbaum's ELIZA, but rather than proving that simple 'unintelligent' rules lead to behaviour that could be dubbed as 'intelligent', he aimed to demonstrate that logical rules can simulate the behaviour of a paranoid person. For example (simplifying the issue greatly), if a normal person were to be simulated, a rule could say

'If the word POLICE is encountered in an input sentence for the first time in a session, then output a "reassured" phrase using the word "cops".'

Reassured phrases might be 'I'm glad that this town has enough cops' or 'I might join the cops some day'. Whereas a paranoid person (depending on the source of the paranoia) may well have a fearful response to the word POLICE, and would select a response among a 'fearful' set using the word cops, in phrases such as

'Cops are dishonest'
'Cops arrest the wrong people'

or more obviously

'Cops are out to get you'

In Colby's program there were many other rules too; for example, the responses would use rules of increasing 'fearfulness' as the session progressed. The beneficial side of this approach is thought to be that the programmer captures what it is to be paranoid in designing sets of phrases and rules for using them that are based on some theory of what it is to be paranoid. Indeed, Colby, a psychiatrist himself, wrote his programs on the basis of Sigmund Freud's understanding of the drives that motivate a paranoid patient. The programs were subjected to tests done by psychiatrists who, on the whole, agreed that they were interacting with a paranoid individual. The argument goes that Colby's program is a much clearer way of describing what may be going on in a paranoid person's mind than a vaguer verbal opinion. Clearly, the fact that the machine 'behaves' on the basis of a set of rules is compelling – enough to encourage us to see the rules themselves as the appropriate representation of the mental condition.

The argument against representations at the neural level is that it would be hard to distinguish between a paranoid and a normal subject by examining the firing patterns of the neurons in their brains. In Chapter 6 we shall show how this criticism has developed and hardened, while in Chapter 7 we argue that the objection is false, as the neural approach might actually go further and model not only the paranoid behaviour but also how it might be that one person is paranoid and not another.

In broader terms, however, it would be wrong to insist that cognitive science can only be practised through the use of computer models. The lasting effect of the computer in cognitive science is twofold. First it is the most sophisticated artificial device that has a behaviour entirely dictated by a complex structure of inner states and which, having a clear blueprint, is amenable to analysis. In that respect it is the most appropriate metaphor of the day for discussing the other dominant machine with a complex structure of inner states – the brain. Second, theories about the nature of the complex inner informational structure of the brain can be tested on the computer. It is often said that the brain is an 'existence theorem' of certain forms of intelligent behaviour (e.g. problem solving, scene understanding) and that a computer is an 'existence proof' when such forms of behaviour are replicated on the machine, and that the program is an explanation of at least one process which might lead to that behaviour.

In the sober light of some future history, it is likely that the major contribution of the computer to a study of cognition will be seen as the dragging of the puzzle of the mind–body problem out of abstraction into reality and revealing it to be analogous to the program–hardware relationship in a computer. AI programs can then be seen as demonstrations of this relationship rather than as explanations of the origins and characteristics of human thought. By the same token, neural computing is beginning to demonstrate how the program of a machine gets into the machine through a process of learning and evolution rather than the intervention of a human programmer. This is a further demonstration of the usefulness of the machine metaphor, and is likely to be seen as having added to the AI contribution rather than having been cast at the 'wrong level'.

But the danger for cognitive science is that its practitioners might take too hard a view of these demonstrations and posit that a computer actually has a mind in the same sense as a human being. That would render the science sterile. Much more productive will be a study of the differences between the computer models and the real thing, which will create an exciting and expanding agenda for the future of cognitive science.

4.5 Representing knowledge

Vague talk of inner states and programs needs to be focused. In order to respond correctly to a particular state of the chessboard, the AI program has not only to contain the rules of the game, but also a search strategy for finding good moves, which in turn requires a recipe for the recognition of good and bad board states. All in all, this could be loosely described as the computer needing a representation of the knowledge necessary to play the game. This can be generalized – whenever one creates an explanatory model of some cognitive task, there is a need to be clear about the way in which the knowledge required to carry out the task should be modelled or represented.

However, the word 'representation' can be used in many ways. Rumelhart and Norman (1983) (as quoted in Aitkenhead and Slack (1985), where many other interesting extracts on cognitive modelling may also be found) raise awareness of the fact that whenever the issue of representation is raised, it should be stated clearly what it is that is being represented, and what the representing medium is. They describe three common examples:

1. The world we inhabit may be represented by brain states
2. Brain states may be represented by conscious experience
3. Brain states may be represented by theories of representation

We have already hinted at the fact that in the neuron/symbol debate it is the nature of representation that is at stake. Connectionists believe that the states of neural networks provide a representation of the world we inhabit and, moreover, may be used to develop a theory of representation of the

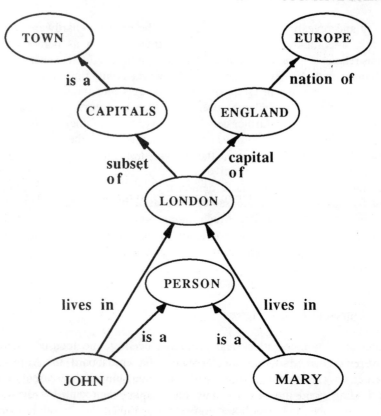

Figure 4.1 *A semantic network.*

dynamics of brain states in general. Here we concentrate briefly on the symbolic techniques of representation which have dominated cognitive science, and which, as may be expected, are closely aligned with the formal ways in which things may be represented on a computer. The first of these is the 'semantic network' which is deeply couched in the properties of sets. Say that we wish to represent the world statement 'Mary and John are people who live in London, which is the capital of England, a constituent nation of Europe'. A semantic network for this is shown in Figure 4.1.

There is a technical consistency here from the point of view of doing this on a computer, as all the programmer needs is to be able to store tables headed 'Object 1', 'Relation' and 'Object 2'. In computing terms this is simply a database. Part of the database that stores the semantic network of Figure 4.1 is shown below:

Object 1	Relation	Object 2
Mary	is a	person
Mary	lives in	London
. . .	. . .	. . .
London	capital of	England
London	subset of	capitals
capital(s)	is a (are)	town(s)

Clearly this database could answer questions by following simple rules, such as

'Who is X' requires that the computer finds X in the Object 1 column and 'is a' in the Relation column. The answer to the question is found in the Object 2 column.

Note that if the task were one of verifying a statement such as 'Mary lives in England' it would take longer to extract this from the database than 'Mary lives in London', as the computer would need to acess the data at least twice to discover whether there was a link between Mary and England. This indirectness is called 'inheritance' which is a useful property as it saves on the number of entries in the database. That is, 'Mary lives in England' is implicit in the database without a separate entry having been created for it.

In fact, the notion of a semantic network arose from tests on humans carried out by Collins and Quillian (1969), who found that human subjects could verify statements such as 'a canary is yellow' more rapidly than 'a canary eats food'. This suggests that, in some way, the brain uses linked inheritance properties to save on its database entries in the same way as has been done in the above example. In the neuron/symbol context, it is interesting that Rumelhart and McClelland, in trying to work out how the brain may become a semantic store, came to the conclusion that a connectionist system is ideal for the purpose. They virtually coined the phrase 'Parallel Distributed Processing' to mean 'connectionism' in the edition of the seminal pair of volumes under that title (1986).

It should not be thought that semantic networks are the only form of representation of factual knowledge developed by cognitive scientists. A glance at a textbook will reveal concepts such as 'frames' (where information in different databases may be linked by things called pointers) and 'schemas'. Schemas are generalized databases organised in a hierarchical manner – schemas contain subschemas and so on. Each schema is a bit like the 'script' we described in connection with language understanding in the previous chapter. It is designed to provide a context for artificial reasoning. So 'high chair' in the phrase ' . . . McEnroe shook the high chair . . . ' would be distinguished from its meaning in ' . . . baby Joe shook the high chair . . . ' as 'McEnroe' in the first case would evoke the TENNIS schema, while 'baby Joe' in the second would evoke the HOME WITH BABY schema.

The above types of representation are called 'declarative' in the sense that the knowledge is simply declared to the computer (in a more or less structured way, depending on whether semantic networks, frames or schemas are used). There is another style of representation, which is generally known as being 'procedural'. For example, the detailed move-searching algorithm employed by a chess-playing program is procedural knowledge. Even the method of verifying indirectly linked concepts in semantic nets such as that described for Figure 4.1 is a procedural representation. The division between these forms of representations has led to partisan support and is on occasions described as a controversy. However, it seems obvious that a properly designed computer model of cognition will make use of both of these methods of representation.

The key issue for discussions about neurons and symbols, however, is whether the neural domain can support these metaphors of mechanisms of human thought. Later (in Chapter 6) we describe the arguments of those who suggest that connectionism is particularly deficient in the representation of procedural knowledge and argue (in Chapter 7) that there is little difference between conventional and connectionist computers in so far as being able to sustain the representations discussed in this section. The important contribution to be made by the neural paradigm is concerned with how such representations could enter a machine through learning rather than programming, thus facing squarely this most important aspect of cognition, which enthusiam for programming has tended to eclipse.

4.6 The mind machine

The models discussed above have the characteristic that they each refer to a circumscribed area of cognition – language understanding, problem solving, and so on. But some cognitive scientists had greater ambitions – the development of a comprehensive representation of mind itself. Of course, such ambitions have to be relegated to the level of theory and philosophy rather than something that may be demonstrated on a computer. Even the simple properties of an average human mind (e.g. knowledge of a million and one things) would currently be rather difficult to enter into a computer, never mind getting the computer to use these in an active way. The first contribution to a formal theory of the working of the mind which should be noted by those interested in the neuron/symbol question is that of Philip Johnson-Laird (1983).

Consider this simple experiment. A subject is given a sequence of statements such as:

the glass is to the left of the bottle
the bun is to the right of the bottle
the cup is in front of the glass
the ashtray is in front of the bun

This is what Johnson-Laird calls a *determinate* description, as there is only one way of visualizing it. This is shown below:

glass   bottle   bun
cup   ashtray

He also presents some subjects with *indeterminate* descriptions such as:

the glass is to the left of the bottle
the bun is to the right of the glass
the cup is in front of the glass
the ashtray is in front of the bun

There are two ways of visualizing this (if interpreted precisely). The first is

glass   bottle   bun
cup   ashtray

while the second is

glass   bun   bottle
cup   ashtray

Subjects were then shown diagrams and asked to judge whether these were consistent with the description or not. They were also given simple memory tests. The results suggest that subjects actually visualize the determinate descriptions and remember the 'scene', whereas for the indeterminate descriptions they remember the linguistic statements and come to conclusions by replaying these to themselves. The first of these processes leads Johnson-Laird to conclude that there are mechanisms in the mind that are not easily described as being either declarative or procedural. They are truly 'mental models'. When seemingly deprived of such models by indeterminate descriptions (multiple models may be hard to store and access) the mode of thinking appears to change to something that could be described as procedural and declarative (e.g. 'if X is in front of W and Z is in front Y and Y is to the right of W then Z is to the right of X'). Readers may notice that a visualization of this statement appears to be easier than some logical assessment, so the latter would be used only when the visual representation appears to be faulty or ambiguous.

These observations actually pose a challenge for neural system research. Mental models may well be explicable in neural terms, while the symbolic mode is better suited to the representation of declarative and procedural knowledge. The connectionist who sees the task as being that of explaining how the brain works, will need to explain how the declarative and procedural knowledge may be learned by a neural system, while the engineer will recognize that designing intelligent systems requires the best of AI in cooperation with the best of connectionism – it is truly a hybrid discipline.

But Johnson-Laird is not the only one who has attempted to formalize the properties of mind on a grander scale. Several authors have suggested that the mind, being a product of a parallel brain, is in itself modular, where the modules are specialists 'who' can be described in declarative ways and who cooperate as a society to create what can be described as 'mind'. Notable are Minsky's 'Society of Mind' (1985), Fodor's 'Modularity of Mind' (1983) and Dennett's 'Multiple Drafts' model (1991). These are appealing metaphors which unfortunately unanimously fail to indicate how such structures are created during a person's lifetime. To be fair, Dennett's and Minsky's models postulate complex evolutionary processes which are at work in bringing these gangs of experts into existence and action.

Fodor is seen by Dennett as being out of step in suggesting that modules of mind are logically powerful and therefore inherited. We believe that this is fruitful hunting ground for connectionism. Cognitive science has embraced the power of logic, but cannot reconcile this with the inability of computer-based models to do anything without the intervention of a competent pro-grammer. Take away the programmer and cognitive science is left with appeals to a vague notion of evolution in answer to the question: how do these specialist modules come into existence? The neural paradigm can be helpful in answering some deep questions, such as the extent to which physical structure (which is the only thing that can be inherited through genetic action) can carry 'specialisms', and to what exent evolution is responsible for developing appropriate flexibility and adaptivity which eventually gets rid of the programmer.

4.7 Memories are made of this

Much of what has been said so far on cognitive science has depicted those interested in cognition borrowing concepts from computer science and using them as metaphors in informationally based theories of cognition. But one of the oldest metaphors, which travelled in the opposite direction, is the idea of memory. Memory is an essential component of any computer. It is a standard measure of the size of a computer, it exists separately from the body of com-puters as magnetic tapes, floppy disks and, in days gone by, as streamers of paper tape with information punched in as patterns of holes. The memory of a computer was central to the celebrated report by John Von Neumann in 1947, in that he suggested that not only can data be stored in a computer (as had been done in machines using electromagnetic relay switches and valves prior to his design), but also the program which makes the machine do its work. The program could be held in a specific part of the memory and accessed sequentially to get the job done.

Indeed, Von Neumann's design was explicitly cast around a metaphor of a human being doing a calculation. She generally knows what she wants to do (the program is 'in her head') and she keeps only a limited amount of intermediate data in her head. The possibility of making intermediate data stores of proportions much greater than those that a human can keep in her head and programs much more complex than a human could ever remember led to much of the reputation of computers being super-smart and the fears that they might, some day, take off on their own and dominate the world. The useful side of this evident exaggeration has been the fact that it draws attention to the difference between the electronic memory and its metaphoric parent – the brain.

Where a computer memory is like a vast filing cabinet (all its data sits in filing folders with coded labels called addresses), human memory is an active, responsive organ which constantly retrieves information useful to the survival of the organism. Where the computer memory needs to be searched by scanning its coded labels, human memory is addressed by content. It is this difference that makes it very difficult for pattern recognition programs to run on a computer, while the retrieval of the meaning of patterns is the natural memory mode in brains. In parenthesis, neural computers have redressed this balance. As has been seen in Chapter 2, the memory mode in neural nets with feedback is associative and reactive to content. In the next chapter we present the basics of a general theory which allows formal descriptions of different kinds of memory (automata theory). Now, it is interesting to note that where computer memory was loosely based on human memory, the influence then began to work in reverse, and models of human memory started to look like the block diagram of a computer.

As computer technology and jargon became better known and used, cognitive psychologists started using computer memory components in models of human cognition. For example, descriptions of short-term memory could be found along the lines of 'a buffer register with a feedback loop for rehearsals' and long-term memory could be depicted as a computer store. So the metaphor has done a complete circle.

To explain this in greater detail it is worth looking at what is possibly the most influential example of a computer-based model of memory, that of Atkinson and Shiffrin (1968) (shown in a simplified form in Figure 4.2). Any sensory stimulus is seen as being stored in a 'buffer register' (in electronics, a register is a group of two-state elements – called flip-flops – which can be set to hold a binary message – such as 000101 – in the expectation that it will be transmitted to some other part of the system in a short while). From this buffer, the information is passed into a short-term memory register, which has limited capacity and in which information is expected not to last for more than fifteen or thirty seconds. But the organism is capable of shifting this information into a 'rehearsal register' if it is of any importance. After rehearsal, some information is admitted to a computer-like store where it is more securely lodged – but not as securely as in a computer (it could be confused by external influences).

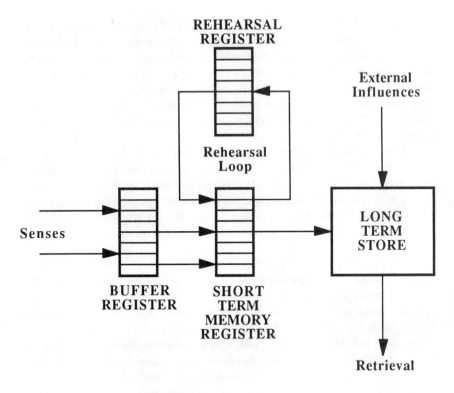

Figure 4.2 *A typical memory description (simplified Atkinson–Shiffrin model).*

While these models fit data generated by experimenters, unfortunately they do not have any power of explanation. They are merely a language for the expression of such results in the realm of information processing. Using a computer store as a model of memory begs more questions than it answers: how are the address labels for information retrieval from the store generated and controlled? Why are certain things harder to recall than others? But above all, where is the grand master that controls what should go into the rehearsal register and what enters the long-term store? The computer metaphor has its pitfalls: computers need control programs (called operating systems). Using a computer model for some aspect of cognition requires that something should be said about the operating system that makes that model tick. This is rarely done . . . .

To be fair, more recent work on memory has concentrated on why it is that some things are remembered and others not (for a review, see Baddeley, 1982), what the effects of context are, and how what is being remembered is influenced by what is known already. Both the issues of the memory of faces and of remembering words in and out of some context have occupied researchers in the years since the Atkinson–Shiffrin model was first postulated, and psychologists have moved towards explanations that take into account the difference between the recall of factual stories (episodic memory) and recall dependent on the meaning of observations (semantic memory – such as 'he was being unpleasant' as a recall of a scene where he was shouting abuse).

The point we wish to highlight is that the simple neural models seen in Chapter 2, and some of the neural automata that will be discussed in the next chapter, have, as a natural emergent property, some of the features that explain that there need not be a grand operating system which controls long- and short-term memory. A neural net will recall events by association and a single net shows both short- and long-term memory characteristics, depending on the way it is structured and exposed to the information it is supposed to learn. This is fertile ground for the appropriate modelling of the results of experiments in the memory domain.

4.8 Solving more problems

In the last chapter we saw that the seminal approach to mechanisms that solve problems was Newell, Simon and Shaw's General Problem Solver. Its appeal to the method of reducing the gap between 'where you are' and 'where you would like to be' resonates well with a mode which humans use and is therefore often quoted as a contribution to cognitive science. Its performance, too, was interesting, as the system could be demonstrated to resolve some well-known puzzles such as that of the 'Towers of Hanoi' and 'Cannibals and Missionaries'. However, this line of modelling of human problem solving was gradually abandoned, as there are clearly many problem areas in which solutions are needed where the 'means' and 'ends' are not immediately distinguishable, and reasoning becomes central to the endeavour. From the point of view of the arguments presented in this book, however, the GPS is historically very important. It represented the establishment of the philosophy that human reasoning is a symbolic affair. The outward solving of problems was accomplished by an inward representation of the problem by a set of symbols and rules for manipulating – this is a powerful metaphor which dominates cognitive science even now.

However, it is of some interest to look at the way in which Simon (1979) reviewed the process of problem solving seven years after the appearance of GPS. The confirmation of the use of symbols comes from the fact that Simon now no longer talks of goals, but of nodes of a problem space. Each node is a 'state of knowledge'. Instead of insisting on global means and ends, Simon now sees the transition from one state of knowledge to another as depending not only on global arguments, but also on local ones associated with that particular node. Instead of cost functions or 'distances' Simon refers to some measure of 'getting warmer'.

So far, this represents only a shift in terminology rather than methodology, but more significant is the addition of several new concerns. The first of these takes cognizance of some psychological experiments, during which it was observed that subjects faced with a problem perform mini-experiments in order to gather information. The mini-experiments are not so much ways of reducing distances from goals as ways of generating batches of problem nodes, one of which might be recognized as easily leading to a goal. Say you have 15 apples, and you want to divide them between Mary and Jane, so that Jane gets twice as many apples as Mary. (Assume also that you know no helpful algebra.) You might try a few things. Try giving Jane 8 apples, leaving Mary with 7. You recognize that 8 is not twice 7. However, you have also gathered the information that 8 is not big enough and you try 11, say, for Jane. Mary gets only 4 which is now less than half of 11, so 11 is too big. You have now learned that the answer must be to give Jane either 10 or 9 apples, and 10 is recognized as being right while 9 is not. In formal terms, the experimentation leads to knowledge being added to the states of the problem, and this helps with homing in on the solution.

A second added mechanism is that of a better use of pattern recognition (or perception in cognitive terms). Given the apple division problem, many would immediately recall that the 10–5 split has the necessary properties. The mapping of the statement of the problem into this conclusion may be akin to the mapping that takes place when any perceptual input is recognized. Indeed, there are echoes here of the game-playing situations mentioned in the last chapter. Good chess players sometimes rely on this technique – a board position is recognized in terms of a good next move, without endless lookahead computations.

But how does Simon reconcile this pattern recognition activity with his faith in symbols? His examples are similar to:

If X <is red> AND <is round> AND <has a stalk> THEN X <is an apple>.

(Words in <chevrons> are symbols.)

Unfortunately, this runs into the problem that pattern recognition is one of the aspects of cognition that can least well be described in a symbolic, logical way. Say the task were one of recognizing whether a face is smiling or frowning. The number of measurements of features could be several millions, and the pre-processing this implies quickly convinces that this is not appropriately described as a symbolic process. It is often a massively parallel task best done by an adaptive mechanism which learns the rules rather than having them specified beforehand by a designer. This is the task for a neural net – indeed, the WISARD neural net has been shown to be capable of carrying out the smile/frown task extremely rapidly as a demonstration of how neural nets can step in where the symbolic approach collapses (Aleksander and Morton, 1990, Ch. 5).

Other extensions of Simon's work are in the area of problem representation and the resolution of ill-posed problems. The first is often tested using verbal descriptions of problems (e.g. ' . . . there were three missionaries and

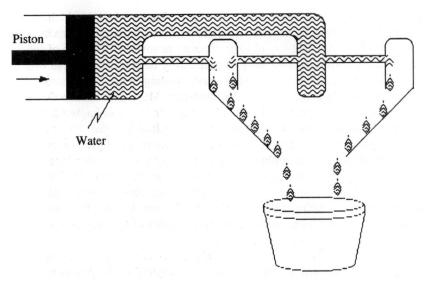

Figure 4.3 *A hydraulic puzzle: how long will it take to fill the bucket?*

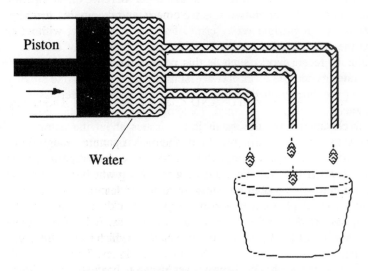

Figure 4.4 *The hydraulic puzzle redrawn.*

three cannibals . . . '). The modelling of this process relies heavily on language understanding and does not rely on models of problem solving.

However, Simon showed that people create representations very closely related to the problem description as given, even if an alternative description might be simpler. For example, a visually presented problem, as in Figure 4.3, is solved with less ease then exactly the same problem as re-drawn in Figure 4.4.

We have carried out tests with students in electrical engineering with an electrical version of this problem (where the difference between the two representations is even greater) and found that very few actually 'redraw in their heads' the difficult version to create the easy one. The few who do 'redraw' solve the problem, and many of those who don't never solve it at all. The point of all this, which is also evident in the way that people approach ill-structured problems, is that strategic aspects of problem solving are very much a function of the experience and knowledge of the individual problem solver – all a long way from the means–ends analysis of the GPS.

4.9 A postscript on cognitive science

The picture of cognitive science which we have painted in this chapter is undoubtedly that of a symbolic enterprise. The question so far unresolved is whether this is complete without a consideration of the neural mechanisms that are being described by a symbolic methodology. While the details of this debate are matters for the rest of this book, here we draw together some of the domains that cognitive science covers and comment on where some opportunities might lie.

On the whole, philosophers have tended to keep away from the neural domain. In recent work, such as that of Dennett (1991), details about the firing rates of neurons, connectivity measurements and the like are dismissed as being too fine-grained to say anything grand about deep issues such as consciousness and the brain–mind problem. This could be criticized by analogy. Is it irrelevant to discussions of grand issues about the nature of matter to refer to molecular structure, and the way in which the behaviour of atoms contribute? While a carpenter who describes the properties of different forms of wood in symbolic ways (e.g. 'if you want lasting furniture you must use hardwood') need not know about physics to do the work, this does not mean that a physical understanding of what differentiates wood from plastic, say, is not useful. In fact, one would argue that the more general understanding of the world is the physicist's, while the carpenter's view is specialized.

Cognitive science has perhaps not yet grown to the level of maturity where the continuum between the microscopic and the macroscopic has been recognized. Moreover, it is false to think of connectionism as operating solely at the microscopic level. While some connectionists are very much concerned with the details of the operation of single neurons, their arguments form part of a continuum of the science of artificial neural networks that is capable of attacking questions such as how language is learned, and how the learning of language leads to the evolution of the 'memes' that Dennett (1991) relies on so heavily for his explanation of consciousness. Successes in such enquiry will surely not leave the philosophical end of cognitive science unaffected.

We have discussed the modelling enterprise based on empirical data. The days of denying the existence of mental states are, thank goodness, over. An area of uncertainty, however, is the link between the models and operations of the brain. The opportunity offered by artificial neural networks is to be able to study concepts such as attention and the relationship between different types of memory in the abstract and as a theoretical construct. The common idea that to understand the behaviour–brain link you need to understand the detailed neural structure of the brain is mistaken. This does not mean that the endeavour of neurophysiology is in any way empty; on the contrary, theoretical experiments on the principles of brain-behaviour in artificial neural models may be helpful in analysing the results that neurophysiologists generate.

At the heart of cognitive science – where the link with AI algorithms is made – connectionists will have to explain how a neural system could behave in a way that is so well described by rules and how such behaviour could be acquired. Again the use of neural models in an abstract sense (as opposed to a neurophysiological sense) must be brought into this activity. We shall say more about the relationship between the logical representation and the neural in Chapter 7.

This type of argument applies to the area of problem solving too. If we recognize that the acquisition of experience shapes the recall of such experience when solving problems, light may be thrown on differing individual problem solving styles. And our discussions of this problem solving domain should include real-life issues, such as coping with change or bereavement. The fact that some individuals are better at dealing with these difficulties than others is of immediate interest to therapists. It is not being suggested that therapists should now expose themselves to liberal doses of connectionism. It is, however, feasible that neural system science can throw light on the nature of the informational machinery that an individual has acquired and help provide a theoretical backdrop for dealing with pathological cases.

5

Neural automata
The science of the inner state

5.1 Introduction: automata – not zombies but logical machines

The word 'automaton' conjures up a vision of a sullen android – a soulless zombie. The Oxford dictionary definition, whle avoiding this vision, begins with a slightly different sense of the word:

> 'Piece of mechanism with concealed motive power, organism ... whose actions are involuntary, without active intelligence'

In this chapter we shall look at automata as a mathematical phenomenon without forgetting the promise that this book does not rely on a knowledge of mathematics. The mathematics here relies on nothing more than common sense – it starts from scratch. In line with the Oxford dictionary definition, the mathematical automaton is distinguished by the property of having an inner, concealed mechanism. In automata theory, this is called an 'inner state'. For example, it is not likely that we would refer to a pencil as an automaton, but we might describe a clockwork mouse as one.

The reason for this comes from the fact that the clockwork mouse may have an inner state, a concealed inner mechanism. Is the spring wound? This is a secret which the mouse holds until you approach it and undo its catch. If it springs into action you can infer that it had been wound; if not, it either needs winding or repairing. So in this example we have the three main ingredients which we shall find in most things that could be called an automaton. The first is an input. In this case it is the release catch. The second is an output – the action of the automaton. There are only two possible output values – the mouse either goes or it doesn't. Finally, there is the state – is the spring wound or not? (Looking a bit more closely, the state could have more values – since the *amount* by which the spring is wound determines how long the mouse would carry on operating.)

The crux of automata theory is that the operation of this gadget (taking the simpler state description) can be described as a series of logical statements:

IF the <catch is released> AND the <spring is wound> THEN the mouse <will go>

IF the <catch is released> AND the <spring is not wound> THEN the mouse <will not go>

IF the <catch is not released> AND the <spring is wound> THEN the mouse <will not go>

IF the <catch is not released> AND the <spring is not wound> THEN the mouse <will not go>

This is typical of what is referred to in this book over and over again as a 'symbolic'/'logical' description. The phrases written in <chevrons> are called the symbols, while IF, AND and THEN are the logical words.

So, in the microcosm of a mechanical mouse we see that while we could have described its operation in a purely mechanistic way (e.g. as the wound spring unwinds it provides power for the wheels provided that the catch which prevents the gears from moving is unlatched ...) we chose to describe it as a series of logical statements. This is one of the main characteristics of automata theory: it allows us to describe quite complex mechanisms in terms of a series of IF ... THEN statements. We shall see that this method of description is important in neuron/symbol discussions, as it provides a link between a mechanical understanding of neural nets and the logical or symbolic description of what they do.

Before discussing the nature of these logical descriptions, we look at neurons again, a little more rigorously than in Chapter 2, in a logical (IF ... THEN) framework (section 5.2). Then, in section 5.3, we define a descriptive space for neural automata – their 'state space'. A point in this space represents the inner state of the net at a point in time, and links are drawn to other points, also states, that can be reached in one step. So at any instant in time while the neural net is learning, its entire capability can be represented by this structure of points and links – the state structure. As learning proceeds, the shape of the state structure changes. So a formal definition of an automaton is

'A device with defined inputs, outputs and a structure of inner states'

This is out of line with the second part of the Oxford dictionary definition. In normal parlance, when the word is applied to a person or an organism, the definition suggests thoughtless, zombie-like behaviour. The formal definition, however, includes a human being in the class of automata. A human has input senses, a muscular output and an ability to use this to great effect (balance on a high wire, play the violin, paint masterpieces, sing operatic arias or just have ordinary conversations). A human has a state structure of wondrous complexity, which is the seat of consciousness and intelligence. This complexity distinguishes it from a clockwork mouse, but mathematically even Michelangelo could be described as an automaton.

Automata made of neurons that either fire or don't fire have the characteristic that, given an input stimulus and a current state, the next state is entirely determined. This kind of automaton is called a 'deterministic automaton'. However, we have seen in Chapter 2 that a neuron may be described as a device which fires according to a probability related to how well its stimulus is recognized. Placing a neuron into an automaton requires that, given a state and an input stimulus, the probability of a subsequent state be calculated. This leads to the definition of a 'probabilistic' automaton, which is the subject of section 5.4. In this section we also deal with the way in which timing is handled in automata models – some are controlled by a clock, others not. The former are called synchronous and the latter asynchronous. It is most likely that natural neural nets are asynchronous, and it is interesting to note that an automaton can be used for modelling this characteristic. It turns out that the asynchronous probabilistic automaton is the most useful model for describing and predicting the behaviour of a neural net.

This said, it may seem odd that in section 5.6 we need to introduce yet another variant of the automaton – the non-deterministic automaton. We can anticipate its description by saying that it differs from a probabilistic version in the following way. Where in the probabilistic device, given a state and an input, we define the probability of going into each of the possible successor states, for the non-deterministic automaton we define a set of subsequent states, any of which could happen next. Why should we bother? It turns out that this formulation is closely tied to models of linguistic grammars. In fact, in section 5.5, we describe automata each of which is capable of embodying the rules of a specific, 'finite state' linguistic grammar. This requires a definition of a grammar and leads to a description of automata that detect whether a linguistic utterance is grammatical or not. It is here that we refer to the work of Noam Chomsky, which has been highly influential on those who embrace the symbolic way of representing cognition.

In sections 5.7 and 5.8 we consider two specific problems that arise in the context of automata. The first is that of identifying the state structure of the automaton by doing input–output tests on it. It could be seen as a kind of formalization of experimental psychology, one which could be applied equally to human subjects and clockwork mice. It turns out that there are considerable difficulties in doing this, even for clockwork mice, but automata theory helps in clarifying why this is so difficult. The second problem is that of controlling an automaton, given a knowledge of its state structure. This raises the question of whether a set of 'neutral' states can be found from which the automaton stands a better chance of responding appropriately to its input stimuli than if in some inappropriate state. This is a kind of 'relaxation therapy' for automata.

In section 5.8 we look at an application of automata which, at first sight, appears to be a digression – the state structures of systems of biological genes. We look at some extraordinary simulations carried out by Stewart Kauffman in 1969 which modelled the gene as a two-input neuron. This is important to the neuron/symbol debate in two ways; first, his work shows how properties 'emerge' from unstructured cellular systems (in this case it is the stability with which cells grow) and second it may provide a substantive argument that supports Dennett's idea (1991) of the way that consciousness enters the 'virtual machine' that runs on the hardware of the brain. Section 5.9 allows us to conclude that the simple tenets of automata theory are something that should not be ignored by the cognitive scientist.

5.2 Neural logic

(Note: this section has been included for completeness, in order to stress the logical nature of the neuron. Those who wish to forge on and read about neural automata should skip to section 5.3.)

Having announced that an automaton is a device with an inner state structure, in this section we break away from that idea for an interval and discuss neural circuits that patently do not have a state structure. There are two reasons for this: first, it allows us to discuss how it could be said that a group of neurons is performing logical operations, and second, it could be said that these 'stateless' structures may form part of a larger network that does have an automaton-like state structure. The physical difference between systems that have a state structure and those that do not is that in the former there are clear feedback connections (where, put simply, information can circulate), but in the latter there are not. The engineering terminology for these is 'sequential circuits' for automata, and 'combinational circuits' for stateless systems.

Staying with the difference a little longer, combinational circuits, not having states, have only inputs and outputs. Given an input pattern, the output pattern is immediately determined and is always the same. In a sequential circuit (automaton), however, the output is not only determined by the current input, but also by the whole history of inputs (more of this later). Here it should be appreciated that much of the neural net literature is devoted to stateless systems. In these systems, called multi-layer perceptrons, information can only flow forwards through the net and there is no feedback. So in this section we look at some simple examples of such feedforward networks in order to see in what way they can be said to be performing 'logical' functions.

We shall concentrate our attention on the simple circuit shown in Figure 5.1, where only three neurons are involved. Without losing generality we define the output of a neuron (slightly differently from the way it was done in Chapter 2) as either firing ($=1$) or not firing ($=0$) or firing arbitrarily (1 and 0 with equal probability). We call this arbitrary firing 'u'. Say that the neuron processes inputs A and B into output p and that it has learned to fire (1) when the inputs are both firing. When the inputs are both 0 the output is 0, and when the inputs differ then the output is u.

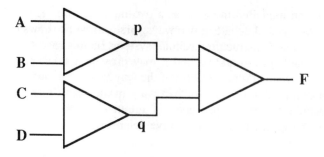

Figure 5.1 *A three-neuron combinational circuit.*

The link between these functions and logic is made through the use of 'truth tables'; the table for the neuron we have just described is

AB	p
00	0
01	u
10	u
11	1

Let us put aside the existence of the u entries in the table above. If they are both replaced by 0, then the neuron would be said to perform a logical function, the AND function: 'p is 1 if and only if A is 1 AND B is 1'. If the two u entries are now made 1, then the neuron is performing the OR function (which in logic is defined as 'p is 1 if A is 1 OR B is 1' where OR includes the case where they are both 1). The other possibilities are making the first u into 1 and the second into 0, in which case the logic function is 'p is 1 if B is 1' or making the first u into 0 and the second in to 1 which leads to 'p is 1 if A is 1'.

One interpretation of this is that at each successive point in time the neuron performs one of four logical functions chosen at random. A more helpful interpretation is for us to say that the truth table containing 'u's defines clearly what the unit is doing – taking this attitude we can show that what the entire circuit is doing can be described in terms of such truth tables. Say that all three neurons may be described by the same truth table as the neuron discussed above. The key question now is, how could we describe, by means of a truth table, what the whole three-neuron network is doing?

The task, then is, to work out the truth table with inputs A, B, C and D and output F. There would be no difficulty if the first two layers generated

0s and 1s only. It is the fact that they generate 'u's that causes difficulties. Consider ABCD=0001. Then the truth table for p tells us that it is 0, while the truth table for q gives u. This simply means that the input to the F neuron is pq=00 roughly half of the time and 01 the other half. Its own truth table then shows that F will be 0 half of the time, and for the other half (being u) it will generate 0 and q equally. We translate all this into a figure that tells us how much of the time the output will be 1. In this case this figure is ¼. Similarly, for an input of 0101, the output neuron has two 'u's entering it, which means that its inputs 00, 01, 10 and 11 each occur about a quarter of the time.

Therefore the input at ABCD of 0101 causes the four equally probable events:

00 which yields 1 at F none of the time (i.e. $0 \times ¼$)
01 which yields 1 at F ⅛   of the time (i.e. $½ \times ¼$)
10 which yields 1 at F ⅛   of the time (i.e. $½ \times ¼$)
11 which yields 1 at F ¼   of the time (i.e. $1 \times ¼$)

Adding up all this we get 1 generated $¼ + ⅛ + ⅛ = ½$ of the time. We can now complete the truth table for the entire circuit!

ABCD	F
0000	0
0001	¼
0010	¼
0011	½
0100	¼
0101	½
0110	½
0111	¾
1000	¼
1001	½
1010	½
1011	¾
1100	½
1101	¾
1110	¾
1111	1

Two observations can now be made. If the terms of the above truth table were applied to the truth table of one neuron, the u could be interpreted as signifying ½. The second noticeable fact is that the 'probabilistic' character of the neuron has been used with logical truth tables to reflect the probabilistic nature of a small neural net. On occasions, Fodor and Pylyshyn (1988) describe probabilistic assessments as being somewhat distinct from and inferior to logical ones. This is a notion that we do our best to dispel in this book, and the above example illustrates that logic and probabilities can be brought together to make clear statements about the behaviour of neural systems. Later we shall see that this methodology links neural to symbolic description in cognitive tasks.

A question which remains in connection with Figure 5.1 is: 'how could such a structure be trained?'. Details of this can be found in Aleksander (1989) – here we discuss the simple principles involved. It is appealing to see the u state of a logical neuron as a state of 'ignorance', and the 0 and 1 states as the 'learning'. So let us assume to begin with that all three neurons in Figure 5.1 have all their truth table (output) entries at u. Let us say that the task to be learned is that the group should output 1 when all the inputs are 1 and output 0 when all the inputs are 0. When the first of these training patterns is applied, as there are only 'u's stored in all the neurons, the output responds with 0 and 1 arbitrarily in time (we assume that there is some clocking mechanism that determines when a neuron is to fire – the details of this need not concern us here). In other words, the network sometimes gives the right answer and sometimes the wrong one. Our training method simply requires that when the net first gives the right answer, all the elements should change the currently addressed 'u's to whichever arbitrary output they were providing at the time. So, say that with ABCD=1111, F is 1 when p=0 and q=1. Then when the second training input is applied (ABCD=0000), the p and q connections will, as a result of 00 inputs addressing 'u's, be outputting 0s and 1s arbitrarily. Again the rule is applied that when the output F is first correct any 'u's that are addressed should be changed. Note now that pq=01 cannot be one of the inputs to the F neuron that cause the correct output, so say it is pq=11. At this point we can note the logic of what has been learned by looking at the truth tables:

AB	p
00	1
01	u
10	u
11	0

CD	1
00	1
01	u
10	u
11	1

pq	F
00	u
01	1
10	u
11	0

We suggested earlier (in Chapter 2) a way of understanding general-ization in neurons. 'u's that have not been addressed during training take up the same value as truth table positions with similar entries. In this example, no such generalization can happen in the first two truth tables, since the 'u's are equally similar to the two learned entries. But in the F neuron generalization would cause the first u to be set to 1 (as 00 is closer to 01 than 11) and the second u to 0. Given an unknown entry now, say ABCD=1110, it will be seen that the network responds with 1. Going through the entire truth table for the network, it will be seen that there is a broad generalization, in terms of whether the input patterns are closer to 0000 or 1111.

In summary, what we have shown here is that neuronal functions have a logical character that can be represented by truth tables. We appeal to this logical character in the sections which follow. There is one question which may arise, of equal interest, in all probability, to connectionism enthusiasts and to their "symbolist" opponents. What has happened to representations of neuronal function by weights and weight changes? The simple answer is that some kind of truth table can be derived for any form of neuron representation. We have chosen to represent neural action directly in truth tables, as we think that doing otherwise has been respons-ible in part for the masking of the fact that neural systems are capable of being described in symbolic terms, which after all, is the focus of this book.

5.3 The formal automaton

In order to understand the definitions of a formal automaton, let us look at Figure 5.2. This innocuous looking device has enormous generality. Let us say now (and justify later) that the heart of any computation can be represented in terms of this model (it is called the Huffmann model, after Huffman (1954). In the first instance it is binary – the terminals shown in the figure have only two states, 0 and 1. These terminals are called 'variables':

il, i2...ip   are the input variables to the model at time t
s1', s2'...sq'   are the internal state variables at time $t+1$
s1, s2...sq   are the internal state variables at time t
o1, o2...or   are the output variables at time t

The idea of time t and $t+1$ comes from the notion that there is a clock somewhere that dictates the time in clicks (as in Chapter 2) so that time can be given values 1, 2, 3, ... Therefore t and $t+1$ are just two successive clicks of this clock. The boxes marked D are where this timing happens: they hold the state variables s1...sq, while the rest of the system is working out the 'next' values of the state variables s1'...sq'.

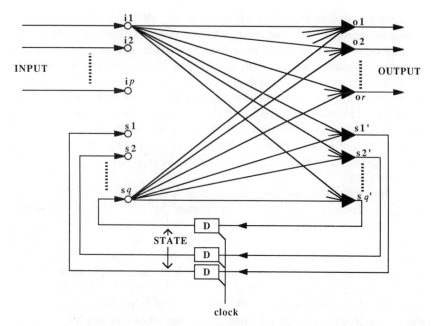

Figure 5.2 *A formal automaton.*

Now this is where the link with logic is made. Each of the variables on the right-hand side of the diagram may be represented by a logic function (i.e. a truth table) of all the variables on the left-hand side. In neural terms, all the right-hand side variables could be the outputs of neurons. And now we can make another connection – the link between the two main protagonists of this book – neurons and symbols. The symbols in this model are the patterns that can occur at each group of terminals.

There are 2^p symbols (i.e. the number of patterns that can be represented by p binary variables) that can be represented at the input variables, these are simply called 'the set of inputs' and written as I1, I2...I2^p. Note that each Ij now represents a whole pattern of 0s and 1s on variables i1...ip. For example, if there are three input variables i1, i2 and i3, the input symbols could be

I1 is i1, i2, i3, = 0,0,0
I2 is i1, i2, i3, = 0,0,1
I3 is i1, i2, i3, = 0,1,0
I4 is i1, i2, i3, = 1,0,0
. . .
I8 is . . .

We are not implying that there are any rules for naming these symbols; we merely require that two distinct symbols be represented by two distinct codes on their variables. Alongside input symbols there are, as one might expect, two other sets of symbols:

the set of State symbols on $s1 \ldots sq$ (with the same set on $s1' \ldots sq'$); these are $S1, S2 \ldots S2^q$

the set of Output symbols on $o1 \ldots or$, these are $O1, O2 \ldots O2^r$

We can now illustrate very clearly the distinction between those interested in symbols and those interested in neurons as a reflection of the difference between two ways of specifying the function of an automaton. The first way relates to the symbolic way of specifying the function and the second relates to the engineering description. This distinction has been around much longer than the current revival of interest in neural systems. The important thing is that these two ways of specifying the function of the automaton are seen in computer science as supporting one another rather than as alternatives.

Figure 5.3 shows a state diagram of an automaton shown solely in its symbolic form. An informal description of this automaton is:

There are three states, A, B and C, each with two possible inputs x, and y. There are two possible outputs p and q.
Output q is emitted only when the automaton is in state C.
The input x causes the automaton to cycle through states A, B, C, A, ... emitting ppqp ....
An input of y stops the automaton in the last found state.

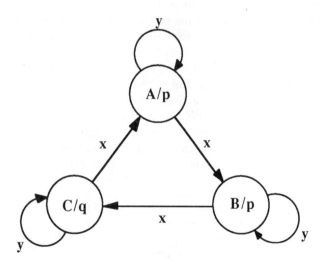

Figure 5.3 *A three-state automaton.*

A more formal symbolic specification is given using five headings:

(i) The Inputs: set {x,y};
(ii) the Outputs: set {p.q};
(iii) The States: set {A, B, C};
(iv) An Output table that relates states to outputs:

State	Output
A	p
B	p
C	q

(v) A Next State table that relates State–Input combinations to the next state:

State/Input	Next state
A/x	B
A/y	A
B/x	C
B/y	B
C/x	A
C/y	C

Now for the alternative (in our context, neural) description, it is necessary to provide a binary coding for the states and the inputs. We note that there are various ways of doing this and this is one reason that 'symbolists' tend to see this description as being unhelpful. One way of encoding the automaton is as follows. Thinking in terms of Figure 5.2, we need three neurons, $o1$ to generate the output (p or q) and $s1'$ and $s2'$ to encode the state (A, B or C). This structure is shown in Figure 5.4.

Say that we encode x by making $i1 = 0$ and y by making $i1 = 1$ (it could have been the other way round – there is considerable arbitrariness in these decisions). Similarly, we can decide that p is coded as $o1$ being 0 and q is coded as $o1$ being 1. An encoding of the states is:

State	Code ($s1$, $s2$)
A	0,0
B	0,1
C	1,1

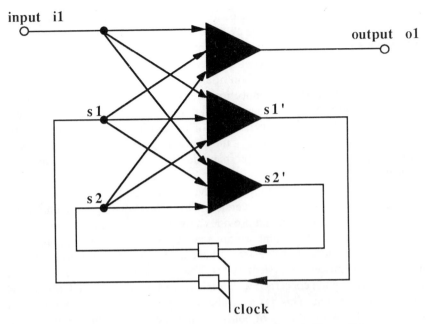

Figure 5.4 *The neural version of the automaton in Figure 5.3.*

This is now a full binary specification for the machine and can be translated into the truth table logic for the neurons as follows:

Inputs			Outputs		
il	s1	s2	o1	s1'	s2'
0	0	0	0	0	1
0	0	1	0	1	1
0	1	0	?	?	?
0	1	1	1	0	0
1	0	0	0	0	0
1	0	1	0	0	1
1	1	0	?	?	?
1	1	1	1	1	1

It is clear from the above that, as the two state variables have four possible combinations, there is an extra state (s1 = 1, s2 = 0) which does not form part of the original specification. In system design, the designer would have to decide how to assign 0s and 1s to positions in the truth table that contain '?'. In a neural implementation, the '?'s are likely to be u values, the effect of which we shall assess later in this chapter.

It is worth summarizing what has been seen in this section. First, there is a complete symbolic description of an automaton. This is best thought of as a diagram of states and connections between them. In somewhat formal terms, it is said that this diagram is drawn in a space of states – 'state space' to be precise. The specific behaviour of the automaton is then said to be represented by a 'state structure' – the actual diagram of circles and arrows. Any changes in the behaviour, perhaps due to learning, are represented as changes in the state structure.

Second, there is a binary representation which, if built in hardware, would behave as the original symbolic version. This representation 'explains' what controls the state structure, and provides a useful link between physical effect and state structure. The point we are making is that these two representations go hand in hand if one desires to have a complete discussion about how an information processing system works. There are those who attack the neural approach as being too concerned with implementation to be included in a discussion about cognition. This has a parallel in physics – a billiards player does not need to know the theory of collisions in order to play the game, but the scientist who is trying to explain what is happening does. So when we talk of neurons, symbols and cognition, do we want to be billiard players or scientists?

5.4 Synchronicity and probabilism

In Figure 5.4 there is a pair of little boxes that somehow or other hold the current state while the next state is being computed by the neurons. These boxes are controlled by a clock pulse which makes the next state into the current state. All this sounds very technological, and thinking of the degree of biological realism of the discussion it is clear that living neural nets do not possess such handy timing devices. Does this mitigate against the automaton as a model?

The answer is no – the automaton that we have described above is called a synchronous circuit as a result of the timing arrangements. There exists an alternative description of an automaton, one that, while still having feedback loops that represent the state, has no timing devices on these loops. This is called an 'asynchronous' automaton. Imagine Figure 5.4 with the timing devices removed, that is s1' connects directly to s1 as does s2' to s2. Now, given an input x, the automaton seems set to whiz around its states, A B C A..., at great speed. There is only one problem with this, and this can only be spotted by looking at the binary assignment. In the transition from state C (s1,s2 = 1,1) to state A (s1,s2 = 0,0), as there is no timing control, two state variables cannot change at precisely the same moment in time. There is what engineers call a 'race' on between the two feedback loops which, as with running races round the track, is almost never drawn.

This is serious, because if s1 wins the race and goes to 0 before s2, the state entered after C will be B and not A. If s2 wins the race then the 10 state will be entered, and this doesn't even have a role in the function of the automaton. If the implementation is neural as described above, state 10 causes the neurons to output 0 or 1 arbitrarily (owing to the u entries in their truth tables) and any state could follow C. So this all seems to be pretty chaotic. There is, however, a simple way out. The problem arises from the way we have labelled the states. In an asynchronous (i.e. untimed) circuit, the states have to be assigned 0s and 1s in such a way that no state transition implies more than the change of one state variable at any one time. This avoids the problems that asynchronism brings, but puts restrictions on the way that certain structures can be achieved, and so, cycles with an odd number of states cannot be achieved. For example, the three-state behaviour in Figure 5.3 could only be achieved by a system encoded using the same principles as in Figure 5.5. Here a pair of states is used to represent each state of Figure 5.3. So six states are required, which, using three state neurons instead of two, allow the choice of a code where no two subsequent states differ in more than one state variable. An input of 0 will now cause the system to whiz around the six states, stopping in the last found pair if the input is 1. To an observer, this behaviour would not be the same as that of the system in Figure 5.3.

The reason we have gone to this level of technical detail is to show that automata theory has the power to describe the sort of constraint that is imposed by technological factors (nature, if you like, in the case of neural systems) on very general descriptions. Indeed, this can be taken further by considering both the effect of asynchronism and the appearance of the probabilistic u states in our logical descriptions of neurons.

In the formal five-element general description of an automaton (discussed in the last section), the fifth part, the Next State table can be modified to define a probabilistic automaton. Given a state–input combination, in a probabilistic automaton, a probability of transition is assigned to transitions to every other state. So the format of the state table is:

State-Input pair	Next state	Probability
A/x	A	P(A,A,x)
A/x	B	P(A,B,x)
A/x	C	P(A,C,x)
A/y	A	P(A,A,y)
. . .	. . .	. . .

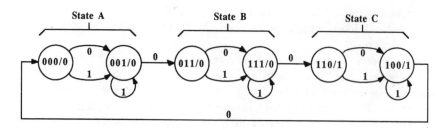

Figure 5.5 *An asynchronous equivalent to Figure 5.3.*

The symbol P(A,B,y) (say) reads 'the probability of changing from state A to state B when the input is y'. This symbol has a value between 0 and 1, and the values of the three symbols associated with one state–input pair (e.g. P(A,A,x), P(A,B,x), P(A,C,x)) must add up to 1. We can flex the muscles of this model by referring to the system in Figure 5.4 with the truth table derived earlier and with the timing elements removed.

In neural nets such as those of Hopfield (1982) it is assumed that when several neurons are required to change, only one randomly selected one does so. This leads to a probabilistic automaton, but alas to one that does not resemble the function shown in Figure 5.3. However, working out what it does lead to we feel may be instructive. So for our system, the troublesome transition

Inputs			Outputs		
il	s1	s2	o1	s1′	s2′
0	1	1	1	0	0

becomes represented as

Inputs			Outputs			Probability
il	s1	s2	o1	s1′	s2′	
0	1	1	1	1	0	0.5
0	1	1	1	0	1	0.5

Finally, we need to represent the transitions that involve u states. The typical one is

Inputs			Outputs		
il	s1	s2	o1	s1'	s2'
0	1	0	u	u	u

Using the probabilistic option this becomes

Inputs			Outputs			Probability
il	s1	s2	o1	s1'	s2'	
0	1	0	u	0	0	0.25
0	1	0	u	0	1	0.25
0	1	0	u	1	0	0.25
0	1	0	u	1	1	0.25

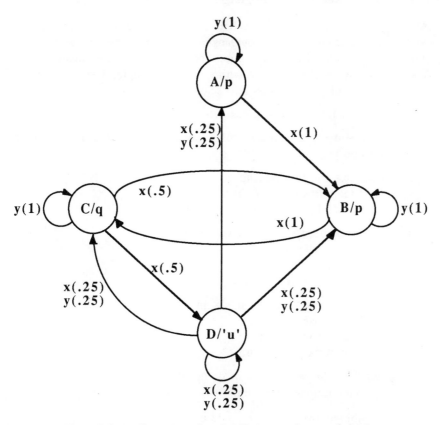

Figure 5.6 *An illustration of probabilistic asynchronous behaviour.*

That is, a transition to any of the four states could happen with equal probability. The u occurring at output 01 should be interpreted as a 50% probability of generating an output of 1.

The best way of describing the behaviour of the circuit in Figure 5.4 is to draw the probabilistic asynchronous state diagram of the full behaviour of the system. This is done in Figure 5.6.

While the good news is that this now accurately represents what the neural system is doing, it also shows up the fact that it is not doing that which its original specification in Figure 5.3 had indicated. As we are simply developing descriptive models at this stage, this does not matter. What does matter, and this is tackled in Chapter 7, is that in the case of neural networks the automata structures built up by a process of training should sensibly represent the information contained in the training examples.

5.5 Automata and formal languages

As we have seen repeatedly in this book, any discourse about cognition cannot be divorced from thoughts about language. Automata theory is very closely linked to the formal side of language – the syntactical or grammatical side. To see how this works, we start with a simple example. The given task is to arrange the following words into sensible sentences:

  Peter, Mary, loves, hates, gives, flowers, eggs.

We make up some 'grammatical' rules (not exactly like the ones we were taught at school):

  A <sentence> can be made up of
          Peter followed by a <peter-verbphrase>
  or   Mary followed by a <mary-verbphrase>

  a <peter-verbphrase> can be made up of
          loves <peter-objects>
  or   hates<peter-objects>
  or   gives<peter-thingphrase>

  a <mary-verbphrase> can be made up of
          loves <mary-objects>
  or   hates <mary-objects>
  or   gives <mary-thingphrase>

  a <peter-thingphrase> can be made up of
          Mary followed by <thing>

  a <mary-thingphrase> can be made up of
          Peter followed by <thing>

<peter-objects> are
      Mary, flowers, eggs

<mary-objects> are
      Peter, flowers, eggs

a <thing> is
      flowers, eggs.

With this set of rules, through a process of starting with <sentence> and replacing items in <chevrons> by one of the things it could be made up of, we can generate all the possible sentences in this simple language. For example:

<sentence>
becomes	Peter <verbphrase>
becomes	Peter gives <peter-thingphrase>
becomes	Peter gives Mary <thing>
becomes	Peter gives Mary eggs

The process ends when all the objects in <chevrons> have been replaced. This type of linguistic analysis is formally stated as follows. A *language* consists of four things:

(i)   a vocabulary of *terminal symbols* (these are the symbols that actually appear in the language, things like 'Mary' and 'eggs');

(ii) a vocabulary of *non-terminal*, auxiliary *symbols* (these are the symbols in <chevrons> that help us along the way, things like <mary-thingphrase> and <thing>);

(iii) a set of *production rules* which indicate all the possible ways in which strings of symbols may be replaced (the above example illustrates such rules);

(iv) a special non-terminal *starting symbol* with which the replacement process is initiated (<sentence> is this symbol in the above example).

It was Noam Chomsky (1957) who defined a taxonomy of language based on the nature of the production rules. Of particular interest are languages, such as the one above, where the production rules are all of the form:

Rule type (A)   <non-terminal> becomes 'terminal' followed by <non-terminal>

or

Rule type (B)   <non-terminal> becomes 'terminal'

This defines a *finite state* language, called thus because such a language is linked with finite state automata as shown below. The link is made by taking three steps. First we let each non-terminal symbol be a state of the automaton. Second, for a rule of type A above, the 'terminal' symbol becomes the label for the transition between the two non-terminal symbols.

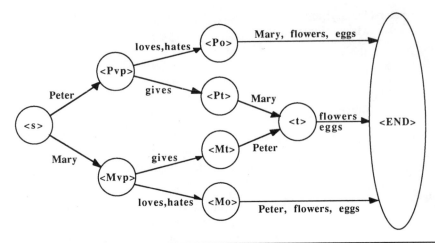

Figure 5.7 *The language automaton.*

Third, for a rule of type B above, the terminal symbol becomes a label for a transition which links the <non-terminal> state to a newly defined <end> state. This simply says that no further replacements are necessary. With these links, we can show the automaton derived from the language featured in the example considered earlier (Figure 5.7).

Not only does this automaton represent every possible legitimate sentence in this language (corresponding to each path between <sentence> and <end>, but also, if built (of neurons, if we like) it becomes an 'acceptor automaton'. That is, starting in the state <sentence> the terminal symbols can be seen as causing state changes. If the input is such that it ends with the automaton in the <end> state, the sequence has been accepted, or to put it another way, it is a legitimate sequence in the language represented by the automaton. It is also possible to add a <fail> state which is entered for any terminal input that is *not* the expected one for the current state. For example, if the current state is <mary-thingphrase> and the next terminal input is 'Mary', 'flowers' or any terminal but 'Peter', the system should take a transition to the 'fail' state.

5.6 Non-determinism and other little problems

Not all language specifications are as well behaved as the one discussed above. The first example of a complication is that, within the latitude offered by the definition of a finite state language, there could be a production of the form

<ntl> becomes ter1 followed by <nt2>

or

<nt1> becomes ter1 followed by <nt3>

Using the rules for the design of an automaton (abbreviating non-terminal to 'nt' and terminal to 'ter') state <nt1> has a transition for ter1 that goes to *two* other states <nt2> or <nt3>. This cannot be physically implemented by a neural net (or anything else for that matter). It is called a non-deterministic situation, and may be interpreted as a statement that transitions to both <nt2> and <nt3> *are allowed* by the rules of the language. The pragmatic approach to dealing with this problem is to realize that while the rules of the language allow this sort of thing to happen, there is always another way in which the rules could have been stated. Such another way is to create one state, say <nt2/3>, where previously there were two (<nt2> and <nt3>).

In other words, the two rules of the language could be collapsed into one:

<nt1> becomes ter1 followed by <nt2/3>

without the ultimate set of legitimate sentences being changed. (Details of this may be found in Aleksander and Hanna (1978), or any other book on finite state machines.) Here we simply take it on trust that non-deterministic automata always have deterministic equivalents. So that was not too much of a problem. Now here is something a little more serious.

Say that we were to relax a little the format for writing the production rules of a language and that we wanted to express something like

'ter1 can be repeated as often as you like, as long as it is followed by a single ter2 and then followed by ter3 repeated the same number of times as ter1'.

This formulation is found in languages where brackets are used. For example, if ter1 is an opening bracket, ter2 is the letter 'a' and ter3 is a closing bracket, then (a) is a legitimate sequence of terminal symbols, as is (((((((a))))))), while ((((a)) is not (because of an unequal number of brackets on either side of terminal symbol 'a'). The production rules for this example are of the form:

<nt1> becomes ter1 <nt1> ter3

or

<nt1> becomes ter2

The number of brackets is the same as the number of times the first rule is applied. The second rule puts in the 'a' and terminates the process. It was in Noam Chomsky's taxonomy of language grammars (1957) that attention was drawn to the fact that finite state automata can accept only state languages. The language we have just encountered in the 'brackets' example is called a *context-free* language. This is generally defined as

<non-terminal> becomes 'any sequence of terminal or <non-terminal> symbols'

The name 'context-free' comes from the need to distinguish this type of language for context sensitive languages where <non-terminal> symbols can be defined depending on the presence or absence of other symbols. This distinction is not of interest here; what is important is the contrast between context-free languages and finite state ones. The context free formulation allows 'nesting' as we have seen with the brackets example. It can be argued that the grammar of natural language is, on the whole, the 'context-free' kind rather than 'finite state'. This is also true of computer languages, such as BASIC or Pascal. So if it is to be argued that neural descriptions are appropriate to the processing of language-like data, it is necessary to show that neural net automata are capable of accepting context-free language structures. We shall return to this subject in more detail in Chapter 7, but for now let us look at some of the principles that are involved.

Were we to say that, in the 'brackets' grammar discussed above, the first rule could be used a maximum of three times, there would be no difficulty in defining a finite state automaton to accomplish the task. This is shown in Figure 5.8. This means that if the nesting is limited the language may be rewritten as a finite state language (The reader may wish to derive the finite state rules related to this automaton.)

In fact, it is impossible to design an acceptor for context-free languages; it is only possible to design approximations, because the amount of 'nesting' (i.e. number of times the first rule of the brackets example is applied) is not known in advance. Turing got over this problem (in specifying a universal,

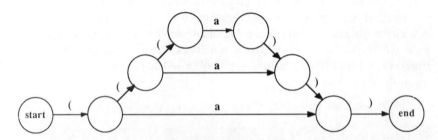

Figure 5.8 *Nested brackets.*

but abstract, computing machine) by endowing it with an infinite tape on which the automaton can effectively make a mark for each opening bracket, and, after the occurrence of the 'a', start crossing these marks off for the occurrence of each closing bracket, thereby checking that the number for opening brackets matches the number of closing brackets. In computing, an electronic version of this tape is provided (the name for it is a 'stack memory') . This can be large, but not infinite; therefore the real, as opposed to the abstract, automaton is only an approximation of an acceptor of context-free language. If the stack is exceeded, the computer will usually output an error message.

Glancing away from automata for a moment and towards cognitive models, it is clear that human cognition is also incapable of acting as a perfect acceptor of context-free languages. The amount of bracketing which a listener can cope with before getting confused is clearly limited. Children enjoy thinking of sentences such as

'In the English examination, Mary, where Jane had had had "had", had had "had had". "Had had" had had more marks.'

While the written version is helped by punctuation, the spoken version becomes an object of curiosity. Similarly confusing is

'The boy who has a dog which has a tail which wags furiously which bit the postman greeted his uncle.''

The nesting does not aid good communication, and sensible writing practice suggests that it should be avoided.

In summary, therefore, what we have tried to establish in this section is that the finite state automaton is an appropriate device for discussing the processing of information which is structured according to some grammatical formulation, even if in some cases this must be seen as an approximation.

5.7 Working with automata: from identification to the nature of dreams

Here, in order to illustrate the usefulness of the concept of an automaton, we look at some of the concerns of those who work with automata. The first question is one of identification. Given a 'black box' for which the set of input messages is known and the set of output messages is known, is there a set of tests that can reveal the state structure (which is not known)? This is an important question whenever the word 'model' is used and is fundamental if the object of some experimentation is to generate a model of the 'inner state structure' of a living organism.

The answer is that this is a very difficult task. The first difficulty that arises is that for a given, measured behaviour there is an infinity of state structures that could represent those results. To explain, say we have an automaton with input messages 'x' and 'y' and output 'p' and 'q' and we discover that it outputs q every third time that x is applied to the input (y making no difference).

We may be tempted to think that the state structure is that of Figure 5.3. Unfortunately, it is not the only structure that behaves in this way – for example, the automaton could have six states that are visited in turn with every third one generating a q. In fact, there is an infinite number of such alternative constructions that behave in the same way. What the automata theoretician suggests in cases of this kind is that only the automata with a minimum number of states be considered as useful models. The second point is that the modeller requires that the automaton that is being tested has no inner 'trap' states: there must be a sequence of transitions that goes from any state to any other.

However, even being given assurances about the minimality of the extracted model, and the full connectedness of the state structure that is being tested, the process of model identification remains a difficult one. The procedure is to apply a sequence of inputs, observe the outputs, and derive all the automata that could give rise to the observed behaviour. Then further tests are designed in an attempt to eliminate some of the candidates, and this process is repeated until the number of candidates cannot be reduced any further. This is a laborious process which is detailed elsewhere (Aleksander and Hanna, 1978). Awareness of these difficulties is a healthy reminder of the possible arbitrariness of descriptions of cognition that treat the organism merely as a 'black box' and take no notice of the possible constraints that the physical structure (neural system) of that organism might impose on the choice of models in an identification exercise.

A second concern that will be found in books on automata theory, is that of manipulating the automaton so that it gets into a particular state. This is called the synchronization problem – it comes from the need to bring an automaton to some initial state before it can do its work. For example, the language acceptor of Figure 5.7 has to be reset to state <sentence> before it can be used. In general, this facility can be built into the design. The theoretical problem relates to cases where the resetting has not been built in. In these cases it is a question of finding a path through a given state space in order to return to a particular state. Again, we leave the details of this for subsidiary reading (Aleksander and Hanna, 1978), but make an important point here.

One of the properties of a neural probabilistic automaton is that if the inputs are fed with noisy patterns, the automaton performs a kind of self-resetting exercise. An impression of this is shown in Figure 5.9. The 'neutral' states in the centre may be those that a brain finds itself in on waking in the morning. The problems and perceptions of the day (input) drive the automaton into a specific area of state space which enables the system to respond appropriately. As the inputs are shifted to noise, the system returns to the neutral area. It is plausible that sleep is the mechanism that has this resetting function in the brain. Indeed, the haphazard way in which states are visited during this resetting trajectory suggests both the mechanisms of and 'reasons

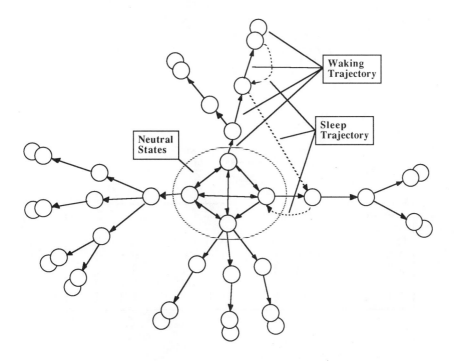

Figure 5.9 *A state structure for waking and sleeping.*

for' dreaming. This notion is unsubstantiated and impressionistic, but it draws attention to the fact that the automata theory may be an appropriate language for discussing aspects of cognition which could be as abstruse as the role of sleep and dreaming.

5.8 Genetic automata

Finally, we look at an application of automata theory to genetics. This is not as distant from cognition as it may seem – a system of genes in a biological cell can be seen as an automaton equivalent to a neural net with two-input neurons whose truth tables have random entries. and in which no learning takes place. This equivalence was first suggested in the work of Stewart Kauffman (1969) who, in the late 1960s was a student of Warren McCulloch at MIT. He argued that, because a gene is just a large molecule that can have either a repressing or an inducing effect on any other gene and that such a gene can only be influenced by two other genes in the same cell, a cell can be represented as an automaton of interconnected two-input binary devices (genes) connected only to other genes in the cell with no inputs from outside

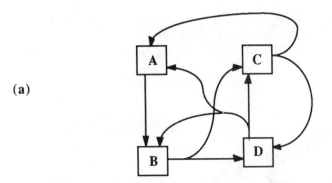

(a)

(b)

The logic of the four genes

C D	A	A D	B	B D	C	B C	D
0 0	1	0 0	0	0 0	0	0 0	0
0 1	1	0 1	1	0 1	1	0 1	1
1 0	1	1 0	1	1 0	1	1 0	0
1 1	1	1 1	0	1 1	1	1 1	1

(c)

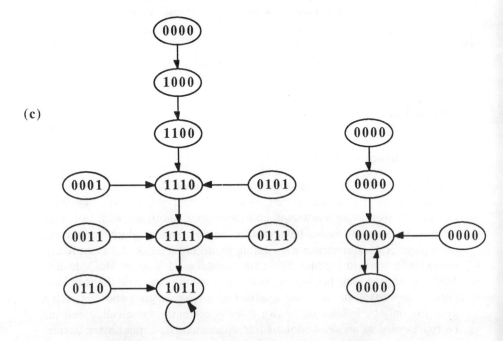

Figure 5.10 *A four-gene network (a) and its state structure.*

the cell. To illustrate this, a four-gene cell model is shown in Figure 5.10. Here (a) shows the randomly connected network, (b) is the set of randomly selected logic functions for the four genes and (c) is the resulting state structure.

To continue the analogy, it is known that the number of genes per cell differs with different species. For example, humans have about 2 million genes per cell while bacteria have about 2000. Automata theory predicts that the network, started in an arbitrary state, will go from state to state, until at some point it returns to a state that has been visited before. At that point, the network has entered a cycle. These cycles are important as they indicate the behaviour to which the cell settles down in time. The analogy is such that each state of the automaton is equivalent to a pattern of chemical activity in the cell and the cycle is equivalent to the repetitive sequence associated with cell division. Kauffman argued that the number of states in a cycle is equivalent to the number of chemical steps required between one division and the next. Now, the net is capable of several distinct cycles – in the genetic equivalent each such cycle corresponds to a different cell type. The phenomena of differing cell types is called 'differentiation' in genetics, while the process of division is called 'epigenesis'. If we sum the length of the epigenetic cycles of all the known differentiated cell types, we get, in automata terms, the number of states in the 'cyclic activity'. The example in Figure 5.10 has only two cell types, one with an epigenetic cycle of two steps, and the other of one. Its cyclic activity therefore is three.

Now for a bit of arithmetic. For a net with n genes there is a total of 2^n states. These are astronomically large numbers. For example, the 2000 gene bacterium has a state space of 10^{700} states (1 followed by 700 zeros) and in the human being this is $10^{700\,000}$ (i.e. 1 followed by 700 000 zeros!). The fact that needs explaining is that for the bacterium it is known that the total number of states in the cyclic activity in the cells of the bacterium is about 80 and in a human about 100 000. These are a minute fraction of the available totals. This limited number in fact, is all that is needed to create the bacterium or the human being. Larger numbers would result in a chaotic situation rather than the sensible creation of a viable species. Even the simplified example in Figure 5.10 shows that only three of the possible 16 states are involved in cycles.

The key question is then what functions in the gene models lead to this stability, and how do they get there? Kauffman's stroke of genius came from demonstrating by simulation that randomly selected functions (i.e. randomly selected content of the truth tables of the genes, randomly connected to one another) lead to this stability. So, to explain the stability of epigenesis and differentiation in cell division it is *not* necessary to evoke evolutionary development or adaptation of any kind. The explanation of this phenomenon will not be reproduced in detail here (it may be found in Aleksander and Atlas (1973)). Suffice it to say that the states in a cycle are those that are supported by information which is capable of circulating in loops in the network. It turns out that such loops are few because of the choice of random functions in the elements of the network. For example one out of eight functions is either the stuck-at-zero function or the stuck-at-one function. Both of these support no information transmission at all. Other functions permit the transmission of changes through just one terminal, effectively shutting off the other one. So, in summary, instead of there being as many state variables as elements of the genetic 'network', there are far fewer, and the low number of states in the cyclic activity can be predicted.

This draws attention to the power of the automaton in linking structure (even if randomly connected) to behaviour (even if surprising) through the function of the nodes (even if arbitrary).

5.9 Standing back

In a sense, understanding automata is vital to the computer scientist. It provides a formal structure for the representation of what a system is doing – the state structure. This is the space in which programs of computers fall; they are state structure representations – a fact which often seems forgotten in the greater debates about neurons and symbols. In some philosophical discussions about the value of artificial intelligence, it has become fashionable to talk of behaviour and programs as if they had a life of their own and exist simply because a programmer has willed them to. This is a result of the fact that a computer is a device that will 'run' any desired state structure. All computers are like this and this gives rise to statements sometimes made by philosophers that implementation does not matter – it's the algorithm (program, state structure) that matters. Given an algorithm for playing chess, it is that algorithm that says something about the nature of playing chess and not whether the algorithm runs on a Macintosh or a VAX machine. The latter is seen as 'implementation' and this word is often mentioned almost in a disparaging tone as if it concerns a lower, less interesting discourse – which, in this example it does, since conventional computers are specially designed to be universal and so not to interfere with the implementation of algorithms. However, what we have tried to show in this section, is that there are many kinds of automata which could play chess, and that for some of them playing chess may be a property linked to their physical structure. Automata theory provides a link between the physical structure and its emergent state structure.

This goes beyond what is seen as uninteresting implementation and is not at the level of whether the algorithm is implemented on a Macintosh or a VAX. It raises the discourse to include structures other than (and different from) VAXes and Macintoshes which *do* have an effect on the state structure. It enlarges the arena of the discussion to asking questions such as 'what is the difference between a human being's playing of chess and the program on the Mac?'. Surely, even the purest of thinkers might admit that this is a proper question. Believing otherwise could be labelled as a kind of scientific blindness akin to saying that explanations of the difference between a baseball bat and a length of hosepipe are valid only at the level that with one you can attempt to strike a ball to propel it into the distance and with the other you cannot. Clearly in this instance any suggestion that molecular structure is 'merely implementation' could be dismissed as nonsense. And automata theory is to discussions about cognitive mechanisms what molecular structure is to discussions about the physical structure of materials. The fact that automata theory does not feature in arguments about models that are implemented on conventional computers should be seen as a specific case of an area of discussion where it does feature in the general case.

Accepting this point also leads into a question which has not emerged earlier in this chapter – what is the representation of learning in automata terms? One of the major differences between symbolic approaches and neural explanations is that the former either explicitly or implicitly assume that a programmer has created the representation, whereas the latter include learning and adaptivity, and it is the structure of the automaton which determines what can and cannot be learned. 'Learnability' is an important concept, and this will be considered in greater detail in Chapter 7.

6

The great debate

Neurons versus symbols?

6.1 Introduction: an alien's tale

Larry Logician was walking home one night when an alien creature suddenly appeared in his path. It was bright orange and had the shape of a large tortoise. A faithful reproduction (in black and white) is given in Figure 6.1.

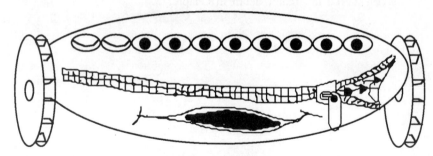

Figure 6.1 *The alien.*

It propelled its way along the ground with a pair of paddle-like wheels. On its underside it had what seemed to be a mouth and on its back it had an array of ten eye-like objects in a row. For Larry this was an exciting opportunity to do some experiments in communication with an alien. He took the thing home. Once inside, Larry, thinking 'there's no time like the present', pointed a finger in the air. The alien closed its leftmost eye. Larry reformed his hand into a fist and the eye stayed closed. Just following a hunch, Larry now raised two fingers in the air. The alien now closed the next two leftmost eyes.

'Maybe it can count!' exclaimed Larry. A little more experimentation showed this hypothesis to be true. Not only could this creature count, but banging one's hand on the table made it 'clear' its last output, saying 'sss' would make it subtract and so on. Larry telephoned his friend Connie Connectionist and told his story. Finally he said, 'so, I now have a full representation of this creature –it's a digital calculator'. Connie was impressed and asked to borrow the alien so that she too could do some experimentation. A few days later, she called back excitedly that she had discovered a zip fastener around the middle of the creature and was able to study its inner structure.

'It's a neural net', she said. 'I found a multilayer perceptron that is particularly sensitive to images of fingers, and will fire in different patterns for different finger patterns or different noises. This feeds a feedback net, a state machine, which, at some point must have learned to count and energize the eyelids appropriately.'

The point of this story (at last) is that the two human protagonists have provided quite different models of the same organism. It's a calculator, says one and is satisfied with that. It's a neural net, says the other. Both representations are predictive in some sense, and could be tested. The logical one predicts an adherence to the laws of arithmetic and the connectionist model describes the patterns which give rise to understandable input ('. . . sensitive to images of fingers . . .'). But which representation is 'right'? Are they perhaps both useful in their own right? Is one more 'appropriate' than the other? This is the substance of the 'great debate'.

In this chapter we discuss in the first instance the opinions of four major contributors to the debate. We then move on to look at the views of a few other commentators on these issues. The opinions are heavily divided, interesting and non-trivial. Our standpoint is that these opinions are cast in too narrow a framework and we suggest a way of remedying this in Chapter 7.

The debate could be said to have started innocuously with a paper by James McClelland and David Rumelhart (1985) of the University of California at San Diego. This was one of the early exposures of the psychological community to the idea of a neural net with feedback. We give a brief summary of the ideas in this paper in section 6.2. The key idea is that an item in the working memory of an organism could be encoded as the state of a feedback neural net. The authors showed that some simulations of word recognition followed the same trends as results obtained in experiments with human beings.

The *Journal of Experimental Psychology*, in which this paper was published, has on occasions the practice of publishing peer opinion at the same time as the paper itself. Thus there was also a criticism of the McClelland and Rumelhart paper by Donald Broadbent (1985) at the University of Oxford, who claimed that, while the distributed model is valid, it is below 'the computational level' and therefore irrelevant to the evidence obtained experimentally. In section 6.3 we discuss Broadbent's view, which makes use of David Marr's three levels of understanding of psychophysical phenomena (see section 3.8). He feels that structural explanations using networks should not be confused with algorithmic (program-based) explanations. Also in

section 6.3 we discuss Rumelhart and McClelland's response to this criticism
(1985), published in immediate sequence to the other two papers. Their defence
is that their model is not implementational (i.e. Marr's lowest level), but
algorithmic, that is at Marr's second level. The effect of this skirmish was,
for the first time, to raise a question concerning Marr-like levels of representation as to which level was the appropriate one to provide valid explanations
of cognitive effects. Marr himself did not raise this question, as he simply
stated that these levels were different and were alternative ways of understanding perceptual prowess in living creatures.

The division became much sharper three years later when Paul Smolensky
of the University of Colorado published a major paper that strengthened the
view that distributed representations (which he called subsymbolic) lead to
new hypotheses about cognitive models which are in some way incompatible
with the traditional computational models. He claims that the subsymbolic
approach offers a physics-like explanation of cognition, which is more
comprehensive than computational models (1988). We take a close look at
his arguments in section 6.4.

Again, published at the same time in the same issue of *Cognition*, came the
counter argument. Jerry Fodor of the City of New York University Graduate
Centre and Zenon Pylyshyn of the University of Ontario, both eminent cogni-
tivists, argued that connectionism is incompatible with and irrelevant to models
of cognition (1988). We shall see in section 6.5 that their argument is based on
the suggestion that connectionism does not have the power and flexibility of
expression that can be found in more abstract, logical/symbolic models. These
two papers drew much comment from a wide range of researchers interested
in cognition. The rest of this chapter will review this highly diverse set of views.

6.2 The distributed memory model

The 1985 paper by McClelland and Rumelhart, as mentioned above, was
responsible for first raising distributed connectionist models as an alternative
to what they called an 'enumerative' point of view. The enumerative model
is what in many parts of this book we have called a logical or rule-based model.
Enumerative models imply that memory is computer-like, capable of storing
associations between items of experience as a large database that can be
explicitly addressed. For example, the enumerative model for distinguishing
the perceptual experience of an apple from that of a banana assumes that some
unimportant processes create symbols such as 'red', 'green', 'round' and so
on. What is memorized are rules such as

'If red or green and round then it is an apple'
'If yellow long and slightly curved then it is a banana'

McClelland and Rumelhart's objections to such models of memory stem
firstly from the assumption that words are identified as a single entity

or symbol. This does not account for ever-increasing experimental evidence that memory has abstractive properties – that is, it creates concepts from a variety of experiences. Concepts such as 'dog' or 'cat' are not merely the internal awakening of a single symbol, but the integration of a raft of experiences involving 'fur', 'legs', 'ears', 'poodle', 'Rottweiler', 'tabby' and a great deal of visual experience. The reason that the rule-based models are called enumerative is that the response to these objections is that all the experiences that go into the concept of 'dog' are stored as individual symbols and enumerated at will. This leads to the second objection. McClelland and Rumelhart argue that the model requires virtually unlimited amounts of storage which, even if available, would require mechanisms of searching of an efficiency not currently known in technology. They question the wisdom of having models which suit the theoretical convenience of making use of logical inferences when such models do not have technological, or even physiological, plausibility.

They acknowledge that their own model draws heavily on neural associative memory ideas such as those of Kohonen and Hinton (see Aleksander and Morton (1990) for an explanation of how these models work) – models that are unashamedly connectionist. The attraction of connectionism is that dynamic networks integrate experience through learning and retrieve it due to the ability of feedback systems to reconstruct complete data from partial presentations. It should be noted that McClelland and Rumelhart present this as a theoretical model and not, in the first instance, as a model of the neuronal structure that might exist in the brain. They refer to neurons as 'modular units' which receive inputs from all the other units in the system. Translated into the notation we have used in this book, McClelland and Rumelhart's scheme is modular and one such module is shown in Figure 6.2. The similarity between this and the General Neural Unit of Chapter 2 (Figure 2.7) should be noted.

McClelland and Rumelhart go on to suggest that a complete model of memory would consist of networks of such modules. Right from the start they assume that such modules are interconnected in some way and that some receive inputs from the senses while others are more abstract and analyse the output of other models. A 'mental state' is a pattern of activation over some modules. These change from time to time, giving rise to a sequence of mental states that is continually assessing perceptual experience. The mechanism for adjusting the behaviour of the entire system is based on the changes of weights that interconnect the units. Thus this leads to statements about the 'knowledge' of these systems being represented by the weight values in the networks. (Recalling our automata models, these weight changes are there represented as truth table alterations.) Finally, the concept of recall or retrieval is seen as the reinstatement of learned patterns of activity. We are not concerned here with the details of the way in which the weight changing is organized – this relies

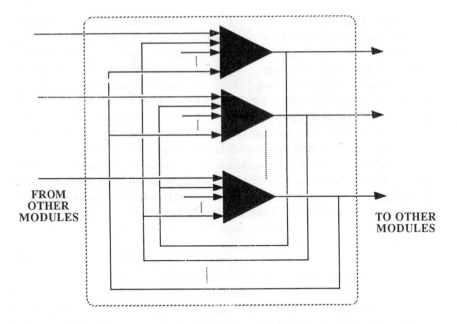

Figure 6.2 *One of McClelland and Rumelhart's memory modules.*

on now well-known convergent procedures. We do, however, wish to look at some of the experiments that have been done with this system.

Their first demonstration was simple and showed that a single module made up of eight units could store at least two retrievable patterns through the adaptation of neuron functions to take care of both patterns. The second demonstration showed that when the system was trained on noisy versions of several patterns, its behaviour was equivalent to having been trained on a prototype of each of the patterns. This was seen by the authors as an important mechanism of abstraction that was missing in enumerative models, which would store the noisy versions and then require a program explicitly added by the programmer to compute a prototype.

Their next demonstration dealt with three patterns that contained two parts – a part of the pattern was meant to be the visual experience and the other part represented the related word. These patterns were represented on a total of 24 units of which eight were the name and the rest stored the visual image. Two of the patterns were visually similar (a cat and a dog) whereas the third was distinct (a bagel). The task, which was to retrieve the whole pattern from a presentation of either part, was successfully accomplished. In general, these three demonstrations all showed successful storage, as did some others where the word labels were removed. The authors arrived at the interesting conclusion that here was a memory model that could account for both abstraction and accurate representation of memorized material – a feat that seemed to them to be in advance of the dominant paradigm of enumerative models.

In the latter parts of their paper they return to how well this model fits some results of experiments performed with human subjects. The first is the area of word recognition. It is known that once a new word has been heard, it is easier to recognize it on subsequent presentations. A theory that covers this effect is the postulate (Morton, 1979) that there exist 'logogens' in memory, one for each word, which 'fire' each time that a particular word is heard. The probability of firing is increased with the repetition of use of a word. So the logogen is a kind of neuron that adapts to a single input pattern. Unfortunately, this theory breaks down when the context in which a word is presented is changed. Not only context, but also a change in the nature of the stimulus (i.e. spoken by different persons, or presented in written rather than spoken form) would require a proliferation of logogens. The powers of abstraction and integration of McClelland and Rumelhart's distributed model overcome precisely these difficulties. It is important to realize here that neither of these contending models (logogens or distributed memory) is being upheld on the strength of its physiological plausibility – the argument simply concerns better ways of accounting for the results of experiments in human learning.

McClelland and Rumelhart's paper continues by giving the results of further experiments, particularly directed at seeing whether the priming effects (that is, say, knowing the names discovered in experimental psychology are accommodated by the distributed model. In their conclusions they broaden the discussion to consider the way in which distributed models might alter thinking in cognitive psychology. Their first target is the issue of episodic and semantic memory. Episodic memory relates to our ability to remember specific experienced events while semantic memory relates to our ability to define things in general terms. For example, we remember that a dog is a four-legged mammal with a hairy body . . . and so on.

The authors argue that their model uses a mechanism (involving the setting of states during learning) in which semantic memory is a residual trace of learning (the actual value of the weights) that lead to episodic memory when the model 'is run'. It also predicts that if a particular item is always experienced in the same context the memory does not easily transfer to other contexts, an outcome that has been observed in experimentation. So, it is clear that distributed models offer a cohesive alternative to a variety of different cognitive models, but why should the distributed mode be preferred? What are its advantages, according to McClelland and Rumelhart?

They argue that despite the seemingly physiological nature of their model, it is just as algorithmic as other enumerative models. They suggest that further work should be done in situations where the distributed model provides difference predictions from other models and that tests would then distinguish the superior model. They suggest that the fact that distributed models may well operate more closely to the physiological level may have a broadening effect on purely cognitive, enumerative models. For instance, ideas of error correction can be brought into the modelling enterprise and, above all, learning can be given a properly based theory, where in rule-based systems it can only be accomplished by the assumption of the existence of smart procedures for concept extraction. In some ways this tends to discredit the rule-based methodology, where learning can only be accomplished through a skilled procedure, leaving unanswered the question of how the procedure became skilled in the first place.

6.3 The initial skirmish: a question of levels

At first sight, the paper discussed in the last section above (henceforth referred to as M&R) appears to be a reasonable addition to the corpus of explanatory theories of human memory. What was it then that led Donald Broadbent (1985) to write a peer comment paper which suggests that the M&R theory is '. . . below the computational level'. He continued: 'It [the theory] is thus irrelevant to evidence from word identification and from response to distorted exemplars of a pattern, to which the authors appeal for support'.

Broadbent makes it clear at the outset that he has no objection to the M&R model at the level of a physiologically valid hypothesis. In fact he sees it as a worthy and correct addition to a dynasty of suggestions that memory is due to reverberations in a network of neural elements. He argues that these explanations are, however, at a different 'level' from Morton's 'logogen' explanations of word recognition. The levels in question are, indeed, those evoked by David Marr (1982) (see section 3.8), largely in connection with vision. At the computational level, Marr suggests that explanations be cast in the form of a broad, clearly stated formal theory. For example, were it discovered that a flea responds to a bang on the table by jumping in the air to a height (h) where h is proportional to square of the loudness of the bang (b), the computational theory would be

$$h = K(b^2)$$

where K is a proportionality constant that would emerge from the experimentation. It is suggested that Marr would see this as a distinct and separate level of explanation from another where the patterns created in the flea's neural cells are related to the force exerted on the flea's leg muscles. Broadbent believes that experimental support for theories of memory is like measurement of the height of the flea's jump, which can only support the computational level of theory and not the more mechanistic notion of distributed processing.

He goes far out of his way not to quarrel with the theory of distribution at its own level, and draws attention to the existence of earlier work on the storage of information in brains and computers, where, in the presence of noise, it is well known that distribution leads to more reliable computation. But, he reminds the reader, such detail would not feature at the computational theory level, where different methods of distribution would all end up as the same program for a Turing machine. In particular, Broadbent is concerned that Morton's logogen theory has been misunderstood. The fact that acoustic input has no priming effect on later visual presentations of the same word suggests, in Morton's computational terms, that different logogens exist for the two models of input. The fact that the distributed memory model produces the results that are modelled by several logogens does not mean that the logogen theory is in any way invalidated by the distributed model. The two, being at different levels of representation, cannot be compared.

On the experiments carried out by M&R with distorted training exemplars, Broadbent comments that a theory of specific, as opposed to distributed, storage could account for the observed responses, depending on the combination rules that are used for evaluating the outputs of specific detectors. He stresses that the behaviour of a recognition system is more an indication of the nature of the patterns that are to be recognized and less an indication of the mechanisms that do the recognition. He argues that the M&R use of evidence from the psychological/cognitive level does not do their case justice, as the evidence is independent of the distributed/specific argument.

How do McClelland and Rumelhart react to this criticism? In Rumelhart and McClelland (1985) (R&M from now on) they have the final word as far as this skirmish is concerned. They recognize that Broadbent raises an important issue – the issue of appropriate levels of description of cognitive activity. R&M point out that, while they do not fully agree with Marr's division into three levels (computational theory, algorithm and implementation), they stress that there are three and not two levels in this philosophy. They suggest that their distributed memory models is cast at the second, algorithmic, level and not at the third, implementational, level and see Broadbent's failure to recognize this as the invalidating flaw in his argument. They also quote Marr as writing 'each of these levels of description has its place' and they are 'logically and causally related'. Therefore, R&M argue, the insistence that one level is 'appropriate' and can be supported only by some evidence solely directed at that level is mistaken.

In this framework R&M argue that it is not only their model which is stated at the algorithmic level but also many other cognitive models, including Morton's logogens. The computational level is not intended to be concerned with ideas of performance, merely with an abstract relation between input and output. It is to the algorithmic level, where two different algorithms for accomplishing one computation are seen as two distinct theoretical entities, that cognitive models belong. Cognitive models are concerned with why some things are harder to remember than others, and therefore theories which account for such differences belong to the algorithmic level.

Another point that R&M feel needs clarifying is the contention that the distributed and localized models are computationally equivalent. This leads them to question Broadbent's reference to such computational issues, as, they assert, this misses the very point of their paper –in the discussion of distributed versus localized models of memory such models are only validated by performance in terms of the success of their predictions. R&M suggest that there is more to the attack against connectionist models. They note that many will see connectionist descriptions as discussions of language 'at the machine code level', where a clearer description of what goes on is available at the 'Pascal level'. The latter is code that makes sense to a human program writer, while the former is code that makes sense to the hardware of the machine, and there are very precise mappings (through compilation) between the one and the other. R&M warn of the inappropriateness of this distinction. Connectionism is distinct because it has a behaviour of its own, due to functions that emerge from the characteristics of network structures (e.g. the automata descriptions in Chapter 5). Not understanding this results in missing the point that these characteristics represent the heart of the connectionist mechanism. No such emergent properties can be found in the Pascal/machine code argument, thus making the analogy inappropriate.

At this point we step out of the role of reporters and make a comment of our own (which is amplified in Chapter 7). The differences that have arisen between Broadbent and M&R/R&M are focused by Marr's definition of levels at which cognitive effects can be understood. Returning to the jumping flea, the computational level answers the question 'what is related to what?' when studying jumping fleas. The algorithmic level requires a statement of the mathematical function that relates observed effects, while the implementational level actually concerns itself with the way that the flea's nervous system relates bangs to muscular jump movements. Our point is that discussions about artificial neural systems do not belong to just one of these levels, but relate to all the three. At the highest level we have broad computational theory, automata theory perhaps, which copes with the structure/function problem; at the middle level we need to instantiate parameters of a neural system (e.g. the overall connectivity) in order to distinguish between different models of behaviour; while at the implementational level it is possible to use connectionism to throw light on very specific physiological structures.

We also note that the arguments between Broadbent and R&M/M&R concentrate for much of the time on the distinction between distributed and localized representations. This is wholly a connectionist argument, one that a designer of any connectionist machine must determine before encoding the data on which this machine will operate, and indeed one that features very much not only at the algorithmic level, as maintained by R&M, but also at the implementational level, where physiologists speculate on the existence or otherwise of 'granny cells' (that is, a localized cell which fires only when you see your grandmother).

6.4 Smolensky's subsymbolic world

Paul Smolensky (1988), in his major effort to establish a proper treatment of connectionism (PTC as he calls it) makes no reference to the above skirmish. But without any doubt his argument is about levels of representation, one of which he has dubbed 'subsymbolic' to distinguish this from the classical analyses of congition, which are at the 'symbolic' level. In the broad, he sees the subsymbolic connectionist explanation as bubbling through into the symbolic level, in the sense that the symbols and the relation between them are dependent on the activity at the subsymbolic level. Therefore, an understanding of the subsymbolic is a way of understanding the symbolic. On the whole, Smolensky sees an understanding of this relationship as leading to an improved understanding of cognition. Now for some detail.

First, some of the author's beliefs. On the one hand he believes that:

- connectionism is less expressive of high-level cognitive tasks than symbolic methods;
- connectionism does not model human cognitive performance, in the sense of easily fitting empirical data;
- connectionist models may not be adequate even to represent real neural activity;
- connectionism does not invalidate conventional cognitive science methods.

On the more positive side, he asserts:

- cognitive science is impoverished, and connectionism will contribute long-lasting ideas;
- connectionism will offer some contributions to the modelling of human cognition;
- connectionism restores discussions of competence and performance to the science of mind;
- connectionism will make significant progress in the mind–body problem;
- connectionism will stimulate improved studies of neural phenomena;
- connectionism will lead to new computational machinery, probably of an analogue (non-digital) nature.

Smolensky's paper is wide-ranging and needs to be read to be fully appreciated. The best we can do here is to focus on some of his central arguments, without attempting to provide his full justification. Some of the early hypotheses relate to the formalization of knowledge. Whatever 'cultural' knowledge may be, it is defined by the fact that it may be formalized by rules couched in natural language. Application of the rules happens at a 'conceptual' level, as the operation of a 'virtual machine'. A virtual machine is a computing machine that is emulated on another more general computing machine – a bit like a calculator which appears on the screen of a computer, but which may be used just like a real calculator. (Note that the idea of consciousness

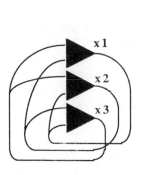
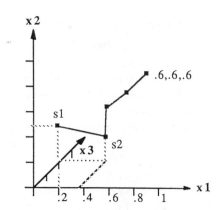

Figure 6.3 *An embryonic intuitive machine: a continuous form of automaton. (a) The circuit; (b) the state trajectory.*

as a virtual machine appears in Dennett (1991), with no attribution to Smolensky's formulation.) There is also another virtual machine, the 'intuitive processor', which is not driven by a sequential execution of linguistically express-ible rules, but is driven by connectionist principles instead. In the terms used in this book, the intuitive processor is a state machine. Smolensky defines a state by a set of state variables, each of which is a number. This contrasts with our defini-tion of states as simply 0s and 1s. Smolensky's numbers are capable of changing continuously in time, and therefore the state can change, not in jerks (as for a finite state automaton) but smoothly, through a continuously evolving state picture. This type of machine is illustrated in Figure 6.3. Here, in (a) the three state variables are drawn as neurons, but for Smolensky they would be abstract calculators of the value of the state variables $x1$, $x2$ and $x3$.

Let us digress from a discussion of Smolensky's ideas to work out how the little system in figure 6.3 might work – it will help to understand Smolensky's notion of a continuously changing state. Say that what each unit is doing (as a completely arbitrary function) is adding the numbers it receives from the output of the other two, but never allowing this sum to exceed 1. It then outputs half of this sum and adds a bias of 0.1, which works as follows. Say that the state variables initially can, somehow, be set to $x1=0.2$, $x2=0.5$ and $x3=0$. This is shown as s1 in Figure 6.3(b), where $x1$, $x2$ and $x3$ are orthogonal axes in a three-dimensional space. Now the units calculate their new values according to the connections in Figure 6.3(a):

$$x1 = 0.1 + (0.5+0)/2 = 0.35$$
$$x2 = 0.1 + (0.2+0)/2 = 0.2$$
$$x3 = 0.1 + (0.2+0.5)/2 = 0.45$$

If we call the starting state s1, then the new calculated state could be s2. This transition is shown in Figure 6.3(b), as are the subsequent states, ending in

0.6, 0.6, 0.6. This is the final, stable point owing to the fact that we do not allow the sum of the inputs to exceed 1 before it is halved (0.5) and augmented by 0.1 (yielding 0.6). In fact, whatever the starting state here, the end state will be the state of 0.6, 0.6, 0.6. While we have referred above to smoothly changing variables, it is clear that the changes are, in fact, rather jerky. This is because we have tacitly assumed that the calculations are done at discrete intervals of time. Smolensky allows that the state variables could change gradually and that the calculations could be done continuously.

Returning to Smolensky's main argument, the salient hypothesis is that the outputs of the units generate information at a subconceptual level, whereas the conceptual entities of the intuitive processor (its conceptual level if we like) are the patterns of values that occur over the whole system. In automata language, the state variables carry subconceptual information, where the conceptual information is found by observing the state variations of the system.

Any precision in the specification of this system exists only at the subconceptual level. For example, in Figure 6.3 our definition of the calculations done by the units was precise enough and was cast at the subconceptual level. The resulting behaviour of the system seemed to emerge as a result of our definition and came as a bit of a surprise. This leads Smolensky to suggest that the subsymbolic paradigm does not start with the requirement of a precise definition of the (conceptual) behaviour of the system. Instead, the behaviour emerges as a function of the subconceptual specification, but it is not the starting point of the theoretical discourse. It is this difference that leads Smolensky to say that the symbolic and the subsymbolic are incompatible – their starting points are different: the symbolic is a statement that starts in some sort of state space while the subsymbolic is a statement of state variable functions and an emergent state space behaviour.

Readers of Smolensky's paper, having convinced themselves that connectionism is related to neural structures, will be surprised to find that one of the tenets in this paper is that the subsymbolic lies somewhere between the neural and the symbolic. What is meant by this is that the subsymbolic is not an exact modelling exercise based closely on all that is known about the properties of neurons. Rather, it concentrates on those properties that are characteristic of a class of systems of distributed, linked processes. This is very much the attitude we ourselves have adopted throughout this book.

Much of the second half of Smolensky's paper is devoted to the relationship between the subsymbolic level and a symbolic description of its function. The links between the two tend to go from the subsymbolic to the symbolic, but not the other way round. To explain – in the subsymbolic system, a state or a pattern of activity may be interpreted as a symbol. It is linked to other symbols by the development of these patterns in time. So far so good, but the real questions lurk around concepts of interference and language. Is there anything at the subconceptual level that can be interpreted in these terms at the conceptual level? Smolensky argues that the competence to process and represent linguistic structures is a matter for the intuitive processor in humans, and hence should be characterized at the subconceptual level. But how?

This point is not tackled in any detail in Smolensky's paper. We shall attempt to tackle it in the next chapter. Smolensky points at the evolution of subconceptual states as being a process of prediction based on learned experience. In a sense this is language-like, if one thinks of language at the symbol string (i.e. state sequence) level. One effect of this way of thinking is that semantic information is more easily incorporated into subsymbolic models rather than symbolic ones. Internal learned states reflect the environment (as seen in Chapter 2 and again in Chapter 7). But also, part of the state could represent environmental events while another could be encoding the linguistic sequences linked to those events. An example of this is the mechanism in Figure 2.14. L and R in the central part of the state shown in Figure 2.14 could be seen as a semantic twin of the sequence of (syntactic) background bars.

Moving through an argument for the powers of continuous as opposed to digital connectionist systems, Smolensky reaches his final point – the way in which the functions of the subconceptual, intuitive processor reflect into the conceptual formulation. The emergent generalization properties of a connectionism system appear, at the conceptual level, as a 'best fit' principle – the output of the process is one of a set of symbols which best fits the input. Another example is the fact that a connectionist system can behave in the same way as a semantic network (Chapter 3). This refers to an experiment where a connectionist network was taught to associate sets of objects with the kind of room in which they may be found. The presence of a basin and a bath will lead to a completion of a stable state which suggests what other objects might be found in that room (e.g. a WC and bathmats). This is a common task carried out in artificial intelligence, the difference being that the subsymbolic system learns the structure of the schemata and generalizes beyond the training examples, where the symbolic representation requires a programmer's full statement of the relationships involved.

In summary, Smolensky's view is that subsymbolic processing addresses intuitive processing in cognition. Its characteristics may be compared to the symbolic ones as in Table 6.1. Figure 6.4 gives an impression of these characteristics in the subsymbolic domain.

It is now widely accepted that the subsymbolic is an interesting way of looking at things – it draws attention to an alternative style of computing with alternative properties. In the next section we consider the major assault on these ideas.

Table 6.1 *Symbolic and subsymbolic characteristics*

Characteristic	Subsymbolic activity	Symbolic equivalent
Inference	Transition between states	Application of a logical rule
Schemata	State structures in state space	Data structures in a database (e.g. semantic networks)
Categories	Stable regions in state space	Sets of objects and their attributes
Categorization	State trajectory leading to a stable region of state space	Execution of a logic program
Learning	Gradual shaping of state structure	Editing of logical expressions

6.5 Cognitive edifices need symbolic bricks

In this section we review the attack on Smolensky's notion of intuitive, subsymbolic processing by Fodor and Pylyshyn (1988) (F&P from now on). F&P's argument centres on cognitive architectures, that is, the nature of information processing structures which support the corpus of effects that may be called 'cognition'. They quickly recognize that 'Connectionism' produces different modes of computing which contrast with what they call 'Classicism'. What they question is whether connectionism has anything to add to the modelling powers of classical methods and come to the conclusion first that the two are incompatible (which in a sense is Smolensky's view too), and second that connectionism is irrelevant to the enterprise of rigorous modelling of cognition (where Smolensky argues that it *is* necessary for the modelling of 'intuitive' cognitive processing).

Early in the paper F&P agree that both classicists and connectionists believe in representation, that is, that the world is somehow modelled inside the system. But while they see localized representations (i.e. when one node represents a concept, as in grandmother-recognizing cells) as being fully representational of cognitive ideas, they question Smolensky's subsymbolic notion and presume it not to be representational in this sense. This is mildly surprising as Smolensky goes to a lot of trouble to define the *set* of subsymbolic variables that make up a state as being the representation symbolic entity. This is not a strong

SUBSYMBOLIC INFERENCE   " IF   A   THEN   B "

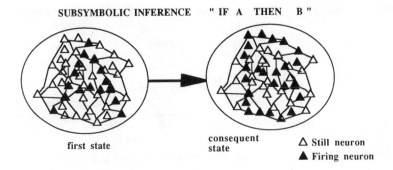

first state

consequent
state

△ Still neuron
▲ Firing neuron

State space shorthand for this transition

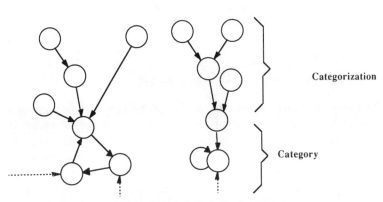

Categorization

Category

Figure 6.4 *Smolensky's subsymbolic functions.*

disagreement – F&P leave room for stronger ones. One of the problems is
that they sometimes refer to localized representations in connectionism and,
at other times, to distributed ones. We shall try to keep the narrative clear
on this point.

F&P identify the main differences between connectionists and classicists
as being founded on two architectural properties of classical formulations that
appear to be missing in connectionist models.

1. 'Thoughts' in classical formulations are language-like (it is not a coinci-
    dence that in 1976 Jerry Fodor wrote a book called *The Language of*

Thought) in the sense that they consist of symbols that have meaning (semantics), they are governed by rules of syntax (grammar) and they have clear atomic and molecular elements (such as words and phrases in language). Classicists call this representation a 'symbolic structure', and argue that such structures are of no interest to connectionists.

2. In the process of classical representations, mental states are transformed from one to another by productions similar to the production rules in language, as discussed in Chapter 5. Connectionists rely on dynamic evolution of states, which it is difficult to relate to logic and productions.

As an example of these characteristics, the knowledge of block manipulation (seen in section 3.4) may be classically represented as

'If block X is on block Y and block X is clear, then block X can be removed and block Y will become clear'

'Block X' etc. are 'atomic' symbols with given semantics; 'block X is on block Y' is a molecular structure with given sytnax; 'If ... then ... and ...' is the 'production' rule that changes the mental state from 'block X is on block Y' to 'block X is removed and block Y is clear'.

So, the foundation of the F&P objection comes from the fact that they regard cognition as being equivalent to the computations that can be logically expressed in a computer while the computations performed by a connectionist system are limited to a restricted set of possibilities. Whatever that limitation might be, this fact in their view disqualifies the connectionist model from being a proper way of describing cognitive tasks, but what are the restrictions that F&P are concerned with? Here is one of their examples.

An element of cognition has the form

$$P^*Q \text{ implies } P$$

(e.g. whenever a block P is clear and on top of block Q, P is in the set of blocks that could be picked up. Note that this really defines * as the operation 'is clear and on top of'.)

F&P's objection relates to the localized connectionist model where objects are represented by active nodes. This means that a particular node in the net fires for the condition P^*Q and this is lined to another node P in such a way that whenever the first node fires so does the second. They point out that this is specific to objects P and Q and does not capture the general concept of a function which in the classical domain is represented by the combination of objects and an operation such as *. In other words, the classical computer, knowing 'P^*Q implies P' will produce 'A^*B implies A' without any further ado, where the connectionist system will require that a new part

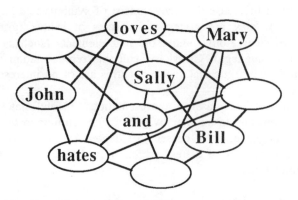

Figure 6.5 *An associative representation.*

of the network be taught, since A*B is a different object, requiring a different node, from P*Q, and the same is true for A being a different node from P. They argue that using P and Q as holding labels that represent any object has no equivalent in connectionism.

Connectionists would not find it difficult to argue against this objection by showing that a part of the network could be activated whenever the relationship * was recognized in some input. It is also possible for a net to map different blocks into the concept of First Block and Second Block, and for the activation to leave only the First Block nodes activated after * was recognized. But we shall resist presenting counterarguments to F&P's objections here. We devote Chapter 7 to the analysis of these objections.

The majority of F&P's objections are variations of the idea that logical syntax and structure cannot be represented in connectionist systems. An example of this is given as the difficulty of representing ideas such as 'John loves Mary and Bill hates Sally'. The problem, say F&P, is with the fact that a connectionist system relates things to one another is by 'associationism'. If the nodes of a network represent all the objects in this phrase, as shown in Figure 6.4, and the sentence is represented by the high activation of these nodes, how would it be possible to interpret the sentence unambiguously? It could just as easily represent 'John hates Bill and Sally loves Mary' or 'John Bill and Sally hates loves Mary'. In other words, while the net is likely to retrieve (John, Bill, loves) given (hates, Mary and Sally), there is no structure in this representation. Therefore associationism is seen by F&P as an inadequate form of representation. The failure is stressed on two counts – the inability to represent syntactical information (the grammar of the sentence) and, even if the grammar could somehow be imposed on

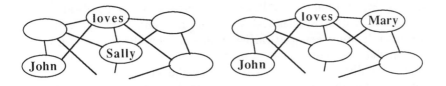

Figure 6.6 *Learning two statements.*

the representation, it fails to represent an unambiguous semantic relationship between the words. As mentioned earlier, we note here that the representation that has been attacked is a localist one, and not the subsymbolic distributed version that Rumelhart and McClelland (in section 6.2) and Smolensky (in section 6.4) have held up as a cognitive model.

Connectionists make much of learning, but F&P attack this too as being logically inadequate. They refer to the fact that the learning mechanism in most dynamic nets is probabilistic. That is, if state X of all the nodes is learned as a stable state, learned also is the probability of occurrence of this state and any other state. Indeed, Hinton sees this as a prerequisite for successful learning and demonstrates that it happens in a particular connectionist machine – the Boltzmann machine (see Aleksander and Morton (1990) for details of this). He suggests that the world needs to be understood not only as containing certain environmental states, but also in terms of the likelihood of occurrence of such states. The Boltzmann machine will, if exposed to two states X and Y occurring with probability $P(X)$ and $P(Y)$ during training, retrieve these states with precisely these likelihoods if allowed to run freely until a state has been found. F&P see this as a further disadvantage, as illustrated by training on the two states shown in Figure 6.6.

The objective of the training is to learn the two concepts:

John loves Mary'

and

'John loves Sally'

The logical interpretation of this should be 'John loves Mary *and* John loves Sally'. F&P argue that the net will not be able to distinguish this from 'John loves Mary half of the time and John loves Sally the other half'. Again, we draw attention to the fact that this objection is illustrated by a localized example of a connectionist system.

In the meantime, connectionists have not been slow to point out that neural structures can be created which carry out parsing tasks and implement semantic networks (Touretsky and Hinton, 1985; Touretsky, 1986). However, this type of work does not impress F&P, as they argue that this is merely an example of implementation of classical symbolic algorithms. In agreement with Broadbent's argument seen earlier in this chapter, F&P come to the conclusion that the best way of looking at connectionism is as a theory of implementation. This, of course, leaves the classical representation as dominant and the existence of connectionism merely at the level of 'the machine on which classical ideas run'. This effectively denies the claims made by connectionists that a new approach to representation has been found. These claims are dismissed in their conclusion that connectionism is as important to cognitive science as the statement that a cognitive model runs on a VAX or a PC (or on a cardboard model of a Turing machine?).

6.6 A few points from the arbiters

Were we umpires at a Wimbledon final, we would describe the contest so far as one in which some powerful services had taken place on both sides, and the opponents had not attempted to return the ball. First, the power of distributed representation, extolled by both Rumelhart and McClelland (1985) and Smolensky (1988) has not been appreciated by F&P. Evidence for this power comes from the fact that inference and linguistic ability are represented by the relationship between the states of a network (i.e. in state space). Most of F&P's criticisms apply to localized representations, and it is precisely the limitation of this representation that leads connectionists to look at distributed styles. On the other side, the connectionists in this game of tennis have actually not shown exactly how either the syntactic structures that are central in cognitive science, or their relationship to semantics, could arise in distributed systems. Smolensky only hints at the fact that this could happen. In fact, as we show in Chapter 7, there are limitations as to what can and cannot be represented in the state space of a connectionist system.

Returning to shots in the other direction, F&P have shown some reluctance to meet the challenge of the power of learning without the interference of a programmer. This is an area where classical arguments are traditionally weak and do not do justice to learning as a cognitive activity. Classically, machine learning is seen as a process of matching attributes to classifications through editing logical statements. An example of this is Winston's use of semantic networks (Figure 3.6), where an arch is defined as 'having two pillars that support a slab'. But if the two pillars are touching each other this is no longer an arch. Then it is seen as a 'near miss' which leads to the description being edited to read 'having two pillars that support a slab, but where the pillars do not abut'. In connectionism, this process is looked at in a more sensitive way, raising important questions about what can be learned by a cognitive organism and how.

6.7 And the world said ...

In this section we look at some of the peer comment that was published at the end of Smolensky's 1988 paper. (We shall not reference these short contributions separately.) What is remarkable about this commentary is, first, the large number of contributions it received from eminent thinkers, and also the fact that the debate gave rise to a host of interpretations of what the debate is actually about. Since in the next chapter we discuss a model that attempts to clarify some of the confusion that has arisen from these alternative interpretations, here we look at some important peer contributions selectively, rather than trying to give a description of them all.

Hubert and Stuart Dreyfus, of the University of California at Berkeley, well-known critics of the AI paradigm, express shock at the fact that Smolensky did not meet their expectation by demonstrating that connectionism would eliminate representationalism altogether. Instead, they found a presentation of cognition at *two* representational levels, the symbolic and the subsymbolic. The thrust of their contribution is that Smolensky's point of view may be interpreted as not being committed to representationalism at either of these levels. They draw attention to the fact that the intuitive processor in Smolensky's theory does not require that *all* intelligent behaviour should involve symbol transformations. There are 'hidden' units that do not necessarily have activities that could at the conceptual level be mapped into symbols. Not every subsymbol has a representational identity. Dreyfus and Dreyfus argue that this provides a healthy alternative to what they see as the over-rigid symbolist view of Fodor and Pylyshyn, an alternative which goes towards explanations of cognition that are more plausible [our interpretation] than those that do not allow for intuitive, non-representable elements as occurs when looking for a 'language' of thought. The commentary is arranged in such a way that the author has the final word. Here, Smolensky does not disagree with Dreyfus and Dreyfus, pointing out that, indeed, the microfeatures or subsymbols may encode arbitrary but nonetheless helpful entities, which Dreyfus and Dreyfus may well call non-representational.

Alan Price of Brandeis University and Stephen Pinker of MIT suggest that Smolensky's subsymbolic model suffers from several flaws. First, the claim that it is a radical departure *because* it enshrines subsymbolic information may be questioned. What Smolensky calls subsymbols (e.g. phonological features in speech) are, in fact, part of classicist trade. They have been incorporated in cognitive explanations that are formal and, by all accounts, symbolic. Price and Pinker go on to question whether the emerging dynamic properties that underpin the computations in the subsymbolic intuitive processor are in fact useful in connectionist explanations of cognition. They point out that connectionists often use specially wired networks, the design of which, the action of wiring, is a process akin to classical programming. This undermines the credibility of Smolensky's suggestion that spontaneous dynamic activity provides a new slant on cognitive science. Another criticism they offer is that of associationism not being capable of representing the structures that are needed to represent linguistic activity – this point is similar to the one made by Fodor and Pylyshyn in their criticism. Indeed many of the commentators, for example Robert Lindsay of the University of Michigan at Ann Arbor, see associationism as an abandonment of a mature symbolic way of dealing with inference. Lindsay sees the connectionist association of A with B as a central computing mechanism as a dangerous return to behaviourism and an impoverished view of what classical symbolic representations have actually achieved.

Smolensky's first reaction is that Price and Pinker have cast their criticism at the distinction between connectionist and linguistic theories, and that this is not the same as subsymbolic–symbolic relationship which is at the centre of Smolensky's article. He points out that the subsymbols of connectionism, while on occasions bearing a similarity to symbolic objects, such as phonological features, are not the same as the symbolic microfeatures quoted by Price and Pinker. These subsymbols could be arbitrary and could exist solely as a result of the demands of the connectionist system, which does give the connectionist model novel and greater scope. Smolensky argues that associationism needs much more development before we fully appreciate its strengths and real weaknesses. We shall show in the next chapter that 'associationism' within a single state of a network is not the only emergent property of a connectionist system. To see it as the only thing that a connectionist can do fails to appreciate the power of state-to-state changes which put connectionism into the same framework of computing capacity as the classical approach. We agree with Smolensky that pointing to the computational inadequacies of associationism as the Achilles' heel of connectionism may be premature.

A supportive comment for connectionism is provided by Douglas Hofstadter, also of the University of Michigan. He is heartened by the much needed opportunity for the formalization of common-sense reasoning through subconceptual arguments. Smolensky confirms that Hofstadter's call for a 'proper treatment of common sense' was behind some of the ideas that went into his 'proper treatment of connectionism'. Wendy Lehnert, of the University of Massachusetts at Amherst, however, expresses scepticism about Smolensky's conclusion that symbolic and subsymbolic processing, while recognized as being different ('incompatible' is the word he sometimes uses), still allow theories in the two paradigms to coexist. She argues that the clarity of the way in which knowledge is represented in symbolic systems cannot be replaced by the vague 'kludge' of distributed representations and is worried by the fact that this may lead researchers into developing methodology rather than solving real cognitive problems. Smolensky responds by drawing attention to the fact that proper representation is a major target for connectionism. He does not fail to point out that connectionism is a much younger, developing field and it is its potential that is under the microscope. This counters the method orientation accusation, as it is clear that classical AI has had many years of method research on the basis of which problem orientation can be developed. Connectionism just has not got there yet. This particular skirmish is of some interest to us because we argue that the relationship between the classical, symbolic and the connectionist is not one between two incompatible sources, but one of different extremes of a continuum. Assuming this to be true would remove many of Lehnert's distinctions and make Smolensky's response unnecessary.

An important criticism is made by one of the doyens of symbolic processing – John McCarthy of Stanford University. He questions Smolensky's assertion that intuitive processing *requires* a subsymbolic engine. McCarthy believes that symbolic representations can capture intuitive reasoning. He also shows concern for the fact that most connectionist models are unary, that is of the kind 'the kitchen contains a stove'. In this sense they are intolerant of elaboration – for example the net holding the unary knowledge cannot elaborate it into, say 'the butler's pantry is between the kitchen and the dining room'. Smolensky entirely agrees with this criticism, but sees it as a pointer to the way that connectionism has to develop – more-than-unary relationships can be represented by networks that have been trained on more-than-unary patterns. But McCarthy goes on to state clearly that he is not concerned with the way in which such complex relationships are learned. Well, if connectionism offers anything new at all, it must be about the way things can be learned. So if the connectionist cannot rise to McCarthy's challenge and show how certain complex greater-than-unary relationships can be learned, and the symbolist states that he is not interested in this process, cognitive science would be left with a gaping hole. This is where the true challenge to the connectionist lies – the impoverished nature of symbolic approaches to learning is beyond doubt.

Some of the commentators, such as Chris Mortenson of the University of Adelaide, bemoan Smolensky's detaching of subsymbolic from neural representations (that is, detailed neural models of the brain). There is evidence that some aspects of consciousness have neurological correlates. It would be helpful, Mortenson argues, to explain such results if subsymbolic theory were deployed at the neural level and phenomena such as the waxing and waning of conscious states could then be considered. Smolensky does not argue against this view, but feels that it is important to draw attention to the gap between abstract neural models that exist in the literature and neurological findings. Abstract neural models should not be confused with those connectionist models in which a great deal of

cognizance has been taken of neurophysiological detail and which may have
close neurophysiological correlates. Many connectionist models of language
and vision processing do not have such correlates. Smolensky's view is that
this does not make them any less valid, and that the subsymbolic is the
appropriate level for their analysis. This book is based on the view that it
is important that connectionism provides a general link between the structure
of a network, what it has learned and how it behaves. This is likely to throw
light on the relationship between neurological structures and linguistic or visual
capacity of human brains even if these are not *precise* models of structures
in the brain. Understanding this relationship leads to informed speculation
about the true nature of the cognitive process, including, perhaps, a proper
treatment of consciousness.

6.8 And, philosophically speaking ...

The debate on connectionism and its contributions to cognitive thought
did not stop with the publication of Smolensky's paper and reactions to it.
In 1991 Ramsey, Stich and Rumelhart published a collection of invited
papers that focus on the effect of connectionism on philosophy. In this
section we review some of the views expressed in this publication. Again,
we do not reference these individually, and comment only on the contributions which are relevant to the concerns of this book. One of the points
that emerges from the review of debates in the earlier parts of this chapter is that the obvious difference between symbolic and connectionist
approaches – learning – is given short shrift. We argue that what can
and cannot be learned by a connectionist automaton focuses attention
on the limitations of connectionism. Here, therefore, we have been particularly primed to discover the views of the contributors to the question of
learning.

Robert Cummins, of the University of Arizona, claims, as do we, that
there is not as much difference between classicists and connectionists
as the literature seems to suggest. He is more concerned about the fact
that connectionists reject 'language of thought' models for reasons of
belief rather than the demands of connectionism. Recent developments
in connectionist architectures show that rule-based production systems
are not out of range. He, with many others, sharpens up the notion
that connectionist and classical models share the property that they are
both virtual machines that run on conventional computers. Where we
would differ from him is that he has harsh things to say about the claims
made for learning in connectionist systems. He does not see that function
(weight) adjustment is any different from the editing of formulae in conventional systems. Our argument is that the difference lies in the fact
that connectionist learning discovers algorithms from among a different

set of algorithms from that available to orthodox editing. Sometimes, but not always, each technique reaches algorithms that are not available to the other.

Another interesting aspect of learning is raised by William Ramsey of the University of Notre Dame and Stephen Stich of Rutgers University. They point to Noam Chomsky's argument that human beings must have a rich store of innate knowledge in order to learn language because the stimulus that children receive is so poor as to make it implausible that they can reconstruct from it the complex structures that language entails. They argue that connectionism offers an interesting challenge to this, but that the point has not yet been proven. Our view is that this is a very important area of research which requires attention. The main issue is one of structure and function. Could specific structures exist that facilitate the absorption of language, where the repository of language is not the structure itself but the speaking adult population? Then it could be said that such structures could be inherited (it is very difficult to inherit anything more than physical structure), but that language with all its richness is not innate but easily absorbed by these special structures.

From a philosophical standpoint the raising of such structure/function questions is important, since suggestions of language innateness have given rise to theories of 'the language of thought' (Fodor, 1976) which, in turn, have entered into the symbolic/subsymbolic debate. We feel that clear understanding of the way in which the physical structure of an automaton affects the state structures that such an automaton can learn is a profitable area for research in neural systems.

6.9 Looking back

In this chapter we have sketched out the controversies that have arisen as those working on connectionist systems have begun to argue that this methodology is challenging the dominant paradigm in cognitive science – the logical/computational representation. One point is clear. In order to mount such a campaign, the idea of highly localized representation (one neuron per concept) has been abandoned. Smolensky's somewhat vague definition of a subsymbolic representation allows for a completely arbitrary assignment of values to connectionist units, which, when taken together, have some semantic value. In our automata-oriented thinking, Smolensky's symbol is what we call a state of an automaton, the state variable being the node value.

In a sense, Fodor and Pylyshyn's attack turns out to be superfluous, as it is focused on these largely abandoned localized representations. Taken seriously, their arguments should be seen as a challenge to connectionists, who have by no means proved, as yet, that the intuitive reasoning functions raised by Smolensky can be learned. Our view is that in the rush to prove that one form of representation is better than another the question of learning remains neglected. In the final count it may be just this property that turns out to be the central contribution of connectionism to a cognitive science that has developed without giving it a great deal of attention.

7

The divide is illusory

The path that goes from neuron to symbol (and beyond?)

7.1 Introduction: no weights, just state machines

The central objective of this chapter is to show that the neural, the subsymbolic and the symbolic are compatible aspects of traditional system analysis. Each, in its own way, can contribute to cognitive science, while at the same time providing methods for making cognitively competent computing machinery. So in this chapter we aim to refute the notion set out in Chapter 6, that connectionism is inappropriate to the understanding of cognition and incompatible with it. We recall that Smolensky's definition of 'subsymbolic' excludes accurate models of the living brain. We do not wish to apply the same exclusion and therefore use the single term Artificial Neural System (ANS) to refer to connectionist, subsymbolic and neural systems.

We aim to show that the symbolic/subsymbolic divide is artificial and that the two styles of computing may be seen as variants of one computational modelling technique drawn from automata theory – the use of state machines. We suggest that the basic model of neural computing is an adaptable state machine with clearly understood and predictable properties, some of which are introduced as global features (e.g. generalization and structural parameters) and some of which are emergent (e.g. the tendency for networks with feedback to be stable). The key character of these state machines is that they have a logical function which is not defined in advance – it is defined by a process of training instead. So neurocomputing, we argue, is not a species of information processing which is alien to the logical, symbolic or Turing style. Neurocomputing may be shown to be totally compatible with this style. It also makes the added value of neural properties stand out clearly.

In using the term Artificial Neural Systems we support the broader view of the neuron as a variable function device with generalization which we have explained in Chapters 3 and 5. This 'weightless' outlook enables us to avoid theories that concentrate on the altering of connection strengths and which can lead to unhelpful statements such as 'the knowledge of a connectionist system is represented by a weight vector'. In weightless systems the way that neurons store information, and how this storage contributes to the behaviour of networks, helps us to explain both the classical and the connectionist nature of the ANS. In this chapter we also begin to look at the interests of those who aim to build systems with cognitive properties. We shall argue that the neural model performs naturally some tasks which could be said to be cognitive and which the classical method achieves only with some difficulty.

In section 7.2 we review and refine some of the concepts of neural automata, drawing particular attention to the fact that conventional models found in connectionist literature are specific cases of a more general, automata-theoretic case. Then in section 7.3 we show how the more general case may be approached through the weightless formulation, which enables us, in section 7.4, to underscore the general emergent properties of connectionist systems. These emergent properties, we feel, should be given a great deal more prominence in neuron/symbol discussions than has been done in 'the great debate' of Chapter 6. In section 7.5 we introduce the concept of 'cognitive competence', which rank orders the set of cognitive models, whether these be classical or connectionist. The resulting ranking is based on the degree of match between an implemented model imagined to be in communication with a human, and the human. In section 7.6 we introduce a Neural State Machine Model (NSMM) which lies on a continuum between being a Turing-like universal machine and being a neural system with emergent properties. By returning to this model we show that discussions of alternative models can be based on 'learnability' – another continuum between learning by exploration at the one extreme and blatant programming at the other. Armed with this concept we revisit Fodor and Pylyshyn's objections and argue that they were directed at too narrow a view of connectionism. In sections 7.8 and 7.9 we suggest that an important impact of connectionism on cognitive science will come from the ability to coordinate the neural and the symbolic in areas of learning, mental imagery and cognitive architectures.

7.2 The neural automaton revisited

In the neuron/symbol debate it is not stressed often enough that in the neural paradigm there are two major types of connection – recursive (where feedback exists between the outputs and inputs of a group of neurons) and feedforward (where there is no feedback). In automata-theoretic terms, the former are state machines with a variable state structure, while the latter are combinational systems with a variable logic function. The latter can always be seen as single-state degenerate forms of the former, and from here on we shall assume that the general form of a neural net is recursive. Therefore the net can be represented by a set of input terminals I, a

set of state variables Q and a set of output terminals Z. It is not necessary
to assume that these terminals can only carry binary information – this model
holds for continuous, discrete and binary encoding of data.

In popular embodiments, such as the Hopfield net (1982), or the Boltzmann
machine (Hinton *et al.*, 1986) there is no input I, and nets are initiated by
a process of 'clamping', which is the forced setting of the initial values of
some of the state variables in Q. There are other models such as the 'weightless'
General Neural unit (GNU) (Figure 2.7), where the set of inputs of the
recursive system is defined. (The input is also defined in some of Rumelhart's
memory modules: see Figure 6.2.) As seen in Chapter 5, in the general case
every state variable (say, $q(j)$ for the jth state variable) is a function of a
selection $I(j)$ of input variables (where $I(j)$ is a subset of I) and of a selection
$Q(j)$ of state variables (a subset of Q), whose values are measured at time
$t-1$ in a timed system (time $t=1,2, \ldots$), where $q(j,t)$ is the value of $q(j)$
as measured at time t. The 'selections' are made according to a connection
scheme which could be arbitrary or based on some strategy. (In the Hopfield
and Boltzmann cases $Q(j)=Q$.) We write the general case as

$$q(j, t) = f_j(I(j,t-1), Q(j,t-1)) \qquad (7.1)$$

This is not simply a state equation for a state machine. The difference to be
noted is the dependence of each output $q(j)$ (now called a neuron) on restricted
sets of state variables (embodied in I and Q). This in itself introduces some
'blindness' of the state variables to which we shall return later. However,
as will be explained below, the key factor which turns this general relation
into a neural one is that f_j is created first by training and then by generalization based on this training.

Training provides spot values of $I(j,t-1)$ and $Q(j,t-1)$ together with their
related $q(j,t)$. We refer to a pattern $IQ(j,k)$ as the kth training input of the
system and $q(j,k)$ as the output value assigned to this pattern by some
training procedure. Generalization is a property whereby input patterns in
some way similar to the training patterns are assigned outputs similar to the
trained ones.

7.3 The weightless/weighted distinction

We have suggested above that weightless formulations provide a novel view
of the way in which learned information is represented in a neural net. In
this section we expand on this theme by a formal comparison. The reader
who wishes to get on with the argument, and is not interested in such
detailed distinctions, can skip to section 7.4 without losing the thread of what
is being said.

In the weighted formulation, the input pattern is turned into an 'activation',

$$A_j = [i(1) \times w(1)] + [i(2) \times w(2)] + [i(3) \times w(3)] + \ldots \quad (7.2)$$

for the jth variable (neuron, where $w(k)$ is the adjustable weight of the kth input. Each output $q(j)$ is a 'sigmoid' function of A_j. That is, as A_j increases from 0, $q(j)$ first hardly changes from 0 and then, as A_j steps over some threshold value, $q(j)$ changes rapidly to 1. Training algorithms do their best to adjust these weights so as to keep the values of $q(j)$ as close as possible to the values demanded by the training set. Generalization is obtained through the fact that small changes in the values of $i(k)$ will lead to small changes in A_j. Not all combinations of inputs to outputs can be achieved, the set of 'linearly separable' functions being the formal description of the set that can be achieved with these classical formulations (details of such arguments may be found in Aleksander and Morton (1990)).

The 'weightless' GNU mentioned earlier is not restricted to linearly separable functions and any measure of similarity can be adopted to obtain generalization for input patterns not used for training. In weightless work it has also been assumed that there are input states for which the output has not been determined either by training or by generalization. In such cases these inputs are assumed to lead to a probabilistic output which generates arbitrarily chosen values of $q(j)$. A neuron operating in this way is said to be in a probabilistic mode. If during the operation of the state machine some neurons enter a probabilistic mode, the state machine becomes probabilistic in the sense that there is a set of probabilistically chosen next states arising from the current state of the machine. In the weighted formulation, hidden or auxiliary units are required to compensate for the limitations of linear separability. Because of this, much has been made of the difficult problem of training such units (e.g. error back-propagation). This training difficulty disappears in fully connected weightless formulations. In the state machine formulation we have allowed the possibility for some neurons to be blind to the values of some state or input variables. In such a case hidden units are required in some form of pyramidal structure.

A general understanding of the difficulty of adjusting the functions of hidden units comes from Stephen Judd (1990), who approaches the task from a point of view of the complexity of searching for appropriate functions. Judd shows that this problem has awkward exhaustive characteristics, and is an example of what mathematicians call an 'NP-complete' problem. These characteristics need to be recognized by designers. The lengthy computations required by error back-propagation are one specific manifestation of this problem.

7.4 Emergent properties

In the symbolic/subsymbolic debate discussed in the last chapter, so much attention is paid to issues of how cognition is *represented* in the two modalities that the fact that the artificial neural system has some properties of its own becomes somewhat neglected. In what we see as a continuum between the general purpose state machine that operates in the classical computational mode and the neural state machine, there is, at the neural end, a gain of emergent properties which we discuss below.

7.4.1 Pattern recognition

This is the fundamental property which is at work even in static systems. The recognition of inputs not seen during training is precisely determined by a chosen generalization strategy.

7.4.2 Re-entrant states

As seen in Chapter 2, the training examples may be used to create re-entrant states in the state space of the system. That is, the pattern on the feedback connections may be made to repeat itself by training and become related to an input pattern. The input pattern is then said to retrieve the repeating state pattern.

7.4.3 Attractors

If the neurons generalize by reacting in the same way to similar inputs, the above re-entrant states become attractors in the state space. That is, if some input–state pair is more similar to training pair IX than to training pair IY (where I is the input pattern and X and Y the trained re-entrant states) then the final re-entrant state of the system will be X. This property is sometimes referred to as 'reconstruction', as prototype states may be reconstructed from presentations of distorted versions of such prototypes. It has been shown (Aleksander and Morton, 1991) that the ability to retrieve trained states depends on the average balance of information (number of connections) that each neuron receives from the state and the input.

7.4.4 Memory

The re-entrant state can be more or less resilient to change resulting from changes of input. The resilience to change depends on input/state connectivity balance and the number of re-entrant states that have been created. This is a subject of current study.

7.4.5 Input temporal sensitivity

As first discussed in Chapter 2, the state machine definition of a neural net allows several forms of temporal training, depending on the time sequence of the training set. For example, say that re-entrant states for the input–state pairs C/C', A/A' and T/T' have been created. Now say that C has occurred and the system enters state C'. Then, while the training mechanism is switched on, the input changes to A. This leads to the learning of the transition to state A' from state C' as a result of input A. Similarly, the transition from state A' to T' for input T can be learned. The result of this is that if the sequence CAT were input, the states would follow a C'A'T' trajectory. However, were the symbols presented in some other order, the system would enter an unrelated set of states. So, the fact that the state representation follows a previously experienced sequence can be interpreted as the system having recognized that sequence. Clearly this can lead to the neural net becoming an acceptor of finite state languages. Ludermir (1990) has suggested ways in which this behaviour can be extended to some context-free languages.

7.4.6 Output sequences

The model is capable of relating either constant input or input sequences to learned output sequences.

7.4.7 Unsupervised learning

It is possible to allow the neural system to develop its own coding for internal states. If it is assumed that before training takes place all the neurons operate in a probabilistic mode, any input will lead to the machine taking a 'random walk' through its state space. Training can then make an arbitrarily self-selected state re-entrant and generalization will make this state an attractor. The degree of generalization determines the range of the 'basin of attraction' (the set of states that eventually lead to the re-entrant state), so novel inputs may be made to create novel re-entrant states.

7.4.8 Capacity

In terms of the finite state machine model, it is important to be able to ask how many re-entrant states and how many transitions between them are possible with a given structure (i.e. a given feedback balance and total number of inputs per neuron). It is easy to show that given n feedback connections per neuron, the largest number of re-entrant states, for a given input, is 2^n. Also, it has been shown by Ntourntoufis (1991) that for arbitrary patterns the probability of distorting the desired states is $1/e^2$ (i.e. about 13%) when the number of states is equal to the number of feedback connections per neuron. More work is currently being done on such limits but meanwhile these rather low estimates of capacity point a designer of artificial cognitive systems in the direction of optimizing the amount and the arrangement of storage used for the implementation of such systems. This type of work also draws attention to the fact that similar effects, which limit capacity, may be at work in the brain. This organ is not a homogenous state machine and it is of some interest to examine neuroanatomical structures taking the point of view that they must have evolved in the direction of optimization of processing capacity.

7.5 Cognitive competence

In this section we ask a question that has been avoided in the discussion so far. What cognitive properties can an engineer, a machine maker, introduce into a human-made artefact? This issue is important not only because reference needs to be made to the performance of various cognitive models even in abstract debates, but also because a performance match between human and machine may eventually introduce a useful distinction between competing cognitive models. As seen in earlier chapters, artificial intelligence is the endeavour which underpins many existing cognitive models. The accepted definition of artificial intelligence is 'doing on computers that which, if done by humans, would be said to require intelligence' (section 3.1). This could be translated to cover artificial cognitive systems, and might read something like 'doing on computers that which, if done by humans, would be said to require thought'.

These are unsatisfactory definitions because they beg a definition of the words 'intelligence' and 'thought'. Cognitive scientists are generally happy to apply such words to machines in the framework of a simplified Turing test (see Chapter 3) – given a human interlocutor, if the machine can make responses indistinguishable from those of a human being, the machine is said to be intelligent, or, at least, to be capable of some kind of thought that could be compared with the thought of a human. This to a machine maker is unhelpful. It is possible to make machines which, in some narrow aspects of behaviour, are much superior to humans (e.g. memory, calculation), whereas things that seem simple to humans (e.g. scene and language understanding) are still the aims rather than the achievements of advanced computer design. A designer finds that the insistence on success being measured by how well the designs masquerade as human is an irrelevant criterion. The target for making machines with cognitive properties should be measured by the extent to which the machine can be understood and used by a human; in other words, can *cooperate* with (rather than replace) humans.

We suggest that part of the target should be the improvement of the human-machine interface, and that the excellence with which the interaction between user and machine is carried out be related to a quality we call competence. To define this we submit that the competence of an artificial cognitive system be expressed in terms of the allowances that the user must make when communicating with the device as compared with communicating with a human being in the context of requesting the same task. We note that this definition includes an element of performance. Speed, for example, is taken into account. If the machine were to take much longer to respond to a command than could be expected from a human, this would detract from its competence.

Does this imply that any machine that does not react to speech is cognitively incompetent? Not necessarily – keyboard communication is sometimes accepted between humans (e.g. electronic mail), so the answer is dependent on the nature of the task. The target for the designer becomes one of ascertaining competence in at least three areas:

(i) the competence with which sensory data are translated into internally usable codes;
(ii) the competence with which the internal codes are related to past experience or might be manipulated as symbols in a logical system;
(iii) the competence with which the results of a request are communicated back to the user.

While it is generally accepted that neurocomputing has a role to play in the first of these three areas, it is also true that both the neural and the logical styles are candidates when designing systems for levels (ii) and (iii). We now look at some specific areas of activity, where competence has a role to play.

7.5.1 Pattern recognition

The most often quoted result of the research of one of the authors (IA) is the WISARD general pattern recognizer (Figure 1.2). One of the tasks that the WISARD performs remarkably competently is the recognition of the expression on a person's face. Is it a smile or a frown? In May of 1982, during a soirée demonstration of the system at the Royal Society in London, rather than simply demonstrating the prowess of the system on a single person, the designers of the system (Igor Aleksander, John Stonham and Bruce Wilkie) decided to perform a semi-scientific experiment. We wished to see on how many faces the system would have to be trained in order to recognize a smile or a frown on the face of a previously unseen face. It turned out to be less than 10. The fact that this could be done at all was surprising, and the fact that this very simple system could develop its own algorithm with very little training could not have been predicted despite the fact that such systems are amenable to an adequate analysis. Unfortunately, while the system is well understood, the images it uses are not. So, experiments of this kind are useful because they tell us something about the nature of the images used in the experiment.

For completeness, the next paragraph provides some detail of the operation of WISARD (but this may be skipped by those who are not interested in technicalities).

The WISARD allows its user to configure very large neurons (they are called discriminators in the literature). In this case only two neurons were used. Each was connected to an input window of 128×128 binary points sampled as random groups of n bits called n-tuples (with $n = 8$ in the experiment we have described above). Being weightless, the samples are looked up in a specially structured semi-parallel store (that acts like a lookup table), the lookup values being built up by training. In encountering an unknown image, the looked-up values are summed, providing a response for that neuron. The neurons start with all the values of the look-up tables set to 0. Training consists of setting to 1 the lookup values of all the n-tuples which occur for a particular input image. In this example, the two neurons were trained, one for frowns and the other for smiles. When tested, the vote is given to the one with the highest response, provided that the difference exceeds a 'confidence' threshold. It has been shown that the generalization of this model may be simply approximated as $(Amax)^n$ where Amax is the area of overlap between the unknown pattern and the pattern in the training set with which the overlap is the greatest (i.e. the maximum). Details of the WISARD may be found in Aleksander and Morton (1990, Chapter 5).

In terms of state machines, the WISARD is the degenerate, combinational form of structure and, to a first approximation, the same thing could have been done with a weighted multi-layer perceptron. The weightless methodology merely provides a high level of performance (training taking about 20 seconds for each new face and the classification of an unknown image taking 1/25th of a second).

The reason for quoting this example is to draw attention first to the competence of the system and second to the very specific nature of the algorithm which emerges from the neural nature of the structure. If we were to approach this task using purely symbolic methodology, what algorithm would be used? A likely route a programmer might take is first to extract the sub-features of the face, such as edges, and then to identify named 'symbols' such as <nose>, <mouth>, <mouth curvature> and <left eye> and so on. Then he or she would try to add the declarative knowledge which could only be obtained by looking at many examples of smiling and frowning faces. It might be discovered that some artefact, such as the geometry of the triangle formed by the corners of the mouth and the tip of the nose, when added to the radius of the eyebrows, gives discrimination between a smile and a frown.

The chances of any such symbolic algorithm being as competent as the neural one are slim, and a system maker would have good reasons for opting for the neural scheme. Particularly attractive is the fact that competence can be achieved after exposure to 10 faces only each for about 20 seconds. Comparing this to the human effort needed to develop a symbolic scheme would make the choice obvious on the strength of development cost alone. The thrust of this discussion is to stress the difference between a cognitive algorithm that is designed by a programmer and that achieved through neural methodology. It may not be entirely coincidental that the neural method, being inspired by the function of the brain, performs more competently than a computational artefact.

7.5.2 Problem solving

We have seen in Chapters 3 and 4 that the solving of problems is often taken as a pinnacle of human cognitive competence. The solving of problems either as a general activity (e.g. Newell, Simon and Shaw's General Problem Solver – see Newell and Simon (1972) and chapter 3) or as a specific task (e.g. robot actions planners – see Fikes (1972) has been seen by AI researchers as a good area for implementation. The common feature of symbolic programs that solve problems is a 'search space'. The problem is conceived as a set of states (e.g. snapshots of the positions of pieces on a chessboard), a set of applicable actions for that state, and the new states generated by these actions. Some of these programs have ways of evaluating the states in terms of how close each is to the required goal (e.g. an evaluation of a chessboard state in terms of the advantage to the simulated player – as in the example given in section 3.3). When the program runs, it spends much time examining each of the possible actions and scanning the search tree to find either a solution or a good intermediate state. To exemplify this, let us return again to the example of the stacking problem seen in Chapter 3. Three bricks A, B and C are stacked on one another in some order and the target is to use a robot arm to stack them in some other order. The conventional program uses a few simple rules such as 'the block at the top can be put on the table' or 'any block on the table can be put on the stack' and 'do not backtrack'. The algorithm then proceeds to explore all possibilities by starting with the existing state of the bricks and moving exhaustively through all available states until the desired solution is found.

In contrast, we (e.g. Aleksander, 1991) and others (e.g. Smolensky, 1988) have drawn attention to the fact that a neural net can operate in exactly the same domain, but with some significant differences. The state variables of the neural state machine have an area to represent the goal, an area to represent the current state of the bricks and an area that represents an action to be taken. Training consists of allowing the system to explore the problem domain and to learn the appropriate action. That is, re-entrant patterns are created which have the goal, the existing state and the appropriate action linked together. So in the neural case too there is an exhaustive exploration of the problem domain, but this happens only once – during training. Subsequently, if the target state is applied to the input of net, the system can produce a set of actions that take it to this state directly from any existing state.

We would argue that the neural system is more competent on the grounds that the amount of computation required while the system is 'solving the problem' is less than that of the conventional system because of the avoidance of the repetition of the exhaustive search. Clearly, there may be heavy penalties to pay in terms of the amount of memory that is required, but, in a very loose way, this may be compensated by the directness of the run-time performance and (dare it be said) the human-like nature of the process. Just thinking of the way that we ourselves solve problems, we note that we are not aware of exhaustive searches going on whenever we solve a problem. The searches for humans, as for neural computers, appear to happen during the process of self-education. This gives the neural system competence in the sense defined in this chapter, as the user of the machine would see the process to be more like his or her own when compared with the process that would be found in a conventional rule-based system.

These points are too controversial to be left at this superficial level. A more telling example is considered in some detail in the next section.

7.6 A cognitive neural automaton

In this section we wish to demonstrate that a simple state machine leads to a model of cognitive behaviour which makes good use of emergent properties in the neural mode. But through an alteration of some of its parameters, the model can operate in a totally conventional way too. These parameters highlight the differences and similarities between these modes. The neural state machine model (NSMM) operates in an environment, and this environment both outputs to and receives inputs from the outputs of the model (Figure 7.1). The NSMM can output one of three possible symbols: a, b and &. The environment also generates four things that are input to the NSMM:

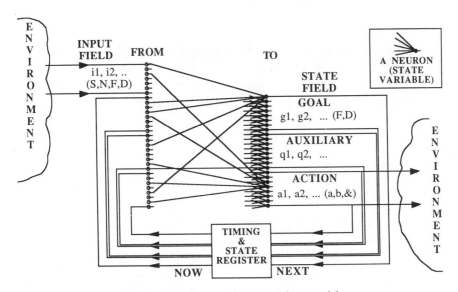

Figure 7.1 *The neural state machine model.*

food, denoted by the symbol F
drink, denoted by the symbol D
a starting symbol S
a neutral symbol N

The objective for the model is to decide whether it 'wants' either food
or drink, and to generate the appropriate sequence of symbols to achieve
its aim (the way the model can 'want' anything will be explained later).

To give some linguistic structure to this task, we make the environment
an acceptor of strings that follow specific grammatical rules:

- It will generate the (F)ood symbol if the NSMM produces a symmetrical
  sequence (in time) of 'a's and 'b's starting with an 'a' (e.g. 'aaaaaabbbbbb'
  or 'ab').
- It will generate the (D)rink symbol if the NSMM produces a palindromic
  sequence that contains both 'a's and 'b's (e.g. 'abba' or 'bbbabbabbb').
- The '&' simply causes the environment to repeat its last output.
- The environment is normally in a rest state in which it generates the S
  symbol.
- While the NSMM is generating symbols that could fit into one of the
  two legitimate sequencing schemes, the environment generates the N
  symbol.

The simplest way to model the NSMM is as a machine with undefined state
transitions which become defined through some learning process. It is assumed
that the state machine has binary state variables.

7.6.1 Base structure

In addition to having a neural net capable of learning, the model must
contain some structure which enables it to adapt to the environment. These
design requirements are not derived from a knowledge of the problem
that the machine is required to solve, but are minimal requirements for
the machine to be able to learn anything at all. To be anthropomorphic,
these are the structural requirements that a system would have had to acquire
by evolution to be able to survive in environments which have 'linguistic'
properties.

The *first structural requirement* is that the state variables of the NSMM
be divided into three groups or areas (see Figure 7.1):

(a) a GOAL area in which target symbols $g1$, $g2$, . . . are encoded (in this
     case they will be F (for food) and D (for drink));
(b) an AUXILIARY STATE area in which states $q1$, $q2$, . . . qj are encoded;

There is the usual INPUT field in which input symbols $i1$, $i2$, . . . are encoded.
These input symbols will be S, N, F and D in this case.

The notation we shall use for the input to the neural net is a list of the form

$$[i(t),g(t),q(t),a(t),] \qquad \text{the FROM list}$$
$$[g(t+1),q(t+1),a(t+1)] \qquad \text{the TO list}$$

The FROM list includes input from the environment and symbols for the current state. The TO list is the output to the environment and the symbols which will FORM the next state. It could be said that our mode of expression is blatantly symbolic, while the physical encoding is subsymbolic.

While in this *first structural requirement* we have not specified the exact way in which the encoding should be done, as a *second structural requirement* we insist that in the output action area the only symbols that can be transmitted to the environment be a, b and &. We shall see that the mechanism of learning depends on these symbols being generated at random. It is assumed that the system can output no other symbols that have any effect on the environment. It is tempting to speculate that this may be a property which is in force in living beings who are endowed with instinctive outputs upon which subsequent learning is built.

7.6.2 Explorative learning rules

We shall identify three ways that the NSMM can acquire the knowledge required to extract food and drink from the environment. These are 'explorative', 'instructional' and 'programmed'. Here we are concerned with the first of these, where the NSMM acquires knowledge by a process of exploration. The procedure we shall discuss is general and not specific to the given problem.

Learning is a process of defining state transitions. Before learning takes place, any state can lead to any other possible state with equal probability. This random action will cause the system to generate random outputs. This is an exploratory form of behaviour, which is a neural property in the sense that the neurons that energize the state variables, while receiving input from the current state and overall input, produce the 'undefined' probabilistic output (Chapter 2). A transition becomes defined when some training mechanism forces a desired next state (or TO state) on the state variables, to be associated with the state which is currently at the neuron inputs (the FROM state). In weighted systems the link is achieved gradually, whereas in weightless systems it is achieved at once.

We now describe a learning rule that allows the NSMM to operate in a predictive way in any symbolic environment with linguistic properties. We call this the LLA, the Linguistic Learning Algorithm. It has two parts, LLA1 and LLA2.

LLA1
When a goal is achieved as a result of the exploration caused by the undefined states of the NSMM, and the environment signals this by

generating, say, F at time $t+1$, the transition from the state at time t becomes *defined* (by being recorded in memory) as follows. Say that the state at time t is originally $[N,gt,q1,b]$ (as it would be for the symmetrical string which always ends in 'b'). This becomes *defined* as the FROM part of a transition as $[N,F,q1,b]$, with the TO part of the transition becoming $[F,F,?]$.

This requires some explanation. First, what determines that the system learns just at that moment? From the designer's point of view, this is the process of recording the last in a series of NSMM outputs which has delivered a reward. Anthropomorphically this points to an innate activity without which an organism would not be able to survive: the unleashing of learning activity (hormonally?) when a basic target such as thirst or hunger relief has been achieved.

Second, there is a subtle step in recording F not only in the TO state, but also in the FROM state in the GOAL area. This was suggested by Eamon Fulcher, a psychology student who was aware of the fact that animals learn maze-searching tasks backward from the goal in multiple goal experiments. In the design of a state machine model of learning, this backward spread of goal information gives state trajectories leading to goals a label of the goal which will be reached. The ? in the TO state indicates that the exit from this state is not defined. Eventually the NSMM will learn that [F,F&F] is a re-entrant state. F in the internal state area is a useful marker of the fact that a goal is expected to be achieved in that state.

Finally, the role of the auxiliary state q1 should be clarified. This is a learned marker which distinguishes between different occurrences of the same output symbol. It could be seen as a counting device of the kind that was identified in section 5.6, where the problem of embedding as exemplified by nested brackets was discussed. The computer system designer solves this problem with a special memory called a 'push-down stack' and the auxiliary area in the NSMM serves the same purpose.

The second learning rule provides linkages between states leading to goals even when the environment is not signalling that a goal has been reached (i.e. when it outputs S or N) .

LLA2
When, through the process of exploration, a transition occurs from an undefined state, say $[N,g,q,a]$, to a previously defined FROM state, say $[N,F,q(j),b]$, then $[N,g,q,a]$ becomes defined as a new FROM state, by becoming $[N,F,q(j+1),a]$ with $[F,q(j),b]$ as its corresponding TO state.

Here too we note that the backward transmission of the goal label provides the crucial forward chaining that eventually leads to the transmission of the correct output sequence for the desired goal state.

At this point it is important to suggest ways in which a goal state becomes 'desired'. There are two steps that need to be understood. First, it is likely that, rather than learning an entire battery of sequences that lead to a particular goal, only one such sequence (a short one is more likely than a long one) will have been learned for each target. It is likely that the learned strategies of the automaton will be as shown in Figure 7.2.

Second, the 'will' to have food or drink cannot occur from within the model as defined so far. From the designer's point of view the system must receive the thirst or hunger signal from somewhere else, in the same form as would normally occur at the input to the NSMM. This symbol is then clamped into the goal area of the state field.

Given this, the major neural property of reconstruction comes into play. Given that F, say, is in the goal area and S, say at the input, q1 and 'a' can be retrieved. From there on the state sequence is determined and leads to the goal. Interestingly, as the sequence can be followed without inputs to the NSMM actually being generated by the environment (the reconstruction emergent property at work again) this can become purely an internal or 'mental' sequence which is a form of 'visualization' of the required actions.

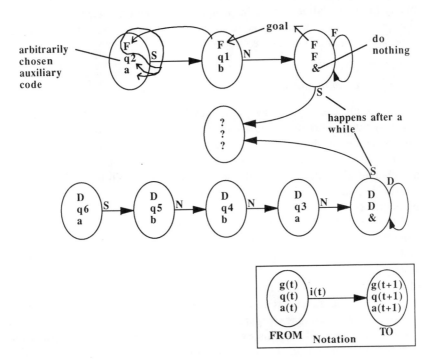

Figure 7.2 *A learned linguistic behaviour.*

7.6.3 Learning under instruction and pre-programming

In the above example of learning by exploration we demonstrated a capacity for an artificial neural system to learn through a process of exploration resulting directly from the properties that emerge from the neural scheme. But the system fails to 'understand' the full nature of the syntactic structure of the environment because it will stop exploring once it has learned a satisfactory sequence. If an agent who *does* understand this structure were now to become an instructor for the system he or she would do this by clamping into the action area suitable sequences that the system might not have discovered on its own. Without going into detail, it can be stated that the model will then build a probabilistic state structure of alternative ways of achieving goals.

Exactly how this might occur depends on the control structures that bring new internal states into playing the $q(t)$ area of the state pattern. One possibility is that the instructor can teach the system to count, by taking control (by clamping?) of these internal states. In other words, the system can learn that a pattern of the first n outputs must be followed by the same number in fixed relation to the first group. At the extreme of this process, the instructor becomes a programmer who maps state behaviour such as shown in Figure 7.2 for Food or Drink generation into the system. We note that the 'hidden' state area has been used as a counter. Something like this would be a requirement of any implementation. Also, the programmer would not use the generalization properties of the neural state machine and would indeed find that the generalization was a nuisance.

7.6.4 Some implications

At the simplest level, we have shown that the difference between a neural and a symbolic version of the architecture for an automaton with cognitive properties lies in the application of a neural function to the state variables of the automaton. This gives rise to the emergence of useful properties at a higher level of description of the system – these abilities are to explore and to generalize from a linguistic environment in order to satisfy some inner 'need'.

We submit that this ability is cognitive, syntactic (it extracts a limited rule from the environment), semantic (it gets the environmental response it 'wants') and, in the case of learning, cannot be understood without appreciating the simple but basic dynamic effect of reconstruction in the neural function of the state variables. Furthermore, it enables the cognitive scientist to study the prime functions required for exploratory learning of complex environments by complex organisms. While we have not carried out such a study systematically in this example, we are merely suggesting that the neural consideration adds a missing dimension to the potential for such studies.

We have also shown that the exploratory activity by itself is inadequate for the model to be able to represent the full mathematical character of the environment – this is better approached when an instructor takes control of the learning activity. The ultimate mathematical model is only achieved when the instructor turns into an analyst, discovers the mathematical structure of the environment, and loads it into the machine. We shall discuss the implications of this relationship between the neural and the rule-based for cognitive science in the next section; suffice it to say here that it is possible to see a theoretical continuum from the symbolic to the neural, which makes it hard to argue that these concepts operate in different, incompatible, planes.

7.7 Where does this leave Fodor and Pylyshyn's attack?

The view presented in this chapter is in contrast with the ideas expressed by Fodor and Pylyshyn (1988) (F&P for short) that what they call connectionism, and we have called Artificial Neural Systems (ANSs), is incompatible with and irrelevant to classical models of cognition. Here we wish to summarize our reasons for arguing that the two are, in fact, compatible and that ANSs extend classical models to provide a richer approach to theories of cognition. We shall divide the discussion into two parts, the first relating closely to the main line of F&P's condemnation of ANSs and the second (in section 7.8) dealing with the way we think that ANSs enrich cognitive science.

One perspective on F&P's paper may be that it was merely written too early in the recent history of connectionism. Like others before them (e.g. Minsky and Papert, 1969), F&P launched their attack on an incomplete and unexplored theory of ANSs. Blame cannot be attached to this – the claims made by early revivalists of the field (e.g. the PDP group: Rumelhart and McClelland, 1986) were also made from a limited perspective. Smolensky's contribution (1988) on connectionist notions of subsymbolic representations (discussed in Chapter 6) are, by his own account, not fully developed. However, maturation of connectionism, we believe, is revealing that concentration on theories of connection strengths stemming from statistical mechanics hides from view a more appropriate approach to computational problems. In this chapter we have appealed to formal methods commonly used in computing (automata Theory, in this case) to clarify the computational nature of ANSs. It is surprising that this has been done by relatively few others. Judd's use of complexity theory (1990) is a refreshing example. We shall discuss below the alternative light that the use of such formal methods casts on some of F&P's main lines of argument.

7.7.1 Association leads to structure I

One pillar of F&P's attack lies in dismissing the emergent property of reconstruction (the re-entrant states and attractors described earlier in this chapter) as leading to 'associationism' which, in their view fails to deliver the syntactic and semantic structures required for connectionist modelling. We have seen in Chapter 6 that they give the example of representing the sentence 'John loves Mary and Bill hates Sally', which, in a Boltzmann/ Hopfield auto-associative net would be represented as a set of coexisting features: John-subject; loves-verb; Mary-object; and-preposition; Bill-subject; hates-verb; Sally-object.

F&P state that the associative mechanism confuses these features and fails to distinguish the correct sentence from utterances such as 'John hates Sally and Mary loves Bill' or even nonsensical sequences such as 'Hates Mary Bill John and Sally loves'. This fear is simply erroneous and based on the fact that the Boltzmann/Hopfield nets are rarely discussed in terms of their temporal behaviour. But another area of connectionism does tackle this problem – Kohonen's ordered maps (1989). Here statements such as 'John loves Mary' and 'Bill hates Sally' would be represented as distinct trajectories of activity in the physical space of the net. They could not be confused.

Alternatively, in an NSMM model such as we presented in this chapter, the two parts of the overall sentence would be distinct parts of two separate states (controlled by an 'and-preposition') retrieved in success. Again there is no danger of confusion. So, it is not that connectionism does not possess the richness of syntactic representation – rather the F&P criticism is valid for only one particular structure and one particular way of using it. It does not apply to the whole of the philosophy of neural systems.

7.7.2 Association leads to structure II

Another of F&P's concerns relating to the linguistic power of the emergent property of reconstruction by state space attractors is that it would be difficult to represent production rules such as

'<sentence>may be replaced by<proper-name>loves<proper-name>'

Again, what has been missed here is that an ANS is a dynamic system. In classical computation, the programmer creates just such systems as virtual machines. These parse and generate strings with syntactic/semantic correctness (e.g. 'push-down stack automata' for parsing grammatically generated strings, or finite state machines for parsing finite state strings).

In our example in section 7.6 we have shown that ANSs enable the possibility of arriving at such structures by exploration or instruction. While the ability to learn from exploration or instruction played a central role in the process, the correct sequences could not be generated without association. Even though the results of the three styles of introducing knowledge into the NSMM lead to different state structures, all three have syntactic content (the generated strings are 'correct') as well as semantic content (the organism 'gets what it wants'). The trick has been to use the associative property of the net in a *dynamic* way rather than the *static* mode which has led to F&P's concern.

We should stress that this argument is not the same as saying that conventional computing can always be achieved by using neural devices as components of an architecture designed to perform a parsing action (Touretzky, 1987). Our position is that a neural system has not only the potential of classical computational power, but because of its emergent properties becomes specialized through feats of learning which are specified and understood at a high level of abstraction. We shall return to this point in section 7.8.

7.7.3 Learning is more than appreciating probabilities

F&P have dismissed learning in connectionist systems for being merely 'frequency sensitive'. This is done in reference to Hinton's demonstration that a Boltzmann machine learns the probability of occurrence of events in its environment. While it is true that this probability is learned, we have demonstrated that this is not all that can be learned by a dynamic ANS. Even in the exploratory learning mode of the NSMM model in this chapter the learning of appropriate strings could not be inferred from probabilities.

While it may be important on occasions to use an ANS in a static mode and to let it adapt to frequencies of events, advanced work in connectionism should be about (and clearly can be about) systems in which the state space representations reflect the time structure of their environments.

7.7.4 Neural systems transcend the 'implementation level' I

In their concluding comments, F&P justify their assertion that connectionism is irrelevant to cognitive science by citing the fact that the latter is expressed at the level of the algorithm while the former casts its descriptions at a lower, implementational level. That is, an algorithm that parses a sentence is a cognitive model of the act of parsing. A description of neuron activation patterns (F&P argue) is neutral in the sense that whether the algorithm runs on the neural net or on any other machine adds nothing to the quality of the algorithm itself. The counter to this argument is that, given a cognitive task, there may be a large number of algorithms that model the task at some surface level. The many competing theories of scene understanding found in artificial intelligence (briefly discussed in Chapter 3) are an example of this. So which of these algorithms is the relevant descriptor? Given this multiplicity, is the algorithmic level irrelevant to cognitive science? Cognitive scientists would rightly see such a question as being absurd. Competing algorithms, they would argue, are like competing theories in any subject – they form part of the scientific endeavour in that subject.

Our view is that ANSs simply add to the selection of alternative algorithms. In the example of recognition of facial expressions mentioned earlier in this chapter, we saw how the neural approach generated an effective algorithm which might not have occurred to a programmer. It should be said in passing that such algorithms did occur to programmers (e.g. Bledsoe and Browning, 1959) but were rejected by early AI workers as not being sufficiently 'rule-based'. The programmer's rule-based approach would in this case be hard to find, and, if found, it would be unlikely to perform in as convincing a way as the ANS approach.

What we have in the facial expression recognition case are two competing algorithms – one generated by an ANS and the other by a programmer. Surely neither can be ruled out as being irrelevant. It is in this context that we have introduced (as an alternative to the Turing test) our definition of competence (in section 7.5) as being a measure of the match between an algorithm and a human user of such an algorithm. This may induce an ordering among models in cognitive science that determines the relevance of such models to the current state of the paradigm. In this new order we may find that some neurally generated algorithms turn out to be more relevant than classical ones. It seems important to keep that door open.

7.7.5 Neural systems transcend the 'implementation level' II

Our choice of using state machines from automata theory is based on the fact that the state machine provides a way of linking the implementation of a system to its behaviour. Designers use the concept to tie algorithmic descriptions (in state space) to the logical functions of the state variables (implementation). In this chapter we have seen that neural generalization of the neurons that control state variables translates to the property of reconstruction which is undoubtedly a property of state space, which is the algorithmic level. F&P's isolation of connectionism at the implementation level is a curious example of dualism mistakenly based on the neutrality of general-purpose hardware. ANSs are not neutral in this way and may be seen (through state machine models as discussed here) as linking implementation descriptions to algorithmic ones.

7.8 The neural extension to cognitive science

Not all the responsibility for the neuron/symbol divide rests at the feet of Fodor and Pylyshyn. Connectionists themselves have argued that a new science has been born purely on the basis of the reconstructive properties of Hopfield nets, the Generalized Delta rule for training Boltzmann machines and the ubiquitous error back-propagation solution to multi-layer perceptrons. In this chapter we have argued that ANSs are much more than that. Of course, we are not alone in looking at a shift of the paradigm beyond these inventive, but constrained beginnings. Notable is the work of Walter Schneider and Prahlad Gupta on the modelling of visual search tasks (1991). They demonstrate sensitivity to the concept of competence and the need to break the task down into cognitive subtasks. This is engineering with state machines. Another example (among an increasing number) is the work of Jeffrey Elman on finding structure in time (1990). He too is conscious of engineering with automata-like structures and the fact that syntactic/semantic structure may be found in the state space (i.e. time sequence) of such systems. We have argued that ANSs, through their ability to learn and reconstruct, add another dimension to existing computational studies of cognition. Here we summarize what might be an agenda for those who wish to develop this contribution further. It also is an agenda for the topics which we discuss in greater detail in the closing chapters of this book.

7.8.1 Learning

Learning has probably received less attention in cognitive science than other areas. While there are exceptions in artificial intelligence (Michalski *et al.*, 1980) these are principally directed at 'concept learning' as a separate effort from the rest of cognition. But almost all that we call cognition in human beings is heavily underpinned by learning. What we are and are not capable of doing is influenced by what we are and are not capable of learning. In our simple example in this chapter we have drawn attention to the way that a consideration of learning in NSMMs leads to a discussion of what is learned under different architectural conditions. Indeed, the study of the difference between exploration and instruction, despite its obvious importance, has hardly entered contemporary connectionist literature.

Connectionism seems to have aimed its study of learning at technological issues such as supervised and unsupervised systems, or the efficacy of error propagation. Again there are exceptions (the work of Judd, 1990), but we expect that as ANSs move towards being used for the making of cognitively competent machinery, more work will be done on developing schemes that learn syntactic/semantic structures. This means that cognitive science will be enriched by a study of how learning is affected by architectural and algorithmic constraints.

7.8.2 Mental imagery

While psychologists have shown considerable interest in mental imagery (see Richardson (1980) and a collection of articles in Hampson *et al.* (1990), this area has largely been shunned by cognitive scientists (with notable exceptions, e.g. Kosslyn *et al.* (1990). The main reason for the neglect of mental imagery is that there are difficulties in generating *formal* representations of the results of experiments executed by researchers in this field. Mental imagery appears too diffuse for the symbolic idiom and it is for this reason that Kosslyn's work is exceptional. He has suggested a rule-based structure which closely represents some experimental findings.

In contrast, the ANS provides an ideal medium for modelling mental images at various levels of abstraction. The internal state of a NSMM is a recallable image. Suffice it to say that theoretical studies on the retrievability of such images form cues, and their retention under different architectural conditions (e.g. Aleksander and Morton, 1991) are likely to have at least two effects. First, they will help to formalize the concept of 'mental imagery', and second, they will bring the role of mental imagery into the discourse on language understanding, where it clearly has an important and a yet largely unexplored role to play.

7.8.3 Cognitive architectures

There is a difference between the way that classicists and connectionists use the word 'architecture'. The former refer to cognitive architectures as those formal processing objects that incorporate symbolic rules. Connectionists pitch their definition closer to the hardware on which neural nets are emulated or constructed. We would suggest that the former is too abstract and the latter too detailed. An appropriate study of architectures might occur at the level where neural systems such as the NSMM are taken as the building bricks of a grander scheme. While there are some specific examples of this in the connectionist literature – e.g. Touretzky (1987), Schneider and Gupta, (1991), Kozato and DeWilde (1991), Sharkey (1989) – we are proposing a more general approach which stems from the theory of linked state machines. The key questions are deep and difficult. How are desired learning properties mapped into structures made of several general neural units? How does one distribute learning information among such modules? Do useful properties emerge from some prototypical structures of these bricks? These are important questions that need to be answered if the true nature of cognitive architectures is to be understood. The questions are not necessarily new – to engineers they are at the heart of the formal design process, to neurologists they are central in inferring role from physical structure, to philosophers they may touch on the mind–body problem.

7.9 A plethora of algorithms?

Declaring that an interest in artificial neural systems can extend the richness of cognitive science accepts that cognitive science operates at the algorithmic level. But the word 'algorithmic' has to be used with care. The algorithmic style is a good medium in which to represent theories of cognition, but in order to have a theory one needs to have the algorithms. Cognitive science exists by virtue of the presence of a set of algorithms, each of which describes some facet of cognition. But if cognitive science is defined by a set of algorithms, the next question is what the evolutionary dynamics of this set might be. Do better algorithms replace worse ones? What is better and what is worse? How are new algorithms invented? Whatever may be the answer to these questions, it seems clear that the set of algorithms is dependent on the analysis of cognition by human analysts and the creation of new algorithms by such analysts.

The case we presented in section 7.7.4 is that ANSs are tools which help to enhance this pool of algorithms. Indeed, the resurgence of interest in connectionism is partly due to the fact that designers of cognitive machines questioned the credibility of the algorithms in the pool when comparisons are made with the cognitive competence of human beings. So we see a future for cognitive science in which the pool of algorithms contains those generated by human analysis *and* those mediated by ANSs. The competence ordering will embrace both neural and symbolic algorithms while, at the same time, it will provide the necessary competitive evolutionary pressure to keep cognitive science buoyant!

8

Language and neurons

Acquired or innate? Logical or iconic?

8.1 Introduction: flexing the linguistic muscles of the NSMM

Our cards are now on the table. In the last chapter we argued that the connectionist bases for cognitive computation and classical models have the same underlying computational principles. The Neural State Machine Model (NSMM) was introduced as an abstract machine which is capable of carrying both conventional representations that are designed by a programmer and neural representations that are created through learning and generalization. From this perspective we revisit in this chapter some issues related to models of natural language – models that arise both in classical methods and connectionist ones.

This has to be done warily. Language is cherished as the essence of being human – to suggest that machines could make use of it is to rob the human of a unique ticket to the top of the intelligence table. Of course other species communicate and this is a source of some fascination. But the scientific quest of those interested in cognition is directed unashamedly at the language that humans use. This immediately leads to some lively debates about human development – what is learned and what is innate? It also leads directly to a distinction between neural and symbolic models. The latter is based on machinery which represents an extant, working language system and therefore leans towards the innate hypothesis. The neural model, on the other hand, leads to explanations of the way that some of the function of the machinery of language can be created by learning.

In section 8.2 we summarize the symbolic view of language by distinguishing between various concepts that are important in formal models of language. Much of this focuses on the way that different kinds of knowledge may be represented. Lexical prowess, that is a knowledge of the meaning of words as might be given in a dictionary, is distinguished from a knowledge of syntax, that is grammar and semantics, and the study of the meaning of utterances (as opposed to single words). There are other issues of knowledge representation in the symbolic domain that have influenced linguistics. One is the concept of semantic networks already seen in Chapter 3, which we now examine to see how they relate to the NSMM model. A new view emerges from this exploration, a view in which the mental image plays a strong part. This discussion allows us to introduce what we feel is an important new concept in language understanding. It is an *iconic state* in the NSMM which relates to a mental image. It serves a major function in the removal of ambiguity from utterances.

With this background we turn to the work that has been done in language through the use of neural systems. In section 8.3 we look at the study by Rumelhart and McClelland (1986) of models which learn the past tense of English verbs. This is an attempt to explain the curious way in which children first accept and learn the past tense of irregular verbs (e.g. give/gave), then appear to become confused by learning the rules of regular verbs (e.g. walk/walked) before creating representations that cope proficiently with both. Our discussion centres on whether this progression is a general by-product of learning or whether it is specific to the learning of the past tense. Staying with early connectionist work, in section 8.4 we review the work by McClelland and Kawamoto (1986) on the assignment of 'case roles' to parts of sentences. As an example, this involves learning that in a sentence such as 'the boy broke the window', 'boy' has the case role of an agent, whereas another word (rock) in exactly the same position in the sentence 'The rock broke the window' is not an agent but an instrument. Where McClelland and Kawamoto used weighted, connectionist models, we relate this activity to the NSMM in order to comment on the learnability of such case role assignments.

More recently, connectionist considerations of language were directly influenced by the symbolic/subsymbolic debate. In section 8.5 we review the work of Jordan Pollack (1990) who uses what he calls a recursive auto-associative memory (RAAM) to encode representations of syntactic structures. He suggests that this is a counter example to Fodor and Pylyshyn's (1988) thesis that associativism cannot represent such structures. We compare the RAAM approach to the use of iconic states in the NSMM and demonstrate that the awkward nested structures of sentences such as 'Bill knows that John loves Mary' can be represented using iconic states. Pollack's method gives rise to a question of whether there is something special about the way that classicists combine symbols to make formulae, and this leads to a consideration in section 8.6 of work by Tim van Gelder of Indiana University (1990). Van Gelder argues that the way classicists compose their symbolic formulations is through concatenation of symbols, where Pollack's work points to ways of composing formulae which, though symbolic, are not concatenated. Van Gelder argues that connectionism may be richer for allowing this type of composability, and we support this by reference to iconic NSMM representations. The trend is continued in section 8.7, where the idea of the role of hidden units in linguistic representation is considered.

While this is not iconic, we suggest that it could be auxiliary to the iconic representation in utterances that refer to time and sequential order.

This in turn leads us back to language, but this time in a 'language of thought' (Fodor, 1976) sense. In section 8.8 we look at a commentary published in 1991 by Martin Davies, of Birkbeck College in London, on Fodor's *Language of Thought* (1975). Fodor argued that thinking followed rules similar to spoken language. Thus in the neuron/symbol debate the hypothesis by Fodor that language cannot be properly represented in connectionism is translated into an argument that connectionism cannot represent thought processes. We draw attention to the fact that, as the hypothesis may be wrong, the representation of thought in connectionist systems is still an open challenge. Finally, in section 8.9 we summarize the changes that have taken place in the modelling of language since the revival of connectionism and look at opportunities that are still open for improved models.

8.2 Symbolic versus mental views of language

Our source material for this section comes from Greene (1986), and the reader who wishes to study the subject more deeply than we do here is recommended to read this comprehensive and compact text.

First of all, it is worth asking an 'emperor's new clothes' type of question: 'What is the benefit of having formal models of language?'. In this case, linguists argue, the emperor's clothes are real and made of the richest materials. The ability to provide sound, mathematically based models of the structure (syntax) of language, the way that language has meaning (semantics) and the way that experience shapes language (knowledge representation) would lead to a shared understanding of this uniquely human ability. One problem, however, is that such models that have been developed are distinct and integrate badly. Our aim here is to discuss lexical knowledge and to show that there is an approach based on the NSMM which integrates such knowledge with syntactic and semantic knowledge.

The first formalization, which is relatively easy to understand, is in the lexical domain. This refers to the sort of activity that occurs when we look up words in a dictionary of a language we understand. For example, if you hear someone say the word(s) 'holus-bolus' you may not know what it means. The dictionary reveals that, first, it is an adverb, and second, it means 'all in a lump, altogether'. Linguistic cognition, that is, thinking in language-like ways and expressing thoughts using language, is based on knowledge of words that we do not need to look up in a dictionary. In some way, it could we said that we carry a useful part of the dictionary in our heads. For example, in the writing of this paragraph we have used the word 'dictionary'. If someone were to ask what that word means, it would not be difficult to say something like 'it is a noun and it means "a book that contains definitions of the meaning of words"'. Looking the word up in a dictionary we find 'Book, dealing with, usually in alphabetical order, the meaning or trans-lation of words ... '. Our guess was not far out; we just forgot about the alphabetical order, and had earlier restricted the discourse to dictionaries in only one language.

Symbolic modellers do not see the modelling of lexical knowledge of this kind as particularly interesting, as it easily done on simple computers. Indeed, for the price of a few paper dictionaries it is possible to buy an electronic dictionary that fits into a pocket. This electronic version works by converting each word into a number which addresses an area of memory that contains the appropriate definition. The more elaborate examples of these machines will even drive a voice synthesizer and provide spoken output in several languages. The process may be defined as

<word> implies <definition 1, definition 2, ...>

The amount of storage required for this method of lexical look up can be easily calculated. For example, the average dictionary contains 40 000 entries. Giving a code to each of these entries would require each code to consist of only 16 bits (26 bits gives rise to 65,536 possible distinct codes). If each word required two definitions and each definition contained four words (each needing 16 bits of storage), the 'lookup' storage mentioned earlier can be done using roughly $40\,000 \times 2 \times 4 \times 16$ bits. However, we will of course need to provide all 65 536 storage locations to store the 40 000 words, so the total becomes $65\,536 \times 2 \times 4 \times 16$ bits = 8 388 608 bits, that is, what computers scientists call one megabyte. (One megabyte is not very much, and is the minimum amount of storage you would expect even in a very inexpensive laptop computer.)

So what could connectionist thinking possibly add to this? Clearly, the above process can be implemented with an NSMM with input and output only (no feedback) or a multi-layer perceptron. But there is a more sophisticated way of obtaining such meaning associations that makes use of a dynamic process for retrieval rather than a lookup table. Such a process is illustrated in Figure 8.1.

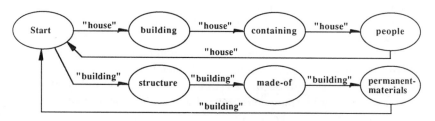

Figure 8.1 *A dynamic lexical system.*

Here the word that needs to be defined (say 'house') is presented as an input to an NSMM-like automaton which moves sequentially through several states, each of which is part of the definition. Given the 16-bit coding of words set out above we would require only 16 neurons (see Figure 7.1) just to encode the words as states of the system. Each neuron would require a maximum of 32 inputs (16 from the word that needs definition and 16 from the sequence of words that form the definitional states). There is no need for auxiliary units shown in Figure 7.1. The chances are that the overall memory capacity is of the same order as the lookup version (i.e. about 64 kilobytes per neuron). But the important point here is that NSMM-like automata are poised to learn associations as they occur, where the lookup scheme has to be programmed.

So far, the discussion has centred purely around technical implementation, and in this context both the lookup and the NSMM are effectively classical computing models. But the key question that remains is whether there are models that are cognitively more plausible than these exhaustive storage methods. The chances are that a human being learns the definition of words in context and not by memorizing definitions. In other words, a child may discover that many things that adults call a 'house' have common features: people living in them, chimneys, gardens, windows and so on. So, on asking a child what a house is, the reply may be a great deal richer than the terse dictionary definitions we have been discussing above. This leads to the thought that the representation of lexical knowledge perhaps cannot be separated from representation of knowledge in general.

Before dealing with the problem of representation, we shall look briefly at the role of syntax in language understanding. In Chapter 7 we saw that the NSMM can learn linguistic structures by at least two methods – exploration and instruction. Perhaps it is the case that the role of syntax is not as central to the modelling of language as is suggested by the majority of models in cognitive science. Possibly the NSMM provides an alternative framework. Consider the difference between the following four utterances:

(1) 'Help ... fire ... child ... trapped'
(2) 'The batsman hits the ball'
(3) 'The ball hits the batsman'
(4) 'Hits the ball batsman the'

(1) is not grammatical but is not hard to understand. In fact, it is a case where the meaning would not be any less available were the order of presentation of the words changed (e.g. 'Fire ... trapped ... help ... child'). On the other hand, (2) and (3) mean completely different things and depend heavily on word order (i.e. syntax), while (4) indicates that there is a word order that has no meaning at all. So we can see that word order disambiguates what would in some cases be ambiguous heaps of words. Now, in normal discourse, utterances are thought to be 'correct' when they accurately represent some world events (this includes both concrete events available to the senses, and

abstract ones that may include words such as 'loves' or 'believes'). In symbolic models of syntax, the correctness of surface language strings is not tested by reference to world events, the difference between (2) and (3) being based on an intermediate labelling of 'batsman' as <subject> and 'ball' as <object> or vice versa. However, if there is a relationship between word order and meaning, we can take the view that meaning can be seen as the driving force behind word order. But what is meaning?

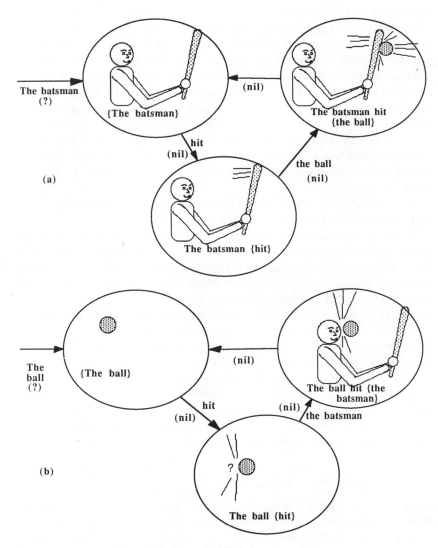

Figure 8.2 *Syntactic NSMM state diagrams.*

With this question in mind, we return to the importance of mental representation and the fact that syntax (alongside lexical knowledge) should not be divorced from representation. Examples (2) and (3) can be processed by an NSMM, as shown in Figure 8.2. This is merely a speculative sketch of the way syntactic and mental representations might interact – it requires some explanation. Consider (a) first. Assuming that the NSMM is in some neutral state, the words 'The batsman' causes a transition to an inner state which, in the way of Chapter 2, is a learned mental image. This represents a lexical retrieval act. As the word 'hits' is perceived, the mental image modifies again (through state development) again to incorporate the new word. This process carries on as the utterance 'the ball' is input, completing the state representation. In (b) the same process is applied to the same words, but in the alternative order – 'The ball hits the batsman' showing that this leads to a different but appropriate mental state representation. In summary, therefore, there is a link between surface word order and mental representation which requires syntactically correct input sequences if it is to be productive. Incorrect sequences such as (4) would fail to elicit any useful mental representation. However, this model also allows for the creation of mental images (that is, understanding) for utterances such as (1), with various word orders leading to the same mental representation of a child trapped in a burning house.

We give this state representation the name **iconic state** and will return to it in later parts of this chapter and in Chapter 9.

There are other features of Figure 8.2 that should be noted. It is proposed that the state is responsible not only for holding the mental interpretation of some kind of image that resolves the linguistic input, but also an echo of the incoming language which corresponds to the mental image as it is being built up. Furthermore, the incremental part of the stored linguistic representation (shown in curly brackets, { }) may be in the output area of the NSMM (see Figure 7.1, and thus the appropriate sentence can be output to describe the mental event. (Transitions once experienced can take place without an input – hence the 'nil' link.)

The reader may wish to refer back to Chapters 3 and 4 to compare the linguistic method proposed here with classical knowledge representation techniques (say, scripts and semantic networks). It seems feasible that connectionism offers new prospects for modelling linguistic cognition which integrate syntax, semantics and knowledge representation.

8.3 Experiments with the past tense

The use of the NSMM in linguistic cognitive models is somewhat different from the early work of connectionists in the linguistic area. It is important to look at some of this earlier work in order to clarify these differences and to see whether the NSMM could be used for similar purposes. Rumelhart and McClelland's work (1986) is a good example of early connectionist effort. This is concerned with learning the rules that lead to the transformation of a verb to its form in the past tense, and we ask whether this task would lie within the remit of the NSMM. This work by Rumelhart and McClelland is central to symbol/neuron discussions, as it suggests that there is more to cognitive models than just a statement of a set of rules that is being followed. Connectionist explanations, they argue, offer explanations which include theories about how such rules are acquired and therefore are more comprehensive.

The phenomenon observed in children goes as follows. At an early stage in language learning, when children begin to appreciate the need to distinguish between past and present tenses, they acquire and use correctly a limited number of past tense words, most of which are irregular, such as *came* and *went*. But there is no evidence that any rule is being used to link the present form of these verbs with their past forms. At an intermediate stage there is evidence that children begin to use a rule which works well on regular forms of verbs, such as *wiped* and *pulled*. But this seems to confuse their knowledge of irregular forms, and they make errors, such as saying *comed* and *goed*. At a later stage, much of this erroneous behaviour has vanished. Irregular verbs are recognized and separated from regular ones for particular treatment. Previously unheard verbs are assumed to be regular and regular rules are applied. This last stage continues into adulthood.

Rumelhart and McClelland use a four-layer network which works at the phonological (sound) level and effectively learns to translate present tense verb sounds fed to the input of the network into past tense sounds at the output of the network. The outcome is that when exposed to present–past pairs of both irregular and regular verbs, the connectionist model develops three phases similar to those observed in children. Here it is not our objective to go into the details of this experiment – there are details aplenty in the original paper, ranging from training regimes to the representation of sounds as firing

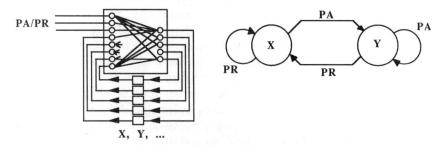

Figure 8.3 *An NSMM that learns the past tense.*

patterns in the net. What we can do, however, is show that the NSMM demonstrates that this three-phase development is a natural, general, emergent consequence of learning with neural versions of the model. Consider Figure 8.3, in which one way of representing this situation is shown. Any relationship between two concepts can be represented as shown in the state diagram of Figure 8.3. In this case the input to NSMM is either PA (for *past* tense) or PR (for *pre*sent tense). So X would be a particular present tense word and Y a particular past tense word. In the early parts of training, the system could learn to build up pairs of states linked in the manner shown in the state diagram. It would be particularly easy to learn given arbitrary pairs, which above we have called 'irregular'. Now say that the volume of trained regular verbs is increased. We need to look more closely at the coding of these to emulate the regular relationships. Regular relationships are characterized by a repetition of the present verb with the addition of 'ed' (e.g. pull→pulled). The coding should reflect this. Say that the present verb is represented by a code on four of the state bits such as 0010, and that the present/past code appears on the fifth bit, so that the whole code for the above verb in the present is 00100, and in the past 00101. (This is in contrast to the coding of irregular pairs, where there is no repeated pattern between the two.) As the number of instances of regular verbs overwhelms the relatively few irregular pairs, the first four state neurons, through generalization, will learn merely to replicate their previous value, while the fifth neuron will learn always to go to 1. This corresponds to the second observed phase. The third phase can then be reinstated by the trainer overriding the generalization through reasserting specific examples of irregular pairs. So the sequence of phenomena encountered in learning the past tense is emergent and typical of an NSMM in the sense that generalization leads to an accommodation to regular patterns, and thus gives the impression of having learned a rule. This rule will misclassify irregular events, and further learning is required to know when to override the generalization.

A key question which arises here and in many comparisons of symbolic and neural linguistic systems is whether the nature of language is in any way dependent on the structure of the brain. The relationship of the present and past tense of a verb is an example of this possible dependence. Putting aside any concerns with the historical development of specific languages and their historical roots one hypothesis is that there is something in the brain that favours certain rules in preference to others. In the above NSMM (Figure 8.3), rules that govern regular cases can be generalized more easily if the change required between X and Y is minimal. As codes go, the change from *pull* to *pulled* is minimal in the sense that the words share many letters. What would a rule that is *hard* to learn be like? Here is an arbitrary example – let the past tense be composed of the present transformed by replacing each letter with the next one in the alphabet. Then the past tense of *pull* would be *qvmm*. This pairing seems hard to learn. So perhaps a natural system is more likely to favour *pull*→*pulled* than *pull*→*qvmm* for most past to present transitions.

In symbolic models it is assumed that we have as an innate, inherited knowledge of what is and what is not hard to learn. Connectionist models encourage an alternative discourse concerned with whether languages reflect that which neural structures (determined by biological rather than inherited rules) find easy to process. The innateness argument is not confined to the work of Chomsky, but may be seen to underpin more recent examples of symbolic modelling as, for example, found in Pinker (1984), where the learnability of language comes under symbolic scrutiny and is fixed as an inherited process.

8.4 Who or what broke the window?

Another early application of connectionism to language processing was McClelland and Kawamoto's study of role assignment to constituents of sentences (1986). They give many examples that illustrate the nature of the problem. These mainly draw attention to the fact that, in a sentence, word order alone does not determine who does what, with which and to whom. For example:

(1) The boy broke the window
(2) The rock broke the window

requires a knowledge of the fact that 'boy' is animate and 'rock' is not in order to label the first noun phrase as *agent* in (1) and as *instrument* in (2). Also

(3) The window broke

requires a knowledge of the fact that a window is a fragile object in order to label the first noun phrase as the *patient*. This could be compared with 'The storm broke' where the first noun phrase is an *instrument*.

In many cases, the cue to the roles of the words in a sentence comes late in the utterance. For example:

(4) The man ate the cake with a fork
(5) The man ate the cake with a candle

Here the last noun phrase is an *instrument* in (4) but a *modifier* in (5). This does not mean, of course, that word order plays no role in the assignment of roles. For example, in

(6) The arrow split the rock
(7) The rock split the arrow

word order is crucial to separate out the *instrument* from the *patient*.

Another very interesting effect in the use of language is the effect of 'priming', where ambiguous sentences can be given word role assignments that depend on the scenario determined by a previous utterance. For example, in

(8) The father photographed his daughter with the new camera

would not normally be seen as being ambiguous – the last noun phrase being an *instrument*. But, had a preceding utterance indicated that the daughter had received a new camera for her birthday, then the last noun phrase would indicate a *possession*, whereas had the earlier discourse said that there were several daughters in the scene, the same noun phrase could be labelled as a *modifier*.

The motivation behind McClelland and Kawamoto's (M&K) attempt to develop a connectionist model that accounts for these effects is that the classical approaches that seek to develop rules for distinguishing between the different cases have been too dominated by syntactic theories. Such theories have a heavy reliance on parsing, which merely treats the semantic content of words as a 'guide'. The M&K model contains two layers of units, one that represents the sentences themselves and the other which represents the case role patterns. The system is trained on pairs of correctly related examples and turns out to have the following properties:

(a) Where a word is ambiguous, it is assigned the correct case role from the context of the rest of the sentence.
(b) The system chooses the appropriate interpretation of the cases of noun phrases linked by verbs (e.g. (1), (2) and (3) above).
(c) It fills in missing parts of incomplete sentences.
(d) It assigns roles to previously unseen words from the context of the sentence.

The focus of this work lies in a semantic coding of the input sentences. That is, it is not the words themselves that are fed into the connectionist network, but encodings of them that capture their nature in a canonical way. For example, nouns such as 'boy' and 'desk' are given binary patterns of values under headings as follows:

Feature	'boy' pattern	'desk' pattern
human	1	0
non-human	0	1
soft	1	0
hard	0	1
.	.	.
.	.	.
.	.	.

and so on.

A similar arrangement applies to verbs and includes different 'frames' in which the verb can be used. For example 'broke' in the context of an agent breaking an object is coded differently from 'broke' in the context of an instrument breaking an object. In addition to these predefined codes, the 'sentence' is presented to the input of the connectionist system in a standard order: verb, subject, noun phrase etc. It could well be argued that the system only learns some fairly basic connections, since much of the work is done in advance through the coding into semantic features and the prestructuring of the sentence. It is at this point that we look at the way in which the NSMM and the concept of an *iconic state* might prove this state of affairs.

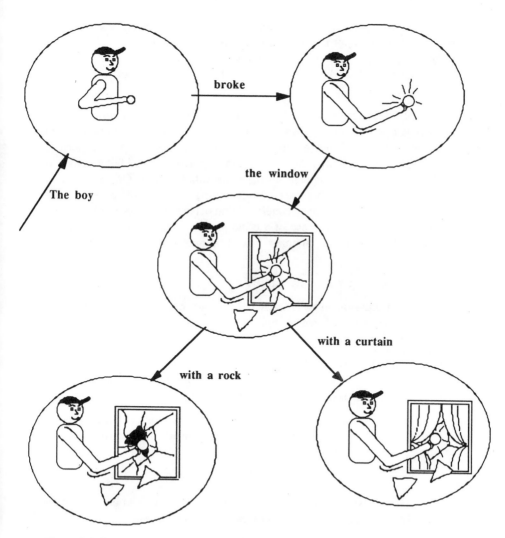

Figure 8.4 *Iconic state sequence that differentiates between two end noun phrases.*

This is really a continuation of the argument presented in section 8.2. Figure 8.4, for example, shows how an iconic state may be used to keep track of incoming utterances such as 'The boy broke the window with a rock' and 'The boy broke the window with a curtain'. In this case the common part of the utterance leads to a common state, and it is only the last noun phrase that modifies part of this state according to the key word that this noun phrase contains.

What we have suggested so far about iconic states in linguistic processing is part of a tentative modelling theory which is still being developed. While this awaits proper demonstration in the laboratory, the features of the idea are worth noting:

- the NSMM can have a rich field in which icons are represented;
- sequences of input can be absorbed from experience;
- this experience can be both iconic and linguistic;
- the state machine keeps track of the history of its input through state modifications.

All this provides a rigorous model for making good use of the neural paradigm in language processing. The concept of an iconic state draws attention to the importance of mental imagery as a mode of the representations of experience (see Chapter 9). It might seem as if the iconic approach would falter in the case of the acquisition of language by the congenitally blind. On the contrary, however, the iconic method can illuminate the interaction of several sensory modalities in order to provide an interpretation of language in terms of memories of sensory events. In the case of a blind person, the mental images needed for the understanding of language would belong to touch, smell and taste.

8.5 I thought I saw a pussy cat...

Sometimes discussion among human beings takes a more embedded or nested form than the examples we have seen so far. Here are a few examples of such sentences:

(1) Bill knows that John loves Mary.
(2) Pat hit the man who thought that John broke the window.
(3) The man who thought he saw John saw Bill.

In symbolic formulations sentences of this type are represented through the use of brackets, and mathematically are known as 'tree' structures. For example, (1) should really be broken down as

Bill knows (John loves Mary).

That is, (John loves Mary) is an item which Bill knows and can be defined separately. Also (3) could be rewritten with brackets as

The man ((who thought he) saw John) saw Bill.

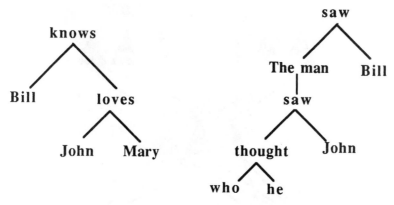

Figure 8.5 *Tree-like language structures.*

The outer brackets act as a descriptor of 'man' which is described separately within the bracket itself. These are known as 'tree' structures, as they can be represented as the tree-like diagrams shown in Figure 8.5.

Taking the connectionist methodology of Rumelhart, McClelland and Kawamoto, these nested representations would be very hard to implement. In fact, this is precisely one of the arguments that Fodor and Pylyshyn (1988) used in saying that connectionism does not have the power to express these very common ways of using language. It was Jordan Pollack who took up this challenge and developed a connectionist way of representing bracketed structures. He calls this the Recursive Auto-Associative Memory (RAAM). The way this works may be illustrated by a simple example using the structure shown in Figure 8.6. This contains an input that contains (say) the codes for two symbols A and B placed on $2k$ binary inputs. There is a hidden layer of k units which feeds an output of $2k$ units. This hidden layer and the output layer are trained to reproduce the input as closely as possible at the output. The hidden layer is allowed to find its own representation in order to carry out the mapping. Say that the task is to find a representation for ((AB)(CD)): the procedure goes as follows. AB is placed at the input and the system is taught to reproduce AB at the output. The central, hidden, units form some sort of a representation which allows this mapping to be repeated – this is called R1. Pollack suggests that this be formed by error back-propagation. In our logical formulation of neurons, this hidden representation could be formed by giving the addressed 'u' states arbitrary binary values. Next, the same is done for C and D at the input (and C and D at the output), this time forming representation R2. Finally, to find a representation for the entire expression R1 and R2 are fed to the input with R1 and R2 at the output, creating hidden representation R12.

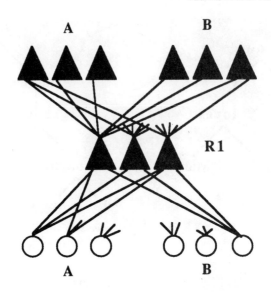

Figure 8.6 *A recursive auto-associative memory (RAAM).*

It is this final representation R12 which is the target of the exercise, since in theory the original structure can be retrieved from it. To do this, R12 is clamped on the hidden units, leading to R1 and R2 at the output units. Then R1 is clamped on the hidden units, retrieving AB, and the same is subsequently done with R2, retrieving CD. Pollack has had some success in representing other bracketed structures, including those of the three sentences mentioned above. But, as he clearly states in his paper, this approach is still hypothetical, since it as yet lacks a system to move the intermediate representations from and to the hidden units. Indeed, a difficulty with this approach is that the structure of the tree has to be known before its constituents can be retrieved.

In the NSMM model with iconic representations, there is an opportunity for representing such nested language structures. The concept implied by these sentences is that of the inclusion of one concept within another. So, the sequence 'Bill knows that John loves Mary' may be represented by the iconic sequence shown in Figure 8.7.

The way in which this works needs some explanation. The opening word 'Bill' creates a state entity (represented by an ellipse labelled B) to represent 'Bill'. The key event is the occurrence of the next word in the sequence 'knows'. At this point we assume that this is a learned cue to indicate that whatever is said next (indicated by '?') belongs to the inside of 'knows' circle. This is in contrast to what would happen were the word 'hits' to occur after 'Bill'. This would set up an expectation that what follows would be

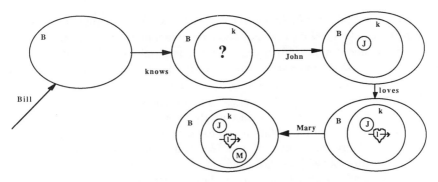

Figure 8.7 *Iconic representation of 'Bill knows that John loves Mary'.*

represented outside the state entity labelled 'Bill'. The word 'John' then becomes an entity inside the 'Bill' area. The word 'loves' at this level is simply a symbol that has a directional relationship (the arrow) to the last word 'Mary'.

Suspending for a moment the specific meaning of words such as 'knows' and 'loves', we note that the iconic representation is clearly capable of representing nested, tree-like structures. The difficulty does not seem to be at the structural level. However, had the sentence been 'Bill believes that John loves Mary', the structure of the iconic representation would be exactly the same. The word 'believes' is seen as belonging to the same class of words that initiates an expectation of an inner development of an entity. A seeming difficulty is differentiating between the two words. The structural requirement for this is resolved by having appropriate labels included in appropriate areas. Whether this deals fully with the problem of semantic representation remains debatable. In symbolic science too, nested concepts create considerable difficulty. Ballim and Wilkes (1991) give a comprehensive account of the way in which 'beliefs' could be modelled. In summary, what is being said is that – contrary to the assertions of Fodor and Pylyshyn (1988) – both the symbolic and the neural approaches are adequate for the representation of structure. The proper representation of semantics remains a challenge both in the world of neurons and that of symbols.

8.6 Composability

There is a considerable body of literature on the topic of linguistic representation, particularly in the domain of artificial intelligence and to some extent in the connectionist area. It is not the intention here to provide a comprehensive review of such work, but only to focus on contributions that require a special mention in the framework of the neuron/symbol discussion. Tim van Gelder (1990) draws attention to the fact that the argument between classicists and connectionists centres on 'composability'. This refers to the ability to create complex structures from simple ones by making use of a set of rules. He makes a distinction between *concatenative composability* and *functional composability* and suggests that classicists are only aware of the former, while connectionists deal with the more general class of the latter.

Concatenative composability refers to the ability in logic and mathematics to express the representation of an effect as a sequence of symbols, that is, a concatenation of symbols. For example, in school physics we learn to represent the force F with which a falling object of mass M hits the ground as

$$F = M \times G$$

where G is a constant 'of acceleration' (change in speed per second). This is a concatenation of symbols which follows certain rules of composition dictated by algebra. These are the same rules that lead to an understanding of expressions such as

$$(2 \times 6) - 3$$

which leads us to a calculation with the result of 9, while a sequence such as

$$6)(2 \times -3$$

though using the same symbols, makes no sense. So, arithmetic and mathematical expressions are governed by rules of composition and use symbols that represent quantities and operations that can be written as strings, or concatenations of these symbols.

In logic too we we have concatenative forms of composition. For example we can write

$$A \ \& \ \tilde{A} = F$$

This is a way of saying: if A is some statement such as 'John loves Mary' and $\tilde{A}$ is its logical opposite, 'John does not love Mary', the two, if strung together by the preposition 'and' (symbol &) always form a false statement (symbol F). Again, the way in which these strings of symbols are written down is governed by rules, which, if broken, would make no sense at all. Finally, the same applies to natural language, where composition is dictated by the rules of grammar and the symbols are words that stand for things in the world, which with other symbols such as brackets or punctuation (for written language obviously – spoken language uses inflections as symbols) lead to the symbolic strings whereby people communicate.

Gelder points out that Pollack's representations (such as R12 above) are typical examples of representations that are not string-like. While they are not concatenative, they remain *functional* in their own way. What they represent has to be obtained by unravelling their function rather than mapping the symbols into their meaning in the world and stringing such meanings together. This is functional *composability*. Our iconic representations clearly belong in this functional class, and, as has been argued repeatedly, are also compositional (as opposed to the weaker description of being merely associative). One question that van Gelder does not ask, but which we feel *is* worth asking, is what the relationship is between concatenative and functional forms of compositionality. The answer, we would suggest, is that the two are linked through the concept of a finite state automaton – both can be represented as specifications for such automata. The input of the NSMM can be concatenatively composed data which is turned into a functionally composed representation of a series of states.

To be more specific, concatenative representations are 'understood' or otherwise by an automaton through being input to the automaton, leading it to a state which either 'accepts' or 'rejects' the sequence. In a functional mode, while the input to the automaton may be partly concatenated (as sequences of input patterns) and partly distributed (each pattern possibly representing many symbols), this input causes the automaton to follow a state trajectory in which every state is semantically meaningful. It is noted that this form of representation is open to pre-programmed state behaviours and therefore does not belong only to the world of connectionism, but could be a somewhat unconventional way of doing classical computations. For connectionists, on the other hand, the functional composition is the natural mode. We feel that one important feature of such compositionality is that it allows important questions to be asked about learning (that is, the way in which functional state representations come into being).

8.7 Hidden representations

Another contribution which shows that the functional/concatenative identification is a sound way of approaching the distinction between the neural and the symbolic paradigms is an article by Goschke and Koppelberg (1991). They argue that connectionism, while allowing perfectly proper compositional inner states, also allows such states not to be related in any obvious, direct way to the concatenative descriptions that characterize classical representations. They extend the discussion to non-representative states or parts of states. It is possible to ask what is the representational role and power of the 'hidden' units in connectionist systems. It is certainly worth asking this question in connection with the NSMM.

In the NSMM the equivalent of hidden units are the 'auxiliary' state variables which can be free to find inner representations that are not directly related to perceptions. These are the units that hold information about repeated occurrences of an event, or the ordinal value of any event. If an event occurs several times the state representation may have an arbitrary code at the auxiliary variables to indicate a count. A linguistic statement such as 'This is the 14th year of Conservative government' is best represented by a counting code. Further, concepts such as 'a short time' as opposed to 'a long time' will require different representations at the auxiliary units. They are not expected to have a relationship to perception that is as vivid as the idea of an iconic model, but, as the name implies, they are auxiliary to the iconic part of the state. While there is much to be done in furthering this idea, the key to the way in which it functions is clear. If an event is present in perception and is transferred to an inner state, and if the system is in some learning mode (where the functions of the neurons fix the relationship of the state to the previous state and input) and, finally, if the input does not change with time, the learning of duration lies in state changes that only take place at the auxiliary units.

When the function of hidden units is being questioned, it seems natural to let the discussion extend to the concept of consciousness. Iconic representations certainly imply some form of 'conscious' contact with these states, that is, a sensation of the firing patterns in that part of the inner state. Arbitrary auxiliary representations may not be what one could call part of consciousness. This points to the danger of getting too enamoured of iconic representations. While these may well exist in the human brain, it could be that they are supported by massive structures of arbitrary, hidden state patterns. The balance between iconic and auxiliary representations is another of the many challenges for those interested in providing a link between cognitive sciences and neural models.

8.8 The language of thought

Much of Fodor and Pylyshyn's attack on connectionism (1988) is derived from an apparent adherence to an earlier theory (1976) of Jerry Fodor's which he dubbed the 'Language of Thought' (LOT for short). The main objective of this section is to look at a recent review of the LOT concept by Martin Davies (1991) which is done in the light of a history that contains the best part of ten years of the connectionist revival. But first of all we attempt to give a brief description of the key features of the concept.

Fodor's LOT hypothesis derives much from Chomsky's view that the human ability to use natural language is innate. This is based on the observation that it would be inefficient for each human to learn complex 'deep' linguistic structures from scratch. Fodor believes that thought is language-like and, being composed of deep structures, it too is innate. In many ways, argues Fodor, LOT is a great deal richer than its communicative counterpart. It must be responsible for dealing with perception, with the acquisition of those parts of language that are learned and with reasoning of all kinds. His explanations of the nature of this language are heavily couched in the classicist computing mode. In crude terms Fodor believes that innate thought can be represented as programs that run on the hardware of brains. These programs instantiate syntactic rules in the sense that 'John loves Mary' is the structure of a legitimate thought mediated by a language-like grammar. The same programs prevent thoughts such as 'John Mary loves' from being generated in the brain. The programs also have semantic content which is characterized by the logic of what the thinker thinks is true. That is, thoughts such as 'John loves Mary' are generated not only as some proof of rule following, but also because the thinker believes them to be true.

Davies' retrospective review draws attention to Wittgenstein's notion that there must be some correlation between thought and the constraints imposed by physiological activity, as there is no reason to suppose that thoughts arise arbitrarily in the brain and have a life of their own (this was published in 1981 in *Zettel*). This supports connectionist models and makes LOT appear to be based on the unsupported assumption about the existence of a deep structure of thought which is unrelated to physiological activity. Fodor is drawn into the belief that thought, like logic, has an existence which, although 'running' on various 'physiologies' is, as seen in Chapters 6 and 7, independent of them. A further general concern about LOT is that it implies an inner user of the language and raises the dangerous possibility of an infinite regress. Davies does not share this concern and counters it by employing an argument similar to that used in parts of this book – LOT correlates with states of the brain, states of activity which do not need an observer because they are *owned* by the thinker. Unfortunately this leads to a further general concern – the sense that LOT, having semantics, syntax and logic, has the character of a public interaction rather than of an internal state. In other words, such properties can be explained as arising in societies of communicating people, but cannot be applied to brains. Again Davies does not share this concern and argues that this is merely a matter of clearly defining the semantic and syntactic nature of LOT as a private object. He sees no reason for assuming that these characteristics should be restricted to public acts only.

If, therefore, LOT cannot be dismissed from first principles, the question needs to be asked as to whether connectionism is displaced by the higher ground that LOT has achieved in its own right. Indeed, LOT provides a comfortable match with our own view of ourselves as thinkers and Davies suggests that, from this perspective, connectionism is an invitation to 'eliminativism' – a process of denying causal, semantic and syntactic attributes in the process of thinking. An eliminativist view can be caricatured by representing a thinker as existing passively in a structured language-containing world from which he or she absorbs only the minimum information necessary for this existence, as opposed to the thinker being a highly structured organism capable of sophisticated behaviour. Respect for the latter, Davies argues, leads LOT ideas to displace connectionism in the quest for a proper and clear explanation of thinking.

We have raised this argument here to draw attention to the fact that LOT is a powerful weapon in the armoury that can be deployed against connectionism. However, when set against the rest of the arguments we have considered in this chapter, it seems clear that what is criticized is a restricted form of connectionism – a form based on associations. In recent years, and increasingly in the future, the task for connectionists has been and will be to show that a connectionist approach does not militate *intrinsically* against syntactic and semantic properties. Such properties, we have suggested, are approached by appreciating state structures that are more extensive than mere associations. Given success in this endeavour, it could be said that connectionism will, at least, stand strongly as an alternative to LOT philosophy, and add to the richness of the debate by including the mechanism of development through learning. This ability to model the origin of cognitive mental structures and the acquisition of language may turn out to be connectionism's ultimate weapon. It may also get rid of the implicit belief that the structures with which we think need to have been programmed in by evolution. Innateness is in fact largely a matter of Chomsky's belief, which for convenience was imported directly into the concept of a language of thought. This is a persuasive belief, but a belief nonetheless – one that should not be impervious to the alternative analysis provided by connectionism.

8.9 Looking back: language and connectionism and icons

The role of language models as one of the foci of cognitive modelling is not disputed. However, we began this chapter by asking what connectionism can add to our understanding of this role. The answer we have provided is something like 'not much yet, but there is scope for fruitful research'. The focus of this future research is the teasing out of semantic and syntactic behaviour from otherwise associationist action in neural systems. Several examples have been given, the earlier ones on learning the past tense and assigning case roles being very specific. These examples leave the impression that linguistic structure can only be introduced piecemeal by designing a new structure for every new linguistic effect. However, the more recent examples cited suggest that this is not the case. For instance, the RAAM (Pollack, 1990) seeks to find general ways of encoding any structure that is tree-like in nature. Further examples involve general definitions of composability (van Gelder, 1990; Goschke and Koppelberg, 1991) which point to more general computational concerns and clarify the character of what still needs to be achieved in connectionism in order for it to say something significant about language. Through these applications we have pointed to a speculation of our own – the use of the NSMM in the definition of an iconic state structure.

The notion of an iconic state is not unique to our work. It has been used in 1990 by Stevan Harnad of Princeton University to suggest a solution to the 'symbol grounding' problem (i.e the problem of relating symbols to perceptual input). What is unique, though, is the proposal that the NSMM is a vehicle that operates naturally on the basis of such iconic states. In theory the NSMM is general enough both to identify the differences between classical and connectionist models of language and to correct some misunderstandings between them. Whether representations are symbolic or subsymbolic is seen as being less important than whether useful representations can be learned or not. Only connectionism provides a platform for a proper study of learning and acquisition. Classicism leans heavily towards the evocation of innateness not only for linguistic ability but also for LOT models. When we say that learning can be represented using the connectionist approach we look further than at what connectionists fondly call 'learning theory' (a concern with techniques for weight adjustment). We refer instead to questions of how appropriate representations can be created and transmitted to the state variables of the NSMM.

It is clear that van Gelder's notion of a non-concatenative representation is crucial in this endeavour. Concatenative structures may well exist in the communication medium between organisms – that is, language. But they do not model well the experience that an organism builds up and which mediates that organism's language. To our way of thinking, the mistake that almost all representationists make in their models of language is to assume that it is language that has to be modelled and not the mediating experience. To remedy this and to encourage work in this area we have introduced the fledgling notion of an iconic state.

The iconic state represents the meaning of an incoming linguistic stream 'so far'. The key to this idea is that, while learning, the NSMM receives linguistic input and sensory 'experiential' input. Learning consists of relating these two in the iconic state, making either retrievable both from linguistic streams and experiential streams. That is, if a child is watching a cat drinking milk and someone says 'the cat is drinking the milk' our argument is that the inner representation for that utterance is the image – the memory of the cat drinking the milk. The memory can then be evoked by the words and, once evoked, can be uttered in language. These states certainly have whatever compositionality exists in the absorbed experience, but this need not be concatenative.

It is curious how some connectionists hope that appropriate inner representations will magically arise from the use of language alone. Iconic representations might change all that. As a concept, iconic representations are totally unexplored and give rise to many questions. Some of these questions have been raised already – what, for example are the representations of words such as 'likes', 'thinks', 'discovers', 'believes' and so on? The suggestion is that much attention should be paid to the experience to which these words refer, rather than the effect that they have in concatenative language. Other questions are more technical and refer to the coding of iconic states. How accurately should these mirror experience? How symbolic should they be? How are they learned? Yet other questions are even more fundamental. How do these relate to cognitive theory? (The work of Johnson-Laird seen in Chapter 4 comes to mind in this context.) How do they relate to the current debate about consciousness?

Despite the contention that iconic representations apply to all sensory modalities, it is their visual aspect that seems be particularly intriguing. It is on this account that the next chapter is devoted to a review of cognitive studies of vision and mental imagery.

9

Seeing and thinking
From perception to imagination

9.1 Introduction: why vision?

Why single out vision for special consideration? In the broadest sense the choice of sensory modality is arbitrary. Our aim in this chapter is to link perception, experience, recall and the relationship of one sense to other sensory modalities. However, vision is featured in this chapter because, from the point of view of cognitive science, it is a phenomenon that elicits great curiosity and attention. The idea of a mental image somewhat directly suggests the inner recall of a visual image. This does not mean that other senses do not evoke inner memories within that particular sense, it is just that vision is the most vivid of these and the one that holds the highest ground in the history of science. Discussions about consciousness stem from a sense of wonder at the sensation that we can 'see pictures in our heads'. Of course we do not wish to imply that an unsighted person is deprived of some area of 'thought' through being blind. On the contrary, we leave open the possibility that there is interaction between sensory modalities and that the lack of one sense can be compensated for by a modified activity in the others.

In this chapter, three main topics are discussed:

- cognitive models of vision
- theories of mental imagery
- NSMM interpretations of both phenomena

These are not separated into distinct discourses; rather, there is constant shifting from one to the other. The aim is to show that the NSMM has an integrative role to play in linking visual cognition to mental imagery and to other sensory modes. The result is a single, neurally based model which contrasts with the many algorithms and model shifts which characterize prior studies of visual cognition. Although we have said that the choice of vision is arbitrary as a focus for this type of discussion, in certain conversations it does appear to hold a central role. Imagine an example from a conversation which might take place after bumping into an old friend whom one had not seen for some time. After an initial exchange, the conversation might develop as follows:

'Why don't you come and spend next Sunday with us in St Margaret's?', we say.

'I'd like to do that, it's one weekend that I'm not on duty at the hospital. St Margaret's, that's near Dover isn't it? I've seen it on a map but I've never actually been there. Do I get there via the M25?'

'Yes, that's the best way if you're coming from Uxbridge.'

'Can you see the white cliffs where you are?'

'No, but you can see the ferries going in and out of Dover harbour. And if you want to see the cliffs we can go for a walk.'

This commonplace conversation contains masses of vision-based thinking. Before looking at these thought processes, pause for a moment to consider the initial phenomenon of people who have not seen each other for a long time being capable of recognizing one another. This ability is quite remarkable, as it seems to be unaffected by quite enormous visual changes, such as baldness, change of hair colour and the appearance of wrinkles. This simply raises a flag that a cognitive model of human recognition ability is by no means a trivial matter.

Returning now to the conversation, in the first part there is an obvious reliance on mental images of previously seen maps and visualization of locations and distances. The widespread use of maps may be a pointer to the fact that exploration of routes becomes visualized in map-like fashion. Many can actually recall maps and plan their actions accordingly. Then the exchange about ferries contains a transfer of visual information through the use of language. This too is a phenomenon that points to the human ability of building up visualizations from purely verbal descriptions. Reading a good book can also create vivid mental images through the use of written language. There is also an element of visually based planning in the promise that a walk to see the white cliffs may be a pleasurable thing to do.

The need for a satisfactory explanation of visual cognition and its link with the rest of cognitive science impinges heavily on the neuron/symbol debate, because symbolic modellers have had to provide explanations of the effect of visual recall such as in the above conversation. But the reliance on visualization and mental imagery does not fit in well with the symbolic idiom, and symbolic models therefore rely on some translation of objects, such as those in the above conversation, into symbolic structures (e.g. frames or semantic graphs). At the other extreme, cognitive psychologists have been interested in the early stages of vision and the way that information is extracted from the output of light-sensitive cells in the eye. The computational models here are akin to the engineering theories of the processing of signals in communication systems. There is also much interest among cognitive psychologists in the interpretation of psychophysical data – data resulting from reports by observers exposed to specially structured visual data. Probably the best known example here is the generation of random dot stereograms by computer which, when observed, give the sensation of depth (Julez, 1965). So the first strand of the discussion in this chapter develops a broad model that cuts across the neurophysiological/symbolic boundary. In section 9.2 the significance of the discoveries of feature-sensitive cells and the effect of these discoveries on computing models and the NSMM are discussed. Section 9.3 is devoted to the way in which information from other senses may be appropriately bound to visual experience and section 9.4 to the link between vision and experience of the way things happen in a consistent environment. Cognitive psychology often benefits from studies of the deficits in cognition in those who through accident or illness have lost some of their cognitive abilities. In section 9.5 we suggest ways in which the NSMM could be used to classify such deficits. In section 9.6 we return to the modelling of visual experience by suggesting a mechanism for the build-up of images and scenes even though the eyes and the body are constantly in motion.

The second strand is concerned with some of the established models of visual memory and imagery, and the effect that the NSMM might have on the thinking underlying these models. In section 9.7 we are concerned with the issue of long-term and short-term visual memory, and suggest that these may be extremes of a single neural process. In sections 9.7 and 9.8 we review some of the issues surrounding the controversial position of mental imagery in cognitive science. The discussion mirrors the neuron/symbol debate, which leads us to suggest that the NSMM strengthens the arguments of those who believe that mental images should not be ignored in cognitive science. Finally, we ask whether, through the NSMM, the desired integration between neuron and symbol is likely to take place in the area of visual cognition.

In the choice of topics for discussion in this chapter, we have been guided by a helpful book by Humphreys and Bruce (1989), which not only sets out in a logical fashion the concerns of cognitive psychologists in visual cognition, but also relates some of these to connectionist modelling.

9.2 The physics of seeing and the chemistry of experience

It is impossible to discuss models of vision without first making reference to the physiological discoveries of Humel and Wiesel (1959, 1968) and, second, to the computational models of David Marr (1982). The importance of the former lies in the discovery that single cells in the striate cortex (of cat and monkey) respond to local features in the receptive field (group of retinal cells connected to that neuron) of that neuron. For example, some neurons will respond to horizontal bars in their receptive fields, others to angled bars, others to edges and still others to moving edges. Therefore, if one were to look at the coding in the visual cortex, one would discover that every event in the visual field is represented by the pattern of firing of a group of neurons with a code that represents the nature of that event (edge, moving bar, orientation, . . .). We have already discussed the work of David Marr (in Chapter 3) in terms of his three-tier philosophy regarding cognitive modelling. His central contribution lies in vision, where again he proposed three different computational processes: the primal sketch (which distinguishes between areas of different texture and shading), the two-and-a half-D sketch (which computes information about local orientation of surfaces) and the 3D model, where the result of these computations is related to stored experience (this being in the form of pipe-cleaner models or models made of differently shaped cylinders).

In a sense, the work of Marr could be seen as an attempt to relate the findings of Hubel and Wiesel (which amounts to cells performing simple computations on patterns falling on the retina) to the way in which such simple computations could actually represent objects in the world. Unfortunately Marr's quest was interrupted by his untimely death, and the three-process model mentioned above is not complete. As a very simple example, seeing a cup and saucer and evoking a suitable inner representation of this does not seem possible using generalized cylinders or pipe-cleaner models. In fact, in the same way that connectionism is seen merely as an implementational tool in the 'great debate' in Chapter 6, it has been argued that what connectionism offers to models of vision is merely an implementational theory of the way that edges or texture changes may be computed (Mayhew and Frisby, 1984). We wish to show here that the NSMM approach to the modelling of vision can contribute to further the discussion beyond Marr's methods of 3D modelling.

In Chapter 8 we introduced the NSMM-based iconic state. Here we develop this further and define a 'principle of predicted experience' (resisting the temptation to turn this into an acronym). Returning to the 'cup and saucer' example, the principle of predicted experience relates to the fact that seeing a cup and saucer leads to an internal representation which recreates the entire experience of interacting with the seen objects – picking up the cup, sipping from it, the taste of the liquid, its temperature, hearing the clink as it is put back on the saucer, and so on. So the principle of predicted experience implies the existence of a mechanism that stands aside from the physics of the processing of signals from sensor cells. Rather than reduce this to pipe cleaners and cylinders, this mechanism must be capable of retrieving experience of considerable richness and detail. This experience should also be capable of being evoked from other sensory modes – spoken language or (in this case) perhaps the smell of coffee or the sound of clinking crockery in the distance. We now wish to show, first, that the NSMM can operate according to the principle of predicted experience including the signal processing activity apparent in early processing, and, second, that it can acquire the necessary experience.

The way in which this ties up with the NSMM is shown in Figure 9.1. This differs from the NSMM introduced in Chapter 7 in the sense that it shows the role that Hubel–Wiesel/Marr early processing (EP) might play in it. Here raw sensory data is processed on a sense-by-sense basis without interaction taking place between sensory modalities. It could also be that no learning takes place in EP. It is the rest of the neural system in which learning takes place and where there may be heavy interaction between

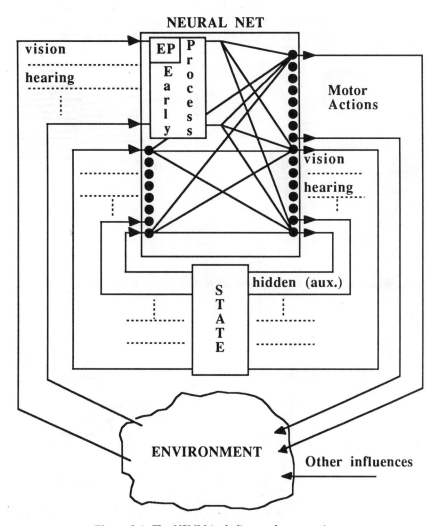

Figure 9.1 *The NSMM including early processing.*

sensory modalities. With this model it is possible to distinguish between perceiving and visualizing. We submit that seeing is the sensation of firing patterns of neurons in the vision area of the EP output, whereas visualizing is the sensation of firing patterns of neurons in the output area of the neural net itself.

As an aside, we can ask where the 'seeing' of subjective contours fits in this scheme of things. Well-known images that have such contours are shown in Figure 9.2. In Kanitza's triangle (a) the edges that make up a borderless triangle may be seen despite the fact that there is nothing on the paper. In the 'dislocation' pattern (b) a contour is seen as a feature. In our model these subjective contours would be seen as the work of the EP box, underlining that this is where the perceptions occur. Taking the dislocation example, we show in Figure 9.3 how this sensation may be created. In (a) there is a description

(a)   (b)

Figure 9.2 *Subjective contours: (a) Kanitza's triangle; (b) dislocation.*

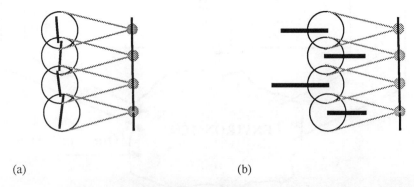

(a)   (b)

Figure 9.3 *The way that the dislocation is seen in the EP: (a) cooperating verticality detectors 'see' a line; (b) cooperating line-end detectors 'see' a line.*

of the way that Hubel and Wiesel detectors are meant to react to a nearly straight set of line segments. The detectors, through being connected to one another, propagate information to neighbours which, if also activated, aid each other to fire. This is called a cooperative activity (or constraint propagation). The end result is that these neurons define a perceptual line. Now, (b) shows that exactly the same thing could happen to a group of aligned neurons if their Hubel and Wiesel task is to be sensitive to end features of lines.

Returning now to the NSMM of Figure 9.1, it is important to state clearly how the specific sensory areas are created and how they may be influenced by other sensory modalities. The areas are created by the following mechanism. It uses a principle enunciated in Chapter 2, where the perceptual input not only acts as input to the neurons, but also creates the state output when the neurons are capable of learning (or, in artificial systems, are in a 'learning phase). What we suggest now is that it is the phonetic output of the EP that controls the creation of these state patterns. This has the implication that the inner state of the NSMM, which includes anything connected with mental images, is represented in the codes generated by the EP. This does not degrade the inner world in any way; it can simply be thought of as a more efficient way of encoding sensory information than the raw codes which are generated by the front-end sensors such as the cells in the retina of the eye.

The advantage of this scheme is that it allows temporary and static information (or temporary information operating on different time-scales – not much in sensory input is likely to be static) to be related and represented within the same system. A sketch of how this is intended to work is shown in Figure 9.4. The EP output of the visual cup is associated with the temporary auditory EP output 'k a p' which at some later stage can be further trained to relate

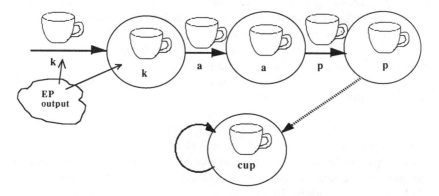

Figure 9.4 *Learning from different sensory modalities.*

both to the written, visual input 'cup'. In Chapter 8 we have assumed in a somewhat cavalier fashion that this is easily done.

9.3 Binding forces

One of the properties of learning organisms that concerns cognitive psychologists is that a system binds the right labels to the right concepts. It is not clear how this is done. Connectionists have had some success in demonstrating very specific architectures that bind concepts in a particular, technological way (see Shastri and Feldman (1986), for example). Here we can demonstrate that the NSMM provides some general principles that carry out this binding as a natural property. Returning to the example of the cup, how could an NSMM get to represent this as a cylindrical, smooth and hollow object? Clearly this must come from some form of simultaneous experience of sensations from different sensory modalities, followed later by the learning of verbal descriptions of these attributes. Babies grasp things and develop a knowledge of the way they feel not only to the hand, but also the mouth and tongue. That is where the precise sensors are, so it is not surprising that babies have a liking for putting things into their mouths. In the NSMM this appears as a feedback connection in which the action outputs form a loop through the limbs back to the tactile input. This is involved in setting up the tactile experience at the same time as the visual one.

The question of how much in this procedure is learned and how much is instinctive can be put aside for the moment. What is very clear is that the earliest experiences will lead to the simultaneous exposure to objects from several sensory modalities. In NSMM terms, vision, touch and smell occurring together will generate multi-sensory images in the state area of the model. Words are heard later, but when they are, they have to be attached to the right sensory attributes. The organism needs to know that the words 'smooth', 'cylindrical' and 'hollow' go with the concept of a cup and that an orange is 'rough', 'round' and 'full'. Then what would it make of a tennis ball? The answer lies in discovering common properties between objects where such properties have unique, common labels. This comes 'naturally' to the NSMM, provided that the experience leading to these attributions is not ambiguous. An example should serve to clarify this issue.

Say that the available objects are a tennis ball (t), a cubic steel paperweight (p) and a billiard ball (b). Also say that the first experience is that of a tennis ball. Let the visual experience result in data V(t) being trained into the visual part of the state simultaneously with the words *tennis ball*, the tactile experience T(t) and the shape experience S(t). As usual, these form a stable pattern in the state field, so that presentation of one or more of the attributes causes a recall of the others through pattern completion. Now say that the paperweight is 'learned', leading to a stable pattern V(p), *paperweight*, T(p) and S(p). At a later stage the organism is 'told' that the *tennis ball* is *rough* and *round* and that the *paperweight* is *smooth* and *cubic*. The stable patterns now are:

V(t), *tennis ball*, T(t), S(t), *rough*, *round*
V(p), *paperweight*, T(p), S(p), *smooth*, *cubic*

The two objects have no common attributes, and therefore, if given an unknown object such as a billiard ball – which has ostensibly T(b) = T(p) and S(b) = S(t) – when questioned it would not be able to retrieve uniquely either of the two patterns. However, had the first two training objects been

V(t), *tennis ball*, T(t), S(t), *rough*, *round*
V(b), *billiard ball*, T(b), S(b), *smooth*, *round*

any round object x, for which S(x) = S(t) = S(b), would perforce find the verbal descriptor '*round*' also attached to it. Ultimately the word '*round*' becomes bound to the correct shape experience. In other words, given an attribute, either spoken or sensed, the NSMM ought to retrieve a series of learned patterns all of which have that attribute in common and discover the sensation (in the case of a given verbal description) or the verbal description (in the case of a given sensation). Therefore, appropriate binding relies on encounters with appropriate, unambiguous training sets, a requirement that connectionism shares with symbolic learning algorithms (see the reference to Winston's work in Chapter 3).

Two points may be worth noting. First, the effect of ambiguity in learning has been observed in children who (for example), after having been shown three blue flowers and four red ones, when shown three red flowers might report that they were blue. (See Ault (1977) for a comprehensive review of cognitive development in children.) This is often used as evidence that number does not have precedence over set properties in learning. Second, the NSMM combines concept learning with pattern reconstruction. This is in contrast to the prevailing view that object naming can only take place once the input has been processed through all three stages of Marr's computational vision model. Again, the NSMM approach seems to straddle the neural and the symbolic.

9.4 A rose is a rose is...

A question often asked in conjunction with visual object identification is how objects that look very different and possibly have no obvious features in common, can be identified as belonging to the same class, sometimes even if they have never been seen before. Some such objects are shown in Figure 9.5. The group on the left are all examples of the letter A, whereas the two on the right are both 'tables'.

We have seen two recent approaches to this phenomenon from the world of conventional computing. That of Clowes (Chapter 3) relies on the

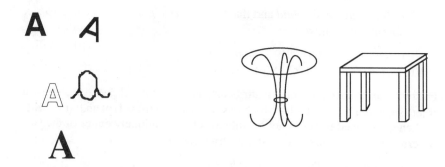

Figure 9.5 *Different objects of the same description.*

identification of cues of simple objects and lists whatever arrangement of such cues befits a particular object. That is, a line drawing of a box permits only a limited number of arrangements of its corner cues in respect to the faces of the cube. The other approach, that of Marr, as already mentioned in this chapter, relies on the few arrangements that generalized cylinders require to indicate an object. No one expects much of these approaches – they are applicable only in restricted worlds. Clowes' work might represent an image where there is a wedge in front of a box, and Marr's cylinders might just capture the difference between a sheep and a giraffe. But how could one capture the class of, say, 'churches', or 'chairs'?

One simple fact is that certain object classes just do have a wide variety of unrelated shapes associated with them, and some form of cataloguing will always be necessary. In trying to approach this through the NSMM, it is clear that there may be many mechanisms for generalization which come into play in creating models for object classes with many differing elements. It is the 'principle of predicted experience' which again turns out to be helpful in bringing into the procedure for recognition not only the shape of an object, but also its function and a prediction of what would happen were it to be handled or used in some way. For example, this would tell us that most objects don't change if one simply moves them about. Hence it is easy to recognize an 'A' rotated through 45 degrees as still being an 'A'. However, this cannot be seen either as an innate rule, or some emergent property of the neural system. Were there an innate rule which said that things do not change if we apply physical action to them, then one would not be able to distinguish between a ball of plasticine and the disc it could become were it squashed, or to attribute differing meanings to '×' and '+' as one could be the other rotated by 45 degrees. So that which changes and does not change under an action from the organism has to be learned by the organism just as much as anything else. In NSMMs this is learned and objects are classed according to the 'prediction of experience' principle. So, for example, if a cup is turned upside down, the predicted experience is that it still is a cup, and that the action does not alter the meaning of the object. But if a ball is squashed into a disc the predicted experience is that the class of the object will change to that of a disc. So invariance must be learned in the same way as any other consequence of an action on the environment and the objects it has within it.

There is another way in which the principle of predicted experience could act in order to categorize objects in an NSMM. This is related to a sector of AI referred to as 'Naïve Physics' (Hayes, 1979). We refer to the 'table' objects in Figure 9.5. On seeing an object with three curly legs and a glass top for the first time, a person may well take a guess and say that it is some kind of a table. The prediction of experience principle is at work as it leads through the thought sequence that a table is a thing with a flat top held up by legs, which is not likely to fall over were downward pressure applied to the flat top. Were the object a square surface supported by three legs at only three corners, prediction of experience would suggest that the thing would fall over were pressure applied to the unsupported corner, indicating a failure of the table test not leading to the retrieval of a 'table' state in the NSMM.

In naïve physics, rules are stored to represent the way in which things might work in the world. These rules may be a bit like: 'IF an object is unsupported, THEN it will fall with acceleration g. In some way this appears to be similar to the principle of predicted experience. However, it may be important to distinguish between the two. Naïve physics in AI is inextricably couched in rule-based representations. A table may be defined as 'a horizontal surface of limited size, supported by legs which form a polygon of at least three points, A, B, C, D, E... on the surface. Any downward pressure within the polygon will be supported, while pressure outside it will not'. In defining a table in this way it is clear that a programmer has imposed his or her view of what a table is like through the use of some computing language. One obvious distinction between this and the NSMM is the fact that the latter would learn from exploration or instruction. A more important distinction is the fact that in naïve physics the process of extracting logical information (e.g. the polygon, the position where pressure is applied etc.) is left for a separate system which remains undefined. Only when all the facts of some perceived object have been extracted will the naïve physics be able to function. In the NSMM, the two (and other) processes are integrated and support each other as a stream of state changes.

We do not wish to create the impression that the NSMM is the answer to all prayers in cognitive modelling in general and concept representation in particular. On the contrary, what has been said about the use of the NSMM is speculative and much research is required to discover the strengths and weaknesses of this approach. What does seem clear, however, is that the symbolic approach and the neural approach have each some attractive characteristics and that the denial of either impoverishes one's ability to model cognitive processes.

9.5 Learning from deficits

There is much in cognitive psychology that benefits from the misfortunes of others. Strokes and head injuries lead to distortions in people's cognitive abilities, which have been carefully studied. This has led to conjectures about the function of the affected parts of the brain as well as the overall link between neural structure and conscious experience. While this may, at times, sound opportunistic, it is often justified by saying that it is better to draw some benefit from misfortune than none. It is possible, however, that cognitive modelling based on a standard form of model such as the NSMM may actually go beyond this and be of some benefit to the patient and possibly permit the development of better treatment of the deficit. Because the NSMM differentiates between sensory modalities by assigning them to different sets of state variables, it is possible to classify deficits by identifying them with specific disconnections in the model. The following example of a visual deficit should help to clarify this point.

Humphreys and Riddoch (1987) present the case of H.J.A. who, after a stroke, was not able to recogize faces, and distinguish the difference between objects and non-objects when presented as line drawings. Yet he was able to recall mental images of objects and to draw things from memory with little sign of impairment. Even more remarkable is the fact that while H.J.A. was able to see, in the sense that he was able to find his way about without bumping into things, he was also able to copy line drawings even if he could not recognize them. Referring to the NSMM of Figure 9.1, it is possible to imagine deficits and their effect. For example if there is a lack of connection between the sensors and the EP system, in the case of vision this would be reported as blindness. Any major break in the feedback loops that are the site for the state of the NSMM would lead to an inability to sustain short-term memory. Clearly neither of these would lead to the deficits found in H.J.A. Rather, H.J.A's deficits could result from a lack of communication in the visual channels between the output of the EP and the input of the state machine. Then, assuming that the output of the EP is an area where perceptions of outer events occur, we would have a model of H.J.A.'s deficit. Mental visual states would not be evoked through perception, but could still be generated by pattern completion from the other sensory modalities. There would not be an impairment in using these states to guide drawing actions. The copying could be done simply by the sensations in the output of the EP (there might be a need for some short-term memory in the EP, which certainly has not been ruled out by our descriptions).

It is also interesting to speculate on some of the cases reported by Oliver Sacks in *The Man Who Mistook His Wife For a Hat* (1985). He discusses the case of Dr P., who could not recognize his brother's face. Prosopagnosia, as the condition is called, is also reported in Humphreys and Bruce (1989). The problem here seems to be that while the patient is able to see the features of a face, instead of putting them together and recognizing the face, he struggles with the pieces of information that the various glimpses provide as if they were part of some jigsaw puzzle, and sometimes comes to the wrong conclusion. An explanation of this deficit in terms of the NSMM involves the interaction between the action output and the movement of the vision apparatus (head and eye muscles). To understand this we need to extend the discussion of the operation of the NSMM and ask first how it could deal with moving images and, in parallel with this, how it could make sense of the images knowing that the head and eyes are moving all the time.

9.6 Going to the movies

One aspect of the visual system of living things is that nothing ever stands still. Eyes are darting about, heads are moving, objects in the external world are rushing about. And yet the sensation we have is a calm one that both easily distinguishes motion yet can remain unaffected by it when necessary. A great corpus of literature exists on the detection of motion and the concept of 'optic flow'. This idea originates with J.J. Gibson (1950) who suggests that successive images of a moving object create a field of 'direction of motion' arrows on the retina to which certain cells in early visual processing are sensitive (as shown by Hubel and Wiesel (1959)). This lends itself well to mathematical representation and has been developed as part of the compendium of algorithms used in computer vision (Marr and Ullman, 1981; Buxton and Buxton, 1983).

However, in the NSMM we step aside from optic flow models and treat them as in the same category as edge detectors, i.e. part of the work of the EP unit in Figure 9.1. Thus, were we looking at a bull in a field it would be the EP that generates the sensation of whether it was advancing towards us, or doing something less threatening. We may react to such evaluations before even becoming 'conscious' of the advancing bull. This raises the question of how one might distinguish between conscious experience, unconscious processing and shades that fall between the two. This question impinges on the weighty issue of models of consciousness, to which we return in Chapter 10. Here the discussion is restricted to an explanation of how the NSMM might act to endow a moving organism with an ability to make mental models of the world. Such models should have the properties of living brains of not being disturbed by motion and being able to make use of it to build mental images that are not only more extensive than the image that falls on the retina of the eye but also retain different levels of detail. Figure 9.6 is used to support an explanation based on the NSMM.

The first factor that we can dispose of is the ocular motor reflex. This is an effect where the eyes can fix on an object and retain that fixation despite head movements. In NSMM terms this is the same as saying that movement detected by the EP feeds directly to action outputs that activate eye muscles so as to keep the gaze fixed. This is a classical control system that has been modelled as if it were an engineering feedback process. What we need to discuss is the process of changing the gaze from one fixation point to another. It is known that when gazing at an image the eyes focus on one centre of interest in the image for a short time and then jump to another (this is known as a saccade). The choice of where to jump is determined by some event in the

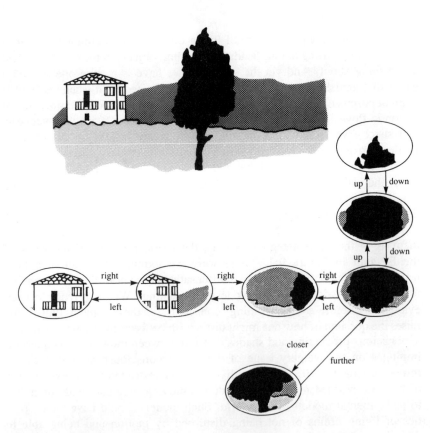

Figure 9.6 *Making sense of images from a roving eye.*

visual field. It should be remembered that the eye does not function like a television camera. In the centre of its field of view (the foveal area) it is capable of a great degree of detail, which we have shown in Figure 9.6 as the content of an iconic state.

The output of the EP not only contains this foveal data, which the rest of the NSMM uses to create stable iconic states, but it also contains information as to where other areas of attention might be. So in any state in Figure 9.6 any iconic state is accompanied by data which (perhaps probabilistically) determines where the next point of the gaze should be. When an extensive scene is memorized (for instance when a newly met face is memorized, and saccadic scanning seems to be targeted on salient features such as the mouth, the eyes etc.) all the information is available to retain the relative positions of the foveal images as a state structure. This has a high degree of economy as it stores important focal points but not areas where little is going on. So if a person looks out to sea and sees a harbour far to the left, and a lighthouse far to the right, while in-between is an unchanging sea/horizon image, this could be stored as a state structure with one foveal state for each of the two end objects, and just one central 'seascape' state with 'far left' and 'far right' links to the other two.

Here we have an embryonic approach to a theory of visual memory which takes account of the highly dynamic nature of vision. To go further, the state structures that retain visual experience need not be limited to transitions that involve saccadic eye movements. Any movement can be involved. So 'getting closer' is a state link that could be remembered by an intentional move towards an object. Indeed, visions of car journeys or walks over the hills are fully covered by the mechanisms we have discussed so far. The only difference is the fact that the 'next point of interest' may be generated in ways other than a peripheral vision signal in the EP. Areas for further investigation may occur in the field of view, requiring getting closer (or, indeed, further away, if a greater perspective is required). Rather than there being an homunculus that is making decisions about where to look next, every perceptual state carries within it options for the action output of the NSMM. These could either be executed arbitrarily, or, if the state carries some intention with it (e.g. part of the state is a code that requires the discovery of an exit from a space), the investigation will be constrained by this intention. A further comment relates to seeing a cinema film. Clearly great visual memories can be created by this experience, without the observer twitching a muscle. This is explained in the model if the rate at which the successive frames are shown is carefully selected to 'create the illusion of motion'. In terms of the NSMM this means that the EP is fooled into activating the motion detectors, thus providing codes very similar, if not identical, to those senses were the observer actually creating the motion.

A cognitive artefact that is embedded in this description of recall of a complex, multi-state image is that of the control of attention. Workers in visual cognition have described this as 'shining a torch' on perceived objects. During direct observation the direction and width of the beam is controlled when something is being observed. However, when a memorized image is being retrieved, the control of attention becomes internal and immediately impinges on questions of conscious control of thought and even free will. These are fundamental questions that extend beyond the realm of vision and are considered in a more general context in the next chapter. Here it remains necessary to look at the vast amounts of storage that appear to be implied by the visual recall mechanisms discussed in this section, bearing in mind the constant bombardment of information to which a living organism is subjected during daily life. In the next section we use the NSMM to suggest some necessary properties that achieve appropriate, economical storage.

9.7 I remember you...

This phrase innocently points to a mass of general questions that surround human memory capacity, and specifically the demand that visual memory makes on the facilities available in the brain. There is also the classical issue in cognitive psychology of the distinction between long-term memory and short-term memory. What is forgetting, or failing to remember, all about?

9.7.1 Short- and long-term memories

Dealing with the latter point first, in the NSMM the distinction between long and short term memory is a matter of degree. The main assumption is that the changes in neuronal function demanded, say, by the need to remember a new face do not happen instantaneously. So those connectionists who worry about the length of time it takes for error back-propagation algorithms to work, may derive solace from the fact that these gradual adjustments hold the answer to the transition between short-term and long-term memory. We are not implying that error back-propagation is necessary to the modelling of these two phenomena. We simply suggest that any neural net that is required (in the manner discussed in Chapter 2) to map pattern X into pattern Y will, in fact, map X into Y-δ where δ *is a randomly set percentage of the bits in Y*. δ gets smaller and eventually vanishes as the same mapping is demanded in training, or, in some way, is rehearsed by the organism itself.

Anyone who has tried to learn a foreign language as an adult will recognize the gradual nature of this process. The new language has to be grafted on an existing substructure of the knowledge of the world. For example, the structure for a cup represented in Figure 9.4, in learning, say, French, requires the label 'tasse' both as a phonological input and a written symbol. The teacher may say something like 'A cup, in French is called "une tasse"' while writing the word on the blackboard. The first part of this statement evokes the state structure related to the English word 'cup'; what this now needs is the added symbolism in French. In principle this could be simply done on an NSMM that allows instantaneous changes in the neuron truth functions – the silicon brain could learn new language instantaneously. If, however, the gradual learning model suggested above is used, the need for repetition before the new symbols are bound to the old ones becomes evident. But, so far, this says nothing about the relationship between long- and short-term memory. We have simply illustrated a particular static aspect of learning.

To explain the short/long-term memory relationship, we merely need to translate the principle of gradual learning to dynamic situations (such as implied in Figure 9.6). On first seeing a new scene or a face, the learned state transitions would have a high value of δ. This would have two effects, the first being that the memory would not be as distinct as that of a highly familiar scene. The second effect is that a state structure such as shown in Figure 9.6 suggests a long-lasting memory as a result of its strongly connected nature. By 'strongly connected' here we mean that a transition is more likely to occur between states in the group that represent a given scene than to other states outside the group. The value of δ actually controls not only the clarity of the states but also the probability of transition between them. Without going into technical detail, in the early stages of learning the probability of transition to states within a coherent group is lower than that in more advanced stages. This fading effect has been described in Chapter 2 (Figure 2.16). So here is a curious idea that is an 'aide-mémoire' to the way NSMMs work. NSMMs are connectionist in two ways. First is in the sense that the mapping between states is strengthened through learning. (In conventional connectionist systems this is a physical strengthening of connections beween nodes, while in the more general methods described in this book, it is the entry in a truth table that becomes closer to 0 or 1 – see Chapter 2.) Second, as learning progresses, the cohesion between groups of states that represent memories is strengthened. Auditory information, of course, has an aided route for going from short- to long-term memory – the possibility for rehearsal through the voice-ear loop. Even the faintest muttering (not even voiced) will provide temporary storage of, say, a telephone number while the inner state transitions are being strengthened.

9.7.2 Memory capacity

How many clusters of states can be supported? How big can these clusters be? These are questions that are easy to answer in general NSMM terms but very hard to answer for the human brain, because details of brain structure and the nature of neurons needs to be taken into account. We can, however, set out three theoretical concepts that relate to the creation of memory in *any* neural mechanism. First there is capacity – and there are calculations in connectionist theory that attempt to estimate this. Second there is plasticity, the ability for neurons to alter their functions in response to training and, third, there is the related question of more recent memories destroying older ones. These deserve a closer look.

One of the most disappointing results of connectionism, where neurons are represented as devices with connection weights linking to other devices, is that a fully interconnected network of N neurons can, on average, only store N states (each state having N state variables). This number gets even smaller if the net is not fully connected. If each of N neurons connects to n other neurons, the capacity of the net becomes n states of N state variables. So if the brain were one great big NSMM (which it is not), and (as is fairly well known) the average value of n were about 5000, the total number of states for memory would be 5000 on a very large number of state variables, since N in the human brain is known to be about 10^{11}. This suggests that we can only think of 5000 things, but in enormous detail. Remember that a single television picture uses about 520 000 state variables (picture points). So this calculation is obvious nonsense – there are two additional factors that need to be taken into account. First, the brain is not a massive NSMM, but is best characterized by many interconnected NSMMs (we are nevertheless justified in thinking philosophically of just one, as the two structures are theoretically equivalent, the one difference being in the assessment of storage capacity). Second, the weighted connection model is pessimistic and the likely capacity of a heavily interconnected group of N neurons, if n is almost the size of N, is somewhere between n and 2^n. So a localized net in a brain of 50 000 neurons with connectivity of 10 000 could store somewhere between 10 000 and $2^{10\,000}$ which is a massive 10^{3000} states. The latter is likely to be a wildly optimistic estimate. So the conclusion here is that much detailed neurophysiological research will be needed before we can adequately relate the architecture of the brain to storage capacity. But what would be most interesting would be to separate out the areas of the brain that are known to be responsible for visual memory, and to try to establish how clustered the architecture is so as to be able to speculate on the qualitative nature of mental imagery – do mental images have loosely linked components that 'run' in different parts of the brain?

9.7.3 Plasticity and interference

The reason that any build-up of memory at all takes place in the brain and in the NSMM is the fact that the neurons can change their functions in response to training. However, this effect is modified by a parameter (plasticity) that determines how likely it is that the demanded change will actually take place. This can be imagined as ranging from full plasticity to none at all where the function of the neuron becomes fixed. A second effect that takes place when n is small with respect to N is that the function of a given neuron becomes overwritten by more recent training. Imagine that a net with N neurons is connected as a feedback net (i.e. a GNU of Figure 2.7 but with no input connections). Then imagine that this is trained to be stable on the all-1 pattern. The next training pattern is half 1s and half 0s. For this second pattern, any neuron that has all its inputs at 1 and requires its output to be 0 is being overwritten, and loses the part of the truth table it learned for the first pattern. Note that, in this example, half of the neurons have their outputs exposed in this way. The chances of any one of these vulnerable nodes having one of their inputs at 1 is ½, having any specific two inputs at 1 is ¼, and having all n inputs at 1 is $1/2^n$. This number gets rapidly smaller as n increases.

Nevertheless, this overwriting does mean that there would be a tendency in a dynamic neural network to be more sensitive to recently learned material and to forget the older information. Clearly this is an undesirable state of affairs in a human being, since early memories (for example, about desirable foods and other basic needs) are necessary for survival and should not be overwritten. One can speculate that there is a beneficial effect that results from ageing. One aspect of human ageing may be that the plasticity of neurons reduces with time. This would compensate for the overwriting effect, and retain a balance between new and old learning. In an early artificial neural system, Mike Fairhurst demonstrated this effect (1973) and achieved this balance by reducing the plasticity of the neurons exponentially with time. In humans this effect often seems to be overstated in the sense that older memories are preserved at the expense of newer ones. In fact, in pre-senile dementias such as Alzheimer's disease, early noticeable signs are the inability to lay down memories of recent events, which points to a total loss of neural plasticity.

9.8 Mental imagery: the measurements

The NSMM works on the basis of the creation of 'mental' imagery and its use in tasks such as language understanding and planning. In cognitive science, mental imagery is the subject of as much controversy as connectionism. In the next section we shall discuss both the nature of this controversy and the effect of the NSMM on such a debate, but first, in this section, we mention briefly some of the experimentation that psychologists have presented as evidence that mental images are not only real objects of cognition, but are measurable entities that can be modelled in formal terms. The details of such work are clearly presented in Humphreys and Bruce (1989).

Among the most influential experiments is that of Shepherd and Metzler (1971), in which subjects were shown pictures of some simple but unknown shapes presented in pairs. They were asked whether these pictures were of the same object or not. The main result of the experiment was that the response time between question and answer was proportional to the size of the angle of three-dimensional rotation between the shapes. This leads to the theory that in answering the question the subject has to 'rotate images in her head' and this takes time. This seems undeniably to point to the ability to understand images and handle them mentally as objects. However, it also involves issues of planning and comparison in which there appears to be much scope for a deeper analysis. That is, the experiments say a great deal not only about being able to rotate images in one's head but also about the way in which experience of handling objects in the world can be generalized to objects that have never been seen before. There is an important question here about the involvement of visualization in the process of understanding and controlling a world that can only partially be known.

Another major contributor to explanations of mental imagery is Stephen Kosslyn who has developed a series of 'block diagram' models of image storage and use. (A recent account of this work may be found in Kosslyn *et al.* (1990), where references to earlier work abound.) This work contains models where images are stored as arrays and scanned by an attention window. The difference between this and the NSMM is that, in the latter, the 'attention window' is the state of the system, and state changes are controlled by inputs to the system. For example, a sentence such as 'He waved his mother goodbye as he climbed into his friend's pocket and drove the tank off the church roof' would be recognized as being doubtful since it creates image states for which links have not been made through experience.

What seems evident in looking at the substantial corpus of work on imagery in cognitive psychology (e.g. Paivio, 1971; Richardson, 1980) is that there is no doubt that the phenomenon must be taken seriously. However, there is much to be gained in incorporating mental imagery into broader models of cognition, particularly in the use of language and planning. This is what the NSMM with its iconic states attempts to do. However, this is currently merely a suggestion which requires much further work.

9.9 Mental imagery: another great debate

In the philosophical debate on mental imagery, no one attempts to suggest that the phenomenon does not exist – that would fly in the face of too much common experience. It is more a question of whether a cognitive theory or a philosophical discussion about mentation can incorporate imagery as a useful ingredient of the discourse. Mark Rollins (1989) has written a comprehensive philosophical text which clearly sets out the arguments against mental imagery while developing his own theme about the inappropriateness of such a view and a defence of a cognitive theory that includes mental images. The arguments are so like the neuron/symbol debate, and the mental image theory is so much like our use of iconic states, that we review Rollins' work quite closely and draw attention to the parallels.

The debate in mental imagery is between pictorialists who believe that mental pictures are appropriate tokens in a theory of cognition, and descriptionalists who believe that mentation is constituted of linguistic, descriptive rules and mental images are merely incidental by-products of following these rules. This division mirrors closely the neuron/symbol debate even to the extent that one of the chief protagonists of the descriptionalist point of view is Zenon Pylyshyn (1979) and that reference is often made to Fodor's 'language of thought' paradigm (1975). These are the two main critics of connectionism, as we have seen in Chapter 6. In fact, the argument against mental imagery is so close to that against connectionism that it suggests that it is the same argument. Connectionism is criticized for being insufficiently expressive in the representation of IF . . . THEN propositions. The same is said of the mental state. Our representation of the state of an NSMM as an iconic state makes this concurrence unsurprising. The connectionist state is a mental image, and therefore the debate is the same one.

Mark Rollins describes himself as a pictorialist who believes that images function as representations of the perceived world. This makes us with our iconic NSMM states pictorialists too. And, further, we have proposed a mechanism for the way in which such representations enter a standardized form of universal machine, the NSMM. In engineering terms all this may mean is that images not only have an important computational role to play in cognition, but they may have an important role to play in computation in general. The suggestion is that the image computing paradigm may have as much power as the linguistic/logical one. Again, we should warn against drawing distinctions between these two as if they were alternatives. Still in the engineering domain, it may be that the two paradigms ought to be brought together in order to make good cognitive machines.

The mast to which descriptionalists nail their colours is unashamedly syntactic. There is a perfectly good ready-made theory here – the theory of well-formed sentences as advocated by Chomsky. So thinking is language-like: a well-formed thought has a well-formed linguistic structure. The argument against pictorialism then stems from the idea that pictures do not have rules that determine whether they are well formed or not. So, if a person thinks of a beautiful sunset over the Mediterranean Sea, according to descriptionalists this either does not exist as a thought until it is properly articulated, or is only a by-product of an articulation which has taken place ahead of the sensation of the image. Another reason for the descriptionalists' attack is the link between mental images and the physics of whatever the brain is made of. This, in different words, is an openly stated objection to connectionism. Theory, it is argued, should depend only on the laws of logic. A good theory should not be mediated by the mechanics of the material which is being described. So Newton's laws of motion form a good theory as you do not have to observe the motion of billiard balls or heavenly bodies to understand the theory. Pictorialism, the critics argue, needs (not in their words, but this is what is meant) an understanding of neurons and their functions – connectionism, that is.

It is our belief that this is where the error is made. The NSMM is an abstract notion. It functions only according to the laws of logic. Structural constraints only affect performance, but this is true of Chomskian theory too. Context-free languages can in theory be recognized by computers, but, as we saw in Chapter 5, this may not be possible if sufficient memory is not available in the machine. So what we are saying is that the NSMM may be just the theoretical artefact that the pictorialist is looking for.

9.9.1 Cognitive penetrability

Rollins points out that one of the attacks from the descriptionalist camp is based on what Pylyshyn calls cognitive penetrability. This requires that if an architecture such as a computer is used to theorize about cognition, the theory and the architecture have to be kept well apart. That is, the architecture must be a pure vehicle unpenetrated by and not penetrating the cognitive theory, if the theory is to be made valid. However, imagery provides a counter-example, since it is seen to be dependent on some architectural effect, as the evidence for mental rotation shows – the time for rotations being an architectural effect for which an architecture-free explanation cannot be given.

Rollins argues that the problem lies with the restricted way in which theory generation is constrained by descriptionalists. Why should architectural effects not form part of the theory? In our NSMM explanations this issue becomes very clear. Though the NSMM shifts from a universal computing machine to a neural system with emergent properties, the theory (automata theory, that is) does not change. The mathematical medium (state structure) does not change, image-like states are easily accommodated, and rotational delays merely become expressed as trajectory distances in state structures. In kind, these are no different from 'unpenetrated' statements about the size of search trees in Chomskian parsing theory. So what Pylyshyn sees as an architectural contamination of pure theory may, in fact, turn out to be an enrichment of cognitive theory.

9.9.2 Qualia

There are mental states that relate to thoughts of qualities rather than objects. Thinking of the colour 'blue' is a different kind of mental state from thinking of a blue boat in an azure sea. Philosophers call such different states qualia. Rollins suggests that if a theory of cognition is ever going to account for qualia it will have to account for the distinction between the two types of image states. This raises the deeper question of the inadequacies of the descriptional philosophy which requires that any cognitive state can be fully represented as a language-like state. Statements such as 'I liked the blue shirt better than the green one, so I bought it' is explained as an expression of desire. It may be that it is due to the fact that the colour blue has different mental associations (neighbouring states, in the NSMM) from the colour green. Again this points to a way in which a theory that accounts for mental imagery is likely to enrich cognitive science.

9.9.3 Economy

'A picture may be worth a thousand words' is a particularly apt adage in arguments that favour accounting for mental imagery. The image of 'trying to fit an elephant in a telephone booth' is an economic representation which, in descriptionalist terms, would require a long list of linguistic statements about the relative size of animals, telephone booths and rules that go with the phrase 'fit in'. This notion extends to the concept of a category, where an economical way of representing a particular category is to store an example of a typical member of such a category. So it may well be that in a theory of language understanding, statements such as 'he came across a cave which must have been inhabited by a very large carnivorous animal – yellowing bones gave evidence of this' have implied images from which their meaning can be construed. There is no harm done at all if the reader of the sentence understands it by imagining a lion or a cheetah as the inhabitant of that cave.

9.9.4 Emotions and moods

Pictorialists find fertile ground in the suggestion that rule-based descriptionalist methods are inadequate at providing a cognitive theory of emotions and moods. These methods describe emotions as being related to statable beliefs and desires. A desire, then, is a statement about wanting a proposition to be true. So cognitive science would model Romeo and Juliet's passion for one another as a 'desire' sentence. This sentence would imply the desire that the proposition that they might embrace be true. Rollins draws attention to this as an unsatisfactory way of dealing with emotion, since emotion seems all-pervasive and distinct from the logic of articulated sentences. For example, depression, which is a complex mixture of emotions, is often characterized by the subject's inability to trade its source or to find modes of thought that allow the sufferer to escape from it. This is where the skill of the therapist or counsellor may be required to help unravel the troublesome feelings.

That mental imagery helps in a proper theory of emotion is still conjecture rather than demonstrated fact. However, Rollins suggests that images help to evoke emotions and therefore move the dry, rule-based view closer to some experienced reality. In NSMM theory, the all-pervasiveness of emotion could be captured by the suggestion that a distributed set of state variables neurons), originally used for fear and pleasure reactions (possibly instinctive), are still at work and could affect other state variables in a pervasive manner. Certainly this would allow for mental states to trigger mood or emotion states which could persist even if the triggering states have abated. Of course, as we shall see in Chapter 10, there is scope in the NSMM to define unconscious areas of the inner state which are not accessible to conscious planning actions and could have a mood-like effect on the conscious state trajectories.

9.9.5 Interpretation

Descriptionalists have not got rid of mental images altogether. Fodor, for example, allows that pictures can occur as fillers in linguistic strings. So, a sentence such as 'I am thinking of John' could not be explained without the speaker being able to visualize John in some way. But, argues Fodor, it is the linguistic statement and not the mental image of John that is a full description of the thought. Rollins suggests that this is not the only alternative. The image of John should be distinguished from a mental image that relates to the sentence 'I am thinking of John'. The latter, in fact, is a bit like Figure 8.7, where the image that goes with the sentence would be an image of oneself thinking about something rather than the something itself.

The NSMM supports this alternative idea in the sense that it shows how linguistic 'interpretations' could work hand-in-hand with iconic states. In fact it is the word 'interpretation' that is misleading. Mental images may not need to be linguistically interpreted; their linguistic and iconic parts may merely be a matter for different, but linked, state variables to take care of.

9.10 Looking back at seeing things

Perhaps the most important thing that has been said in this chapter is that connectionist theory, particularly as generalized in the NSMM, is an appropriate theoretical medium for the representation of visual cognition. While 'visual' cognition is being mentioned it may be important to realize that this is merely an example of the internalization of sensory experience leading to 'images' of such experience and the part that this plays in cognition. It has been suggested that results of early processing lead to the codes that constitute image-like mental states which, through consistent occurrence with auditory input resulting from spoken words, becomes bound to appropriate linguistic labels.

Next is the transfer of the mechanics of things in the world into the dynamics of mental images – this results in something like the 'naïve physics' originally defined in artificial intelligence. The NSMM is shown to be useful in generating hypotheses for the classification of cognitive visual deficits that arise from brain lesions due to accidents or illness. This is possible, as it is easy to predict which of the cognitive abilities of the model are likely to be disrupted by which specific disruption in the model. In moving towards a discussion of mental imagery, we have suggested how the NSMM might integrate eye, head and body movements in the creation of coherent, dynamic imagery that pieces together the output of a sensor system that does anything but stand still.

It has been argued that those who object to the introduction of mental imagery into cognitive science do so for the same reasons that they object to connectionism. It is argued that such objections may be misplaced as, through the NSMM, a theory is used that endows iconic states, that is the states of a connectionist machine, with not only a proper rigorous foundation, but also with the compositional properties on which conventional cognitive science is based.

10

Neural cognitive science
A framework for neurons and symbols

10.1 A fresh look at cognitive science?

In the earlier chapters we have seen that cognitive science emerged from cognitive psychology as influenced by those computing formalisms which have largely been developed in the pursuit of artificial intelligence. This sequence has also given rise to what one might call cognitive philosophy, as exemplified by Fodor's 'language of thought' paradigm. This, in turn, is firmly based on the idea that thoughts are well-formed sentences in a mental language that has syntax and semantics along the same lines as Chomsky's mathematical models of language. Connectionism has come into this picture late, and has had an uneasy passage so far. Connectionists find themselves having to argue that their science has something to add to the existing paradigm. This leads to the important debates that have been discussed in this book. Sometimes the impression is created of a successful and complete conventional theory that does not need the addition of connectionism.

So connectionists are put on their mettle to prove that their models map into those of extant cognitive science and have something to offer within that framework. No harm in that: it is quite right that a newcomer should be given a challenge. But a totally impartial observer may ask whether the extant paradigm has been successful enough to hold this high ground. How, indeed, does one measure success in this type of endeavour? One way is to require that a science should, at best, be predictive. Failing that, it should suggest questions that need to be asked in order to deepen understanding. When subjected to this type of test the totally impartial observer may come to the conclusion that the success of cognitive science lies not in making predictions or suggesting new lines of enquiry, but in providing a formal language for describing cognitive effects – the language of computer algorithms. So it is as a formalizing force, a force that allows otherwise vague ideas to be stated clearly, that cognitive science receives its greatest accolade. But, taking away this cloak of formalization, it may be that the science is still fragile and weak, owing to the difficulty of turning formalization into the form of explanation that would lead to prediction.

So, does it make sense to assess the newcomer of connectionism against just one measure of success of the existing paradigm? The criticisms all seem to fall in the area of lack of formal descriptive power of connectionism rather than its explanatory potential. In this last chapter, we shall approach an assessment of the general automata-theoretic form of connectionism (as exemplified by the NSMM) as if Von Neumann had never suggested the embodiment of a Turing machine and as if Chomsky had never elevated mathematical linguistics to the dominant position from which it influenced the philosophical side of cognitive science to the point at which language and cognition become inseparably fused into one another. We ask the question 'What would constitute cognitive science had the concept of a human-made algorithm never existed and computation been defined as a science of the properties of neural networks?'.

First we define a set of fundamentals that bring out the explanatory strengths of the automata-theoretic way of assessing cognition. These five fundamental targets are: learning, thought control and attention, time and sequence understanding, language and planning. In section 10.2 we summarize the structure and operation of the NSMM as a way of tying together the various statements that have been made about it elsewhere in the book. We set out a definitional framework (by referring to other parts of the book, where these arguments first appeared) within which further questions could be asked and predictions made. In section 10.3 we specify assumptions about the world in which the person modelled by the NSMM does its learning. The various levels at which the learning can be done are reviewed in section 10.4, while in section 10.5 we look again at notions of attention and thought control, which have been tackled only summarily in the rest of the book. In section 10.6 we return to a discussion of language and look at the way in which the content of Chapter 8 ties up with other parts of the book. We show that the NSMM suggests that the evolution of language is an efficient thing to have happened in a society of people. In section 10.7 we state, more formally than has been done previously in the book, the logical character of the state space, which becomes the 'mind' of the object modelled by the NSMM.

Finally, in section 10.8 we speculate on the effect that these arguments have on the nature of consciousness. There are two reasons for doing this. First, Daniel Dennett has provided an ingenious explanation of consciousness (1991), which, though, is rather heavily couched in computational terms (virtual machines and the like). Since we have embarked on computational explanations of non-classical architectures, it is of some interest to see how this explanation of consciousness fares in this context. Actually, it fares well, and we are able to show that some of Dennett's explanations transfer to the connectionist computing paradigm. Second, the reason is that it is possible to think of consciousness as being heavily supported by precisely the five cognitive features mentioned above. An organism would have a rather impoverished consciousness were it not able to learn, attend, understand time, plan, and in the opinion of some, use language. So dealing with these matters is, in fact, dealing with consciousness. In section 10.9 we attempt to suggest a possible future for a novel approach that integrates symbolic and neural thinking.

Before dealing with these matters we need to clear up a possible source of confusion. The word 'organism' is used sometimes to indicate intelligent entities that are not necessarily human. The initials NSMM are sometimes used as if this were some kind of organism. The intention in this chapter is to use the term 'neural cognitive science' to point to the body of theories that, in the first instance, explain the function of a 'person', that is, a human being capable of using language. An 'organism' then is an entity that has some cognitive properties that need not be precisely those of a human being. The NSMM is a theoretical vehicle. As we have already seen, and as we shall state a little more formally in the next section, this is a computational device on which both algorithmic and neural theories may be deployed – it is not an organism in its own right, nor is it a computer or the brain of an organism. Its relationship to theoretical notions is the same as that of the Turing machine to computing theory. In fact, it is a transformation of a Turing machine which shows where the neurons are (thereby making it easier to describe 'learning'), and which instead of having tapes for memory has neural areas that perform in the same way.

10.2 The Neural State Machine Model (NSMM) revisited

There is no need to re-draw the NSMM here; Figures 7.1 and 9.1 show specific embodiments of the idea and are sufficient to support the discussion in this chapter. The main aim here is to list and to discuss briefly the properties of this theoretical device so as to be able to evoke it appropriately when discussing neural cognitive science. So, rather than providing rigorous proof of our assertions we concentrate on the use of this device as a cognitive modelling tool.

10.2.1 Universality

(This may be skipped by those not interested in the link between the NSMM and Turing machines.)

The NSMM is a universal computing model which is equivalent to a Turing machine. It has identifiable state variables for input, output and internal representation. If the internal state variables are split into functional and auxiliary groups, the functional variables represent the body of a Turing machine, where the auxiliary variables are equivalent to the Turing concept of a tape. Some computations may require infinite numbers of auxiliary state variables, in the same way that a Turing machine requires infinite tapes. These computations would be curtailed in the NSMM as they would be in a conventional computer (and indeed could not be done in a person's head).

10.2.2 The variables

No assumptions are made to start with about the representation of variables in the NSMM. They could be continuous and numerical, they could be binary, or they could be probabilistic. In general, discussions involving the NSMM are neutral with respect to these methods of coding. The NSMM in parallel with a person has a finite (but possibly very large) number of variables. These are distinctly labelled into three groups: input, output and internal.

But what, in a person, can these variables represent? We shall see that the NSMM can operate in a mode (the programmed mode) where there is no link between these variables and anything that may be happening in a human brain. But the greatest interest in this model stems from its operation in the neural mode, where the NSMM variables are the outputs of artificial neurons. There is no intention here to suggest that there is a one-to-one correspondence between every neuron of the NSMM and a neuron in the brain. However, in the neural mode the NSMM uses variables that are neural in character. This provides the opportunity of developing a theory that is not at odds with neural function, as may be the case with descriptional theories of the 'programmed' kind. Of course there is nothing to prevent neurophysiologists from using NSMMs.

10.2.3 The input state

The theoretical definition of an NSMM input is a variable that cannot be influenced by any inner activity of the system. An input state is a 'snapshot' of the value of all input variables at some instant. For the purposes of cognitive modelling of a person, 'input' refers to all sensory input to what might be called the brain. In the NSMM the boundary of the model corresponds to any part in a person's nervous system that can sense its environment. In order to concentrate on cognitive issues rather than signal processing, it is possible to introduce some early processing into sensory input as has been done in the EP unit of Chapter 9. There are residual questions as to whether something in a long-routed feedback loop is input or not. For example, inner activity can cause a person to move their arm, which is then sensed – is the sensed data an input or not? We would recommend that such long-routed loops be treated individually when they arise and not be considered in a general description.

10.2.4 The output state

In a person, the twitch of any muscle is output. That includes the activity of vocal chords during the emission of speech. In the NSMM, theory tells us that we can either simply see output as part of an inner state (that is, some variables of the inner state are also the variables responsible for output activity) or define a separate set of state variables that are influenced both by input and inner state variables. The two ways of doing this are equivalent – any prediction or explanation that can be made for the one can be transformed to the other. (In the literature these are known as the Mealy–Moore and the Moore–Mealy transformations; see Aleksander and Hanna (1978)).

10.2.5 The inner state

In a person, the inner state forms the focus of attention of cognitive scientists and philosophers. In the NSMM, some of the glamour disappears and an inner state is said to be the instantaneous snapshot of all of the system's state variables, a state variable being any variable that has not been designated an input variable. In this we have taken the option to define some of the state variables also as output variables. So far, this is classical automata theory as discussed in Chapter 5. In order to direct this model towards cognitive modelling we call for a further partition of the inner state into conscious and unconscious state variables. Conscious state variables, through the process of learning, are those that take part in an available representation of the world. Others (that connectionists sometime call hidden units) are the auxiliary state variables that may be needed to label events internally almost as a private act. We return to these various examples later in this chapter.

10.2.6 The dynamics of state changes

The states of the NSMM are constantly changing. The changes are controlled by the input, and the output activities are keyed to the changing states. The direction (i.e. choice of next state) is determined by the input. Automata theory normally encourages one to think of an automaton with discrete states where the state changes are computed at regular intervals. However, in order to obtain a feel for the cognitive dynamics of the NSMM, the number of states can be thought of as being very large indeed, and the changes between states not very great. In the limit this is a continuous system where state changes are seen as a kind of an internal movie, but one that is continually being controlled by input and in response to which the output takes action.

Is this really an appealing framework in which to model a person? Perhaps not, when blatantly stated as above! However, it is shown in later parts of this chapter that, through learning, the state activity becomes adapted to matching the external world, which leads to a framework that in many ways 'feels OK' when compared with our introspections into the way we ourselves think that we function.

10.2.7 The neural–universal continuum

The NSMM is a theoretical framework which supports a variable degree of what has been called 'the emergent property' of a neural net. At one extreme, the theoretical machine is a blank slate which allows the structuring of any machine as defined by a state structure. At the other extreme the emergent property is that which allows parts of state structure to be created by learning and allows other parts of state structure to align themselves with this in a stable way (this is discussed fully in section 10.4). Here we draw attention to the two variables that take the model from one extreme to the other. The first is the connectivity of the state variables. At the universal end the internal state variables are seen as being fully connected to all the other state variables (inner and input) and capable of performing any function of their input (that is, the state variables are simply the outputs of lookup tables that can be loaded in all possible ways). This has the effect of allowing the structuring of any finite state machine. At the neural end, the internal state variables have a limited connectivity, which in itself causes some generalization, in the sense that variables become insensitive to some of the changes in the state and respond as if these changes had not happened. That is, they respond to similar patterns in similar ways, which is a kind of generalization.

In fact, generalization is the other variable that defines where on a neural--universal axis the model lies. This refers to the degree by which generalization is instituted in the particular state variables. So if spot values of input for a neuron/state variable are programmed or learned (see the next section) generalization means that appropriate responses are given to other inputs similar (in a way to be defined by a generalization algorithm) to those spot values. Clearly, at the universal end the state variables have no generalization.

10.2.8 Iconic inner states

In Chapter 8 much was made of 'iconic' inner states. These are a by-product of the learning process (described in section 10.4 below) where stable perceptual data are transformed into stable internal states that preserve the sensed properties of the percepts. Therefore parts of the set of inner state variables are devoted to iconic representations, one part for each sensory modality. The fact that associations can take place between these stable sub-states, and that one can be retrieved from another, is a central feature resulting from the emergent properties of the NSMM operating in the neural mode.

10.2.9 Time and sequence

The way in which a dynamic neural net can learn sequences has been covered in some detail in Chapter 2 (Figures 2.11–2.16). Essentially, if input A is followed by input B, the NSMM learns to transit to inner state B from inner state A when input B occurs. The method discussed there calls for a timing device which generates the clicks that define the instants at which the next state is computed by the neurons. It has been seen in chapter 5 (section 5.4) that this synchronous activity is not necessary, and NSMMs could be thought of as being asynchronous.

This explains how the NSMM could have a sense of sequence, which really comes naturally to any state-based automaton. More puzzling is how a person can have a sense of time. For example, a person may need to react in one way to an event that has a long duration and in another to a short event. People are clearly capable of making such judgements, and a theory of cognition should account for this kind of understanding of time. The mechanism that provides this part of a model in the NSMM is the auxiliary state. Let us say that the duration of an event is significant. Say that the input is P and this has a duration D1 which has to be distinguished from the same input but of duration D2. As P is perceived and transferred to the internal state, say that the auxiliary state keeps changing and that these changes are learned. It is then quite possible for these two occurrences of P to enter the NSMM's experience as different events which may require different reactions. Note that the auxiliary state does not necessarily enter the 'conscious' part of the NSMM state. It would be an interesting task to use the NSMM in conjunction with what is known about people's ability to memorize duration of events in order to develop a full cognitive model of this phenomenon.

On the subject of sequence and time we must draw attention to the work of Jordan (1986) who devised a state machine type of neural system that was capable of storing linguistic structures. Elman (1990) has shown that by training this type of structure on verbal sequences, it can, in auxiliary units, develop representations of word types from their position in an utterance. In Elman's way of expressing this, the system discovers 'structure in time'. While the NSMM is a more general device that Jordan's dynamic system, it behaves very similarly when subjected to Jordan's or Elman's tests.

10.3 The world

From a point of view of automata theory it would be tempting to say that, having proposed the NSMM for modelling a person's cognitive processes, we should represent the world in which this person does her cognition as another totally general automaton. Theoretically this would not be a problem. But from a point of view of credibility and as a match to life this would be impractical. A general automaton can change output from moment to moment and have a totally obscure state structure. It would be very difficult for the NSMM to 'make sense' of this. But, in many ways the world we live in is somewhat more amenable. Actions and reactions are localized and causally related. This means that things in the world are generally stable. Changes occur locally against a stable background. So if a person picks up a cup to drink some coffee, she can concentrate on that act. Some other things may be going on at the same time, but wild environmental changes are not generally expected.

Therefore the most helpful way of modelling the world may be not as one huge automaton, but as many largely disconnected smaller ones. A person would normally recognize the part of the world with which she was interacting. 'Recognize' in NSMM terms means that the appropriate sector of state space is triggered off through the senses. Switching from working with one automaton in the world to another is an attentional process which we consider later in this chapter.

Another way in which the world is likely to be amenable is that the state structures it presents to people are not too obscure. Mostly, they are the sorts of structures that obey Newton's laws of motion: billiard balls, pendulums, motor vehicles, bicycles and so on. These are all aspects of the world which have inner states described by concepts such as velocity and acceleration. They are learned and 'understood' early in life. For example, a child will, simply by observing a beach ball that she is trying to catch, brace herself appropriately to take into account the force with which the ball will strike her. The observed world state is just change of position, so the child computes (through learned skills in the NSMM?) the world's (ball's) internal variable of acceleration which (as Newton worked out mathematically after millennia of generations of children had done it intuitively) is proportional to the force that requires a reaction. The ability to cope with more complex dynamic properties of the world, such as the driving of a crane or the flying of a jumbo jet, are seen as skills that can be acquired by a great deal of training. So there is a limit to the complexity of the inner state structure of the world that a person can understand and deal with, which, luckily for survival, matches roughly what the world has in store.

Probably the most complex element of the world that a person has to face is another person, or, worse, crowds of people. Here there are hidden states in profusion and total switching from one internal state to another. But this is the province of the social psychologist, who indeed may find it interesting to develop theory based on interacting NSMMs. George Kelly (1955) was aware of this possibility and stated that the extent to which any two people can take part in a social process is mediated by the extent to which they have a knowledge of each other's state structures. He did not use these precise words. Kelly uses the phrase 'system of personal constructs' – these constructs are very much like aspects of learned state structure in the NSMM.

10.4 Learning

Learning is the central feature of NSMM-based cognitive science. What follows below is a continuation of the attempt to create a framework for this science

rather than providing watertight definitions. It is broken down into its
principal features.

10.4.1 Learning

Learning is the transfer of state structures that exist in the world and its
inhabitants to the inner state structure of the NSMM in ways that support
the retrieval of such structures. The existence of static events in the world
becomes represented in NSMM state structure as either single re-entrant states
or short re-entrant cycles. Dynamic events, on the whole, are echoed as state
sequences in the NSMM (more detail is given in section 10.6 on time and
sequence understanding, and in section 10.7 on language).

10.4.2 Motivation for learning

Mechanisms in the NSMM must be such as to stem from and represent 'need'.
The organism that is driven by a NSMM must have means (e.g. physical
actuators, voice) to be able to carry out operations on the world which, given
the appropriate sequences, cause the world to release that which the organism
needs.

10.4.3 Understanding

An organism is said to understand the state structures of the world if, through
the internalization of such structures, it is capable of manipulating the world
so as to cause it to yield what the organism needs. In the case of a cognitive
theory about people, there should be sufficient similarity between the state
structures internalized by different individuals to enable them to take part
in social interactions. It is sufficient for a scientist to represent such structures
in a NSMM to understand what understanding is.

10.4.4 Exploration

Some learning can take place through the application of randomly selected
NSMM output to the world and learning the resulting world responses. What
can be learned during this exploration is limited and (as shown in Chapter
7) may not lead to a full discovery of the world's state structures.

10.4.5 Instruction

More of the world's structure may be learned if another person in the
environment controls the state structure in a way that increases the learning
NSMM's exposure (see Chapter 7). This is a kind of learning-by-showing
procedure.

10.4.6 Teaching using language

In Chapter 7 we took a leap from learning by instruction to programming as it might occur in a conventional computer. Here we introduce an intermediate step, which is learning through the use of language. This is clearly a major route taken by people. We have seen in Chapter 8, and will review later in this chapter, that language serves to call to mind related experience. The years spent at school learning history, geography and the like are a shortcut to an enormous amount of experience. The key to this method lies in an expansion of existing experience, existing experience being represented in NSMM as state structure. So, for example, if one were to explain to a child who had never seen snow what snow is like, some similar substance would have to be brought to mind – finely chopped ice perhaps. The child would then be asked to imagine his front garden, the houses around, and the street covered in this substance and told to label it as snow. Seeing some pictures might help. When later asked by a friend, who too had never seen snow, what he had learned about snow, the first child may say that it was like finely chopped ice and so on.

10.4.7 Programming

The last example is useful in distinguishing between learning by interaction between persons and learning as might occur in direct programming of the NSMM. Programming is done by an entity that can be set aside from the society of NSMM organisms, an entity that has infinite knowledge of the effect of setting functions in the neurons-cum-state variables. This is precisely what happens in conventional computer programming. The 'neurons' are programmed in detail, but not necessarily by the programmer, who may be using a high-level language to express what the machine is to do. It is a special program (the compiler) that takes these high-level descriptions and maps them into the neurons. So it now takes two types of people at least to get computers to do what is required – the programmer and the compiler designer.

In conventional cognitive science the role of these two types is often forgotten, putting the modelling of a cognitive task at the level of a program written by the programmer who, when translated to the level of the society of people, is left in the position of some God-like creature. This argument allows us to question the validity and usefulness of such models. Our own point of view is that models of learning that stem from within the societal structure in which a person operates are likely to be more realistic in terms of defining a cognitive science. After all, the deity could write programs that greatly exceed human ability with the same ease as other programs that don't. This makes it hard to sort fact from fiction.

10.4.8 *Generalization*

Generalization is one of the key factors that distinguishes neural cognitive theory from the conventional, computational version. It operates at many levels, the lowest being that the neuron responds in the same way for inputs similar to those set in training. The next level is that of state structure, where the neuronal generalization causes states similar to those that have been created during learning as re-entrant states or short cycles to transit to the learned states. The effect of this generalization is for the re-entrant states to act as prototypes of world events which are entered internally when variants of these events are perceived.

Generalization should not be thought of as being automatic. That is, the system on only seeing the letter O will treat Q in the same way, but if, as part of training, Q is learned as a different event, then there will be two separate re-entrant states for these two events, and which of the two is entered will become very sensitive to the presence or absence of the distinguishing slash. In a sense generalization may be seen as rule-learning. In the above example, the generalization effect could be described thus – the 'NSMM is learning the rule that a circle with a small slash in the bottom-right region is a Q and that one without a slash is an O'.

10.5 Attention and thought control

Introspection supports the NSMM notion of internal states that mirror the world as it is experienced. An important question is whether this notion of perceived inner states can be extended to feelings of being able to control that which is at the focus of conscious attention. There is a danger here of assuming a homunculus as being responsible for this control. But this is not necessary. The principle of thought control in NSMMs is that the person is capable of controlling exploration of the external world through bodily action and can transfer this ability to exploration of the internal state representation through 'imagined' bodily actions. We therefore look at attention first as an external phenomenon and then suggest a way in which it might become a method of internal thought control.

10.5.1 *Thought hopping and noise*

Having defined world experiences as stable, re-entrant states or short cycles which are entered when the appropriate perceptual input is present and must be recognized, it is appropriate to ask what might happen if the input were to be removed. It can be shown theoretically that the system would remain in that state until a new recognizable input were to disappear. As a mental model this state of affairs is clearly not what one would wish, as it is obvious that such a model should allow for thought-hopping between known stable states. The only way in which the NSMM could be dislodged from this stable state is through the presence of some noise that disrupts the stable state and then abates, to allow another state to be found. This is one of the predictions that can be made about brain function from neural theory – noise is an important cognitive factor and should prompt some neuro-physiological investigation.

There is another example of the possible beneficial presence of noise. If the input is ambiguous, e.g. if the input were half house and half tree, where the NSMM knows of a house and a tree, the inner retrieved image would be either a tree or a house. But once one of these had been seen it would be hard to swap to the other without the presence of noise. In the psychologist's armoury of visual stimuli there are such ambiguous images (woman/duck or old/young woman) and it is difficult to switch between representations. Some people cannot switch at all, whereas others seem to be able to learn how to do it. It is suggested that noise or some other form of general disruption at the disposal of the mechanism is at work. These are arbitrary switches between thoughts – now for something a little more controlled.

10.5.2 Visual attention

This has largely been tackled in Chapter 9. The person generates complete views of the world through a mechanism which relies on an interaction between foveal vision and peripheral vision for 'knowing where to look next'. This becomes internalized as a probabilistic state structure which enables the NSMM to shift attention between memorized states, giving an impression of seeing a complete picture rather than foveal saccades. It also leads to being able to report seeing things at different levels of detail.

However, there is another form of visual attention, which brings the notion of 'willed' thought control into closer focus. A person can imagine a trip down a well-known road that comes to a fork. She may then report that she can decide to think about going to the left or going to the right. Going to the left, she reports, gets her to Alphaville and going to the right, to Betatown. She can think of either and feels totally in control of her 'will' to choose which thought to take up. NSMM theory explains this as state structure in which the fork in the road is an internal state related to an external state which requires a decision as to which way to go. Learning enables the recall of events that occur in going both ways and the results which are experienced. Therefore, as in the linguistic example in Chapter 7, Alphaville and a left turn become associated in one state that follows the fork state, while Betatown and a right turn are the other. This is experienced as an ability to take either path if a goal is not set in the state variables. Making the transition 'mentally' puts the goal data into the state by pattern completion, and can therefore lead to the report that either goal can be accommodated. There is no homunculus there – just a memory of 'when FORK if X then Y' with a complete description of what X and Y could be. Noise may also be at work in leaving one with the feeling that the choice can be made arbitrarily.

10.5.3 Auditory attention

Can the NSMM explain the 'cocktail party problem' as set out by Colin Cherry (see section 4.3)? Before considering switches of attention between conversations (as might occur at a cocktail party) let us remind ourselves what 'following a conversation' might be like in NSMM terms. Say the overheard conversation goes something like:

'Barry has had to give up his house in France due to the recession.'
'Really? He runs a restaurant in Chelsea doesn't he?'
'Yes, an expensive one – people can't afford to eat out these days ...'

The images created in the listener's head will depend on how well he knows Barry – that is, whether he possesses stable states for that person, his house in France and his restaurant in Chelsea. We note that following a conversation depends not only on the heard input but the fact that the states such as 'Barry' and 'his house in France' have possible links between them (i.e. have a reasonable probability of transition between them).

Now imagine that the other conversation goes something like

'... We went to Mitilini for our holidays.'
'Where is that?'
'It's the Greek island of Lesbos, in the north Aegean ...'

If the two conversations are heard simultaneously, the phenomenon is no different from the perception of ambiguous visual input of the woman/duck type. The input is ambiguous and the listener sticks to one conversation solely through being in a sequence of states that have an elevated probability of being linked. This, added to the ambiguous input, will favour retaining attention of one conversation. However, it would not take much in the NSMM to switch to the second conversation. Noise may be at work (and the hubbub of the rest of the party may have a part to play in distorting the input sufficiently to weaken the transition probabilities). Then a word or phrase that has a strong link with a mental image 'Greek island' or 'holiday' may complete the transition.

10.6 Language – use and evolution

Chapter 8 was devoted to the question of language and the NSMM, with conventional cognitive notions in the background. The most significant and possibly controversial point made in Chapter 8 is the introduction of an iconic state that keeps track of the meaning of utterances. This is a novel approach which is different from that taken by some connectionists. However, it may be the approach which, in the long run, reconciles the somewhat uneasy separation between syntax and semantics arising as a result of the rigorous Chomskian treatment of language through syntax alone. There is scope for a great deal of work in the development of this iconic approach.

Another novel possibility is in the area of language understanding. There is connectionist work on this (Sharkey, 1989) where local nodes in a dynamic network represent concepts such as standing in a queue, finding a seat, getting on a bus. Script-like stable activations of these concepts allows the net to group them together under headings such as 'the cinema' or 'a bus ride'. Having activated the appropriate group of units, the system could be made to answer questions about the scenario and order events as they might happen. However, the iconic approach we have presented here is quite different. Objects such as 'standing in a queue' are in fact, iconic states represented in a distributed way by many units. They are linked to other related objects through state transitions, and language understanding would depend on whether incoming utterances would give rise to the appropriate experience represented as a synchronous sequence of states. This is another item of evidence which suggests that the symbols of neural computing are best sited in the states of an NSMM rather than being locally encoded as the 'meaning' of the firing of single neurons.

Another important result of NSMMs is the support of the notion that language need not be innate. The innateness hypothesis is very much part of the computational culture where learning does not play a great part. This can be revised in the light of the learning model that is available for the NSMM. The essence of language as a learned phenomenon is that its development is based on a need to spread information about the world to other members of a species for maximum survival, and then passing this on to new members that are born into the group. As an example, imagine that the world can deliver ten products – edible meat, fire, food, . . . and so on. Further assume that there are ten tool-like objects available – stones, spears, sticks, . . . and that there are further objects that can be attacked, such as chickens, fruit trees, fish, mushrooms, ... Finally, there are ten actions that people in this world are capable of – strike, dig, rub, ...

In some intermediate state, assume that individuals of a tribe, through the use of exploratory learning, have discovered how to obtain some of the products. For example, individual A has discovered that 'rub a stick with a stick gives fire'. Another may have discovered that 'dig the ground with a stone gives mushrooms'. However, exploratory learning is a notoriously haphazard business. Taking ten subjects, ten actions and ten objects, we have 1000 combinations, of which we have said only ten will yield useful products. If there are sufficient individuals, all the ways of generating the products will be discovered in the society as a whole. But, if the society survives only if all the individuals know all the rules, it becomes important for the survival of this society that the information discovered by individuals be transmitted to others. The immediate way of spreading knowledge to other members of the society is to hold public demonstrations of what has been learned. This is known to happen among animals in family groups, where, as among lions, the elders of the group show the younger members how to catch and kill prey.

However, public demonstrations of actions are inefficient in the sense that one must wait for the right opportunity and go to the right place to execute the demonstration. Given the ability to make noises, public meetings are best spent in agreeing which noises apply to which single objects (e.g. HARG is a stick TUUI is hit and KUKU is a chicken). This agreement can come about even without the object being there. Mime actions may do the trick. So the development of agreed signing, that is a language, can be seen as a way of overcoming the inefficiency of exploratory learning. But learning is still required, and the type of iconic learning that has been discussed in conjunction with the NSMM is precisely the technique that would associate objects and actions with sounds.

Finally, it would be easy for this iconic technique to be transmitted directly to new entrants to this society, and it seems inconceivable that such a society should wait for evolution to transfer the structure of sentences into genes (as is implied by Chomskian innateness), when the job can be done directly. We note that the structure of the language reflects the structure of the world (e.g. do X with Y and Z will happen). This would ensure that different isolated societies, though using different sounds to indicate actions and objects, would end up with the same structure of language. The discovery that most languages have similar structures need not immediately imply that this structure is innate.

In summary, the learning mechanisms assumed for the NSMM imply an efficient and rapid evolution of language. The repository of such a language is the societal group itself and not a transfer into the gene pool. What is needed now is the development of a corpus of knowledge gleaned through simulation of NSMMs that suggests ways in which language might have acquired sophistication that is much beyond that used in the above example.

10.7 Logic

Where production rules are the mathematical background to the syntactical side of computing, logic is the other pillar on which the mathematical rigour of computing rests. As we have seen in Chapter 6, connectionism has been criticized for not having the same rigorous foundations as conventional computing. So far we have been content to draw attention to linguistic properties that have been missed in this attack. Here we do a little more in showing that the representational medium of the NSMM, that is the state structure, has a sound logical basis.

Of course, we have shown in Chapter 2 that a neuron itself performs any logical function as determined by training, which is then expanded by generalization. But this is not at stake here. What is at stake is that the mode of representing the world as state structure should be logically sound in the sense that it can represent any logical proposition. This would show that people being modelled using this technique would not be deficient in the 'understanding' of logical principles. Any event that the person believes to be true is

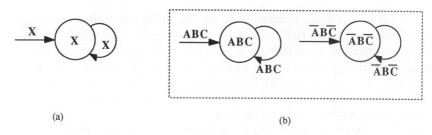

(a)   (b)

Figure 10.1 *The logic of true events in the state structure.*

modelled in NSMM as a recurrent state cycle. An event X is represented as shown in Figure 10.1(a). (Note that this event could be represented by a state cycle in its own right if an event which is true is a sequence of time.)

The way we have described the NSMM is that an event which in logic would be represented by the composite occurrence of true events A *and* B *and* C would appear within a state. In fact, Figure 10.1(b) shows a representation of the logical statement (A *and* B *and* C) *or* (~ A *and* B *and* ~ C) where ~ A reads A is not true. This demonstrates that the state structure can represent any logical state of the three events A, B and C. Also, given sufficiently large numbers of state variables, the logical state of any set of events in the world can be represented.

So logical correctness of the state representations can easily be proved, but what is exciting about these representations is that variables such as A, B and C in the above descriptions could be very rich in the sense that they could be iconic representations of truths in the world.

10.8 Dennett's consciousness

After years of being shunned by cognitive scientists, the concept of consciousness is currently enjoying a revival of interest. One of the most comprehensive recent attempts to provide an explanation of this rather ephemeral concept is Daniel Dennett's book *Consciousness Explained* (1991). It is interesting to ask whether a technique for modelling cognitive phenomena (NSMM in this case) supports or does not support explanations of consciousness. Dennett uses many concepts that belong to conventional computational science in his 'explanation', and since we are proposing that cognition could be modelled using an alternative set of connectionist computational principles, we look at the effect of these ideas on Dennett's theory. Whatever the case, a computational revival of interest in consciousness seems to be firmly on the agenda for the latter part of the 1990s. This could be called 'artificial consciousness'. In a way this makes more sense than 'artificial intelligence'. Acts such as recognizing a friend in a crowd or reacting differently to the statements 'your trousers are on fire' and 'your trousers need pressing' certainly require consciousness, but would normally not be seen as great feats of human intelligence.

The question of whether machines could be endowed with some sort of artificial consciousness is also an important one, not because a positive answer might give rise to new breeds of robots, but because it might clarify some common-sense beliefs about what consciousness is and is not and who could possess it. In this final section of this book we look closely at the elements of Dennett's explanation and consider whether the NSMM notion of cognition supports or contradicts these explanations. We can anticipate now that, on the whole, the NSMM supports Dennett's arguments and, in some aspects, helps to clarify them.

10.8.1 The Cartesian Theatre

In everyday discourse, the word consciousness seems to evoke the inner world, an ability to access experience and a sympathetic relationship with the objects in our surroundings. Dennett warns us to beware of the enticing idea that consciousness has an existence of its own displaying its content to its owner as if it were a play taking place in a theatre or a movie screen with its owner as the only member of the audience. The Cartesian Theatre (as he calls it, because it is reminiscent of Descartes' idea of existence of mind independently of body) is appealing but dangerous, as it leads to an infinite regress – who is watching the movie? Whoever it may be, is he or she conscious?

However, in Chapter 9 we deal precisely with the idea of 'pictures in our heads'. So are we not coming close to saying that there may be something like a Cartesian Theatre there after all? Who is the observer of our 'iconic state'? By starting with the assumption that a sensation is due to the firing of neurons in our nervous system, we not only avoid the Cartesian Theatre, but also explain why the notion of 'pictures in the head' is appealing. Some neurons in the NSMM respond directly to perceptual input – and that is the process of seeing things when they are in front of us. Others are driven by perceptual input in the same way, so when we are actually looking at something they simply take part in generating the sensation of seeing but this latter group, through feed-back, can *sustain* these images even when the sensory input has been removed. So the sensation of seeing is sustained under such conditions – that is, there are pictures in the head. But in the sense that the original sensation of seeing belongs to the owner of the head, so does the sustained vision. There is no homunculus, but there are pictures in the head generated by firing neurons. They can be recalled and manipulated as discussed in Chapter 9.

10.8.2 Multiple drafts

A by-product of Cartesian Theatre philosophy is that the place of the stage and the exact moment of production of any part of the play needs to be identified. Most of the time the person is bombarded with sensory input which different parts of the brain process at significantly different rates. As this does not bother the owner of the resulting sensation, and she manages to string together all this into a reasonably coherent experience, it is hardly surprising that Cartesian Theatre followers will start looking for coordinating, supervisory mechanisms that mould consciousness into a slick production. But having demolished the Cartesian Theatre, this feeling of coherence needs to be explained.

The first point to realize is that there need not be a localized area nor a point in time when the sensory input has to be processed. Dennett likens this to what may be happening among the editorial board of a newspaper where the various editors are continuously revising the state of their drafts as news comes in, but never actually bring all the stories together or produce a final draft. Indeed several drafts may coexist, some of which might be overridden by new evidence while others may linger. By way of illustration, Dennett draws attention to a couple of known psychophysical phenomena. The first is the Kolers colour phi phenomenon (see Dennett (1991) for details). A red dot is turned on and off on a screen, as is a green dot an inch or two away from the red one. The two flash in opposing phase – when one is in the middle of being off, the other is in the middle of being on. There is some overlap when both are on. For some frequencies of this operation a subject will report not only that the dot is moving between one position and the other, but that it changes colour half-way between the two – a localized experience which actually has no localization in the real world. The revised draft of the original experience says something like: 'it *must* have changed half-way'.

Another illustration is that memory can sometimes play tricks. People get confused about who they met when. For example, you may remember going to a party the previous week and meeting two colleagues from work and the woman from the local bookshop. There is consternation when at the next meeting with the woman you are told that she had never been at that party. Your brain has inserted the woman into the memory of the party from some earlier experience. This is an example of a draft revision that has gone wrong, but is as vivid as if it had actually happened. Dennett argues that Cartesian Theatre adherents will look for revisionist mechanisms. The first he calls Orwellian, in the sense that it calls for a series of homunculi in the brain who are rewriting history. The second he calls Stalinesque, as it implies that there is an imaginative producer who, for reasons of his own, is putting on show trials that are so impressive as to hide the truth. These, of course, are vignettes that form part of the armoury for demolishing the Cartesian Theatre – multiple drafts is simply a way of suggesting that the inner state has a dynamic of its own made up of many parts. This dynamic must sometime rationalize the input from perception and parts of it can bind the wrong experience into other parts of a draft. There is no Orwell; nor is there a Stalin.

The NSMM can be used to clarify the multiple drafts idea. If one were to think of single neurons or closely interconnected groups of neurons as 'editors' then the way in which the inner state is controlled by perceptual input could easily be described as a continuous revision of the inner state draft. But there is no boss in the system, each 'editor' does the best it can with the input it receives from perception and the other reporters. Consciousness is a continuously revised report from these editors. Kolers' colour phi phenomenon is due to the same process which we discussed in section 9.6. The exact events sensed by the eyes are captured by the Early Processing (EP) unit in the NSMM. This unit may also activate some motion detectors. The internal states of the NSMM then would go through sequences learned when bodies really are in motion. So a part of the state, though there may only be three distinct states in the input, goes through a much larger set of states where the dot is 'filled in' as being in intermediate positions. A 'colour' part of the state has to bind its content to these. For us to understand how an event that has not yet occurred (the colour change) can be reported as happening ahead of time requires us to step back a little.

How, in the NSMM, can any fleeting event be looked back on and reported? Again we refer to Chapter 9 (section 9.7). The mechanism for shifting from short- to long-term memory requires that any recent experience be recycled as a state cycle in the NSMM. So, when the colour change is reported as being half-way in the trajectory of the dot, this is a synchronization effect between the more detailed changes of the position image of the state and the lower detail of the colour image part of the state. The report (on the action outputs of the NSMM) is based not on the original event but on the cycling of the inner state reaction to that event – a 'draft' that may have been 'revised' many times before the action output responds.

It is the same mechanism of shift between short-term memory and long-term memory that is responsible for putting the woman at a party she never attended. While areas of the state are recycling the memory of the party, the memory of the bookshop woman can, by accident or some other effect (for instance someone resembling her actually having been at the party), become bound to the party cycle. Once this has happened the 'true' report has vanished, and truth becomes simply the badly revised drafts. The thinker has no access to the 'real' truth. So Dennett's cartoon of consciousness being like 'revised drafts' is a useful metaphor with which to displace the Cartesian Theatre. The NSMM suggests mechanisms for this, but also implies that a great deal of work could be done in neural cognitive science to relate data from controlled experiments with people to network parameters, in order to assign characteristics to some of these parameters and thus provide a sound neural model in the area of witnessing and reporting.

10.8.3 *The evolution of consciousness*

Assuming that consciousness is a process of revising drafts as discussed above, where did it come from in people? Dennett proposes that an inheritance process may have been at work in bringing about the development of some basic wired-in functions – looming object detectors, ducking mechanisms, other creature detectors, friend or foe detectors.

In terms of the NSMM, it is the Early Processor in vision (and similar devices in the other sensory modalities) that assumes some form of evolution that leads to pre-wiring. Another evolutionary development proposed by Dennett is one that comes from auto-stimulation – the discovery that the signal which is used to draw another person's attention also awakens responses within oneself. This mechanism is very similar to that which we have proposed for the evolution of language in section 10.6. A third mechanism is also one we mentioned above – the generation of linguistic notions that enter a societally preserved repository. Dennett points to one of Richard Dawkins' theories that there is an evolution of such informational structures based on informational 'genes' which Dawkins calls 'memes'.

Possibly the most interesting contribution that the NSMM can make in discussion about the evolution of consciousness is to clarify that which can and that which cannot be transmitted genetically. One thing is clear: only physical structure can be transmitted through the genetic mechanism. The way we have defined a neuron, the only thing that can be inherited in the NSMM is the connection pattern for the neurons. Therefore a discussion can arise as to whether certain connection patterns serve the evolutionary requirements of the person better than others. For example, is it useful for groups of neurons to be strongly connected within the group and weakly outside it? As there are constraints in living systems in the way in which neurons can connect to one another while the organism is developing, how would evolutionary changes improve on this?

An easy guess is that evolution can mostly provide fixed functions (such as the EP) where this is useful. Beyond that, the best thing that evolution can do is to create as flexible a mechanism as it can so that memories may be stored as efficiently as possible in what is clearly a 'hardware-limited' situation.

10.8.4 *The virtual machines of consciousness*

The conclusion that evolution leads to a mechanism of maximum flexibility is one that we share with Dennett, but we differ on what this mechanism should be. Dennett sees that the most flexible thing that could happen is that a *virtual computer* become installed in the parallel neural networks of the brain. (In computer engineering a virtual machine is a kind of machine in disguise – one machine to be made to act as another. A simple example is one that many people who own a personal computer will have experienced. There may be a 'pull-down' menu which contains a 'calculator'. By clicking a mouse control or pressing a few keys on a keyboard, a calculator that looks like the face of a conventional pocket calculator appears on the screen, and from then onwards the computer behaves just like a pocket calculator. In fact, packages such as spreadsheet and word processing programs are all virtual machines running on conventional computers.)

Dennett's virtual machine on which consciousness occurs is a serial, conventional processor, which explains the dominance of that concept in cognitive theory. This is not presented as a serendipitous event – evolution having designed what was subsequently done by Von Neumann. No, the way it is suggested that this has happened is that the Von Neumann design, or Turing's thoughts about universal computing machines, are a summary, a celebration even, of conscious cognition. But having created this universal machine, what kind of a program does it run on (these machines *only* run on programming power)? Dennett's answer to this important question is that there are two kinds of program – first there is the program that has been put there by wiring through evolution, and second, the 'memes' that get there through intellectual intercourse with other members of the species. Further modulations occur through learning by experience.

But what, according to Dennett, does the final programme on this virtual machine do? The answer is lots and lots of things. Each thing is a separate expert (one that appreciates art, another that plans financial life etc.). There are mental spreadsheets, graphics programs, game playing programs, all interacting as required by the organism's need to think or cope with informational input. This is a veritable 'Society of Mind', to borrow a concept from Marvin Minsky (1985). It has no boss, no organizer and, above all, it produces continually revised drafts, in a way that is driven by the needs of the moment.

This explanation, however, leaves many questions unanswered. Dennett makes much of the fact that any explanation of consciousness should not depend on what he describes as 'and then a miracle occurs'. But to the eye of a computer engineer the idea of the appearance of a virtual machine in the brain does seem to be a bit of a miracle. And having got the miraculous universal machine, the arrival of software to create the various experts seems to require a host of other miracles. It may be that a knowledge of how a conventional machine and its virtual machines work is just too much to ask for from evolutionary processes – it may be the wrong thing to ask for. In the next short section we suggest that the NSMM may be a better thing to be aiming for – requiring fewer miracles.

10.8.5 Consciousness and the NSMM

The observation that has lead Dennett to conclude that consciousness is a multi-expert program that runs on a conventional architecture which is a virtual machine sited in the neural nets of the brain is that people do things that are best described as algorithms on architectures that are best known – conventional ones. So his explanation of consciousness buys, perhaps a little reluctantly (he likes Minsky's models but not Fodor's), the algorithmic view of cognition. We have seen that the NSMM can, through appropriate learning or instruction, carry out, at one extreme, computations that have algorithmic models and, at the other, tasks that can only be learned, for which algorithms may be hard to find.

So from the NSMM point of view, the only mechanical requirement is the neural system with three characteristics – a considerable amount of feedback where state structures can develop the plasticity to do lifetime learning and the ability to generalize from what has been learned. There we have the plasticine in which may be moulded the rest of Dennett's notion of consciousness – the evolution of special detectors, the decomposition of tasks into specialist activities (which occurs on demand from the environment) and the notion of consciousness being a continually changing state that can be likened to a continually revised set of drafts. There is no need for the double feat of building first a virtual Von Neumann architecture and then programming it.

However, with this simple architecture for holding consciousness, a deeper question can be asked. Do all organisms that behave on the basis of an inner state structure have consciousness? The answer we give is positive, but then we hurry on to say that it is important to find quality measures that distinguish between the consciousness of a clockwork mouse and that of a human being. Undoubtedly, people have taken a quantum leap by having developed a consciousness that has a linguistic component tied (in the NSMM way of modelling) to iconic representations of the sensory world. Most other creatures are likely to have the iconic representation but are known not to have the same linguistic links. The clockwork mouse has neither – it 'knows' only if its spring is wound or not. So important quality and quantity judgements are being made here. Although science has not as yet produced useful measures for expressing these assessments, we have drawn attention to the fact that the methodology exists – it is the science of relating structure and function of NSMMs to their behaviour. It now needs some further development.

10.9 A kind of epilogue

What are the overall conclusions that can be drawn in an area of work that encompasses so many topics? Given that the task is to provide models of thinking, top of our agenda has been the appropriateness or otherwise of the tools that might be used in the design of these models. The question has become phrased as 'should these be symbols or neurons?' This is the phrasing of literature on this subject – we do not agree with it. The question is badly posed. Symbolic modelling is too concerned with simulation of effect, too deeply rooted in the formalizations of logic and language and not universally successful in models of cognition. Models of scene and language understanding still leave us in some doubt as to whether they enlarge our understanding. On the other hand, neural modelling as an isolated discipline may be in the process of going down too many blind alleys. It is too concerned with mechanisms of weight adjustment and the behaviour of single, homogeneous nets. It has not been sufficiently exposed to formal assessment as a computing tool. So we have attempted to represent a framework for further development where, with a computational perspective on connectionism and an acceptance that parts of cognitive theory may turn out to be algorithmic, there is scope for the development of a theory that takes the best from each side and finds a new momentum.

To clarify our standpoint, we have introduced the NSMM, which deals both with neurons and symbols, creating the scope for a comprehensive computing theory of cognition where it is clear how the two relate to one another. This relationship can be restated once more – neurons compute the state variables of the computing system on the basis of current state variables and new input. The states or parts of the states are made up of the state variables and are the symbols. The state structures get there through various models of learning and generalization from this learning.

It would be wrong to assert that the NSMM is a fully worked out concept. It is a framework within which there is considerable scope for discovery. For example, the model drives some organism that lives in a world which is not entirely arbitrary and which needs definition. There are many modes of learning and recognizing the role of other similar organisms in the world, and this is largely uncharted territory. Further, there is scope for advancing current theories of attention and thought control. There is scope for developing further the notion of iconic states and the way in which they operate in language understanding and scene analysis. There is scope for developing notions of concept and language acquisition. There is scope for demystifying consciousness and (despite this not having been raised elsewhere in the book) of providing proper models of emotions, their development and their control.

Clearly, much of this is still highly speculative. We have written about a few bones that now may deserve to receive some flesh.

References

Aitkenhead, A.M. and Slack, J.M. (1985) *Issues in Cognitive Modelling*, Lawrence Erlbaum, Hillsdale NJ.

Aleksander, I. (1989) The logic of connectionist systems, in *Neural computing architectures* (ed. I. Aleksander), MIT Press, Boston.

Aleksander, I. (1991) Connectionism or weightless neurocomputing?, in *Artificial neural networks* (eds. T. Kohonen, R. Makinsara, O. Simula and J. Kangas), North-Holland, Amsterdam.

Aleksander, I. and Atlas, P. (1973) Cyclic activity in nature, causes of stability. *Int. J. Neuroscience*, **6**, 45–50.

Aleksander, I. and Fairhurst, M.A. (1970) Pattern learning in humans and digital learning nets. *Electronics Letters*, **6**, 318–19.

Aleksander, I. and Hanna, F.K. (1978) *Automata Theory: an Engineering Approach*, Edward Arnold, London.

Aleksander, I. and Morton, H.B. (1990) *An Introduction to Neural Computing*. Chapman & Hall, London.

Aleksander, I. and Morton, H.B. (1991) A general neural unit: retrievability. *IEE Electronics Letters*, **27**, 1776–8.

Atkinson, R.L. and Shiffrin, R.M. (1968) Human memory: a proposed system of control processes, in *The Psychology of Learning and Motivation: Advances in Research and Theory*, **Vol 2**, (eds. W.K. Spence and J.T. Spence), Academic Press, New York.

Ault, R.L. (1977) *Children's Cognitive Development*, Oxford University Press, New York.

Baddeley, A. (1982) Domains of Recollection. *Psychological Review*, **89**, 708–29.

Ballim, A. and Wilkes, Y. (1991) *Artificial Believers*. Lawrence Erlbaum, Hillsdale NJ.

Bledsoe, W.W. and Browning, I. (1959) Pattern recognition and reading by machine. *Proc. Eastern Joint Computer Conference*.

Boden, M. (1977) *Artificial Intelligence and Natural Man*, Harvester Press, Hassocks, Sussex.

Boden, M. (1981) *Minds and Mechanism*, Cornell University Press, Ithaca.

Boden, M. (1991) Horses of an different color?, in *Philosophy and Connectionist Theory*, (eds. W. Ramsey, S.P. Stichard, D.G. Rumelhart), Lawrence Earlbaum, Hillsdale NJ.

Broadbent, D. (1958) *Perception and Communication*, Pergamon Press, Oxford.

Broadbent, D. (1985) A question of levels: comments on McClelland and Rumelhart. *J. Experimental Psychology: General*, **114**, 189–92.

Buxton, B.F. and Buxton, H. (1983) Monocular depth perception from optical flow by space–time signal processing. *Proceedings of the Royal Society of London*, **B218**, 27–47.

Cherry, E.C. (1953) Some experiments on the recognition of speech with one and with two ears. *J. Acoustical Society of America*, **25**, 975–9.

Chomsky, N. (1957) *Syntactic structures*, Mouton, The Hague.

Clowes, M.B. (1971) On seeing things. *Artifical Intelligence*, **2**, 79–116.

Colby, K.M. (1975) *Artificial Paranoia*, Pergamon Press, Oxford.

Collins, A.M. And Quillian, M.R. (1969) Retrieval time in semantic memory. *J. Verbal Learning and Verbal Behavior*, **8**, 240–7.

Craik, K.J.W. (1943) *The Nature of Explanation*, Cambridge University Press, Cambridge.

Davies, M. (1991) Concepts, connectionism and the language of thought, in *Philosophy and Connectionist Theory* (eds. W. Ramsey, S.P. Stich and D.C. Rumelhart), Lawrence Erlbaum, Hillsdale NJ.

Dennett, D.C. (1991) *Consciousness Explained*, Allen Lane, The Penguin Press, London.

Dreyfus, H. (1972) *What Computers Can't Do: A Critique of Artificial Reason*. Harper & Row, New York.

Elman, J.L. (1990) Finding structure in time. *Cognitive Science*, **14**, 179–211.

Fairhurst, M.C. (1973) The dynamics of learning in some digital networks. *Ph.D. Thesis*, University of Kent at Canterbury.

Fikes, R.E. (1972) Learning and executing generalised robot plans. *Artificial Intelligence*, **3**, 251–88.

Fodor, J.A. (1976) *The Language of Thought*, Harvester Press, Sussex.

Fodor, J.A. (1983) *The Modularity of Mind*, MIT Press, Boston.

Fodor, J.A. and Pylyshyn, Z.W. (1988). Connectionism and cognitive architecture: a critical analysis. *Cognition*, **28**, 3–71.

Gardner, H. (1987) *The Mind's New Science*, Basic Books, New York.

van Gelder, T. (1990) Compositionality: a connectionist variation on a classical theme. *Cognitive Science*, **14**, 355–84.

Gibson, J.J. (1950) *The Perception of the Visual World*, Houghton, Mifflin, Boston.

Goschke, T. and Koppelberg, D. (1991) The concept of representation and the representation of concepts in connectionist models, in *Philosophy and Connectionist Theory* (eds. W. Ramsey, S.P. Stich and D.C. Rumelhart), Lawrence Erlbaum, Hillsdale NJ.

Greene, J. (1986) *Language Understanding: A Cognitive Approach*. Open University Press, Milton Keynes.

Guzman, A. (1968) Decomposition of a scene into three-dimensional bodies. *Proc. Fall Joint Computer Conference*, Thomson Book Company, Washington, pp. 291–304.

Hampson, P.J., Marks, D.E. and Richardson, T.E. (1990) *Imagery – Current Developments*, Routledge, London.

Harnad, S. (1990) The symbol grounding problem. *Physica D*, **42**, 335–46.

Hayes, P.J. (1979) The naive physics manifesto, in *Expert Systems in the Microelectronics Age* (ed. M. Minsky), Edinburgh University Press, Edinburgh.

Hillis, D. *The Connection Machine*, MIT Press, Boston.

Hinton, G.E. and Sejnowski, T.J. (1986) Learning and relearning in Boltzmann machines, in *Parallel Distributed Processing*, (eds. D.C. Rumelhart and J.L. McClelland), MIT Press, Cambridge.

Hopfield, J.J. (1982) Neural networks and physical systems with emergent collective computational abilities. *Proc. National Academy of Science*, **79**, 2554-8.

Hubel, D.H. and Wiesel, T.N. (1959) Receptive fields of single neurons in the cat's striate cortex. *J. Physiology*, **148**, 574-91.

Hubel, D.H. and Wiesel, T.N. (1968) Receptive fields and functional architecture of monkey striate cortex. *J. Physiology*, **195**, 215-43.

Huffmann, D.A. (1954) The synthesis of sequential switching circuits. *J. Franklin Institute*, **257**, 161-90.

Huffmann, D. (1971) Impossible objects as nonsense sentences, in *Machine Intelligence 6* (eds. B. Meltzer and D. Michie), Edinburgh University Press, Edinburgh, pp. 295-325.

Humphreys, G.W. and Bruce, V. (1989) *Visual Cognition: Computional Experimental and Neuropsychological Perspectives*. Lawrence Erlbaum, Hillsdale NJ.

Humphreys, G.W. and Riddoch, M.J. (1987) *To see but not to see: a case study of visual agnosia*, Lawrence Erlbaum, London.

James, W. (1890) *The Principles of Psychology*, Henry Holt, New York.

Johnson-Laird, P.N. (1983) *Mental Models*, Cambridge University Press, Cambridge.

Jordan, M.I. (1986) *Serial order: a parallel distributed processing approach* (Tech. Rep. 8604), University of California Institute for Cognitive Science.

Judd, S. (1990) *The complexity of Neural Networks*, MIT Press, Boston.

Julesz, B. (1965) Texture and visual perception. *Scientific American*, **212** (February), 38-48.

Kauffman, S.A. (1969) Metabolic stability and epigenesis in randomly constructed genetic nets. *J. Theoretical Biology*, **22**, 437-67.

Kelly, G. (1955) *A Theory of Personal Constructs*. Norton, New York.

Kohonen, T. (1989) Speech recognition based on topology-preserving neural maps, in *Neural Computing, Architectures* (ed. I. Aleksander), MIT Press, Boston.

Kosslyn, S., Van Kleek, M.H. and Kirby, K.N. (1990) A neurologically plausible model of individual differences in visual mental imagery, in *Imagery – Current Developments* (eds. P.J. Hampson, D.E. Marks and T.E. Richardson), Routledge, London.

Kowalski, R.A. (1979) *Logic for Problem Solving*, North-Holland, Amsterdam.

Kozato, F. and De Wilde, Ph. (1991) How neural networks help rule-based problem solving. In *Artifical Neural Networks* (eds. T. Kohonen, R. Makisara, O. Simula and J. Gangas), North-Holland, Amsterdam.

Lighthill, J. (1972) *A Report on Artificial Intelligence*, Science Research Council, London.

Longuet-Higgins, H.C. (1981) Artificial intelligence – a new theoretical psychology? *Cognition*, **10**, 197-200.

Ludermir, T. (1990) Automata theoretic aspects of temporal behaviour and computability in logical neural nets. *Ph.D. Thesis*, University of London.

McCulloch, W.S. and Pitts, W. (1943) A logical calculus of the ideas immanent in neural nets. *Bulletin of Mathematical Biophysics*, **5**, 115–33.

McClelland, J.L. and Kawamoto, A.H. (1986) Mechanisms of sentence processing: assigning roles to constituents of sentences, in *Parallel Distributed Processing*, (eds. D.C. Rumelhart and J.L. McClelland), MIT Press, Cambridge.

McClelland, J.L. and Rumelhart, D.E. (1985) Distributed memory and the representation of general and specific information. *J. Experimental Psychology: General*, **114**, (2), 159–88.

Marr, D. (1982) *Vision*, W.H. Freeman, San Francisco.

Marr, D. and Ullman, S. (1981) Directional selectivity and its use in early processing. *Proceedings of the Royal Society of London*, **B211**, 151–80.

Mayhew, J.E.W. and Frisby, J.P.(1984) Computer vision, in *Artificial Intelligence*, (eds. T. O'Shea and M.Eisenstadt), Harper & Row, New York.

Michalski, R.S., Carbonell, J.G. and Mitchell, M. (1980) *Machine Learning, an AI Approach*, Tioga Publishing Co., Palo Alto.

Miller, G.A. (1956) The magic number seven, plus or minus two. *Psychological Review*, **63**, 81–97.

Minsky, M. and Papert, S. (1969) *Perceptrons*, MIT Press, Boston (revised in 1988).

Minsky, M. (1985) *The Society of Mind*, Simon & Shuster, Boston.

Morton, J. (1979) Facilitation in word recognition: experiments causing change in the logogen model, in *Processing Visible Language 1*, (eds. P.A. Kohlers, M.E. Wrolstal and H. Bullman), Plenum, New York.

Newell, A. and Simon, H.A. (1972) *Human Problem Solving*, Prentice-Hall, Englewood Cliffs NJ.

Ntourntoufis, P. (1991) Storage capacity and retrieval properties of an autoassociative general neural unit. *Proc. IJCNN*, Seattle, p. 959.

Paivio, A. (1971) *Imagery and Verbal Processes*, Holt, Reinhart & Winston, New York.

Pinker, S. *Language Learnability and Language Development*, Harvard University Press, Cambridge MA.

Pollack, J.B. (1990) Recursive distributed representations. *Artificial Intelligence*, **46**, 77–105.

Pylyshyn, Z.W. (1979) Imagery theory. *Behavioural and Brain Sciences*, **2**, 561–2.

Pylyshyn, Z.W. (1981) The imagery debate, in *Imagery* (ed.N. Block), MIT/Bradford, Cambridge MA.

Ramsey, W., Stich, S.P. and Garon, J. (1991) Connectionism, eliminativism, and the future of folk psychology, in *Philosophy and Connectionist Theory* (eds. W. Ramsey, S.P. Stich and D.C. Rumelhart), Lawrence Erlbaum, Hillsdale, NJ.

Ramsey, W., Stich, S.P. and Rumelhart, D.C. (eds.) (1991) *Philosophy and Connectionist Theory*, Lawrence Erlbaum, Hillsdale NJ.

Richardson, J.T.E. (1980) *Mental Images and Human Memory*, Macmillan, London.

Rollins, M. (1989) *Mental Imagery: On the Limits of Cognitive Science*, Yale University Press, Boston.

Rosenblatt, F. *The Principles of Neurodynamics*, Spartan, New York.

Rumelhart, D.E. and Kawamoto, A.H. (1986) Mechanisms of sentence processing: assigning roles to the constituents of sentences, in *Parallel Distributed Processing* (eds. D.C. Rumelhart and J.L. McClelland), MIT Press, Cambridge MA.

Rumelhart, D.C and McClelland, J.L. (1985) Levels indeed! A response to Broadbent. *J. Experimental Psychology – General*, **114**, 193–7.

Rumelhart, D.C. and McClelland, J.L. (eds) (1986) *Parallel Distributed Processing*, MIT Press, Cambridge MA.

Rumelhart, D.E. and Norman, D.A. (1983) Representation in Memory. *CHIP Technical Report No. 116*. Center for Human Inter. Proc., San Diego.

Ryle, G. (1949) *Concept of Mind*, Hutchinson, London.

Sacks, O. (1985) *The Man who Mistook his Wife for a Hat*, Summit Books, New York.

Samuel, A.L. (1959) Some studies in machine learning using the game of checkers. *IBM Journal of Research and Development*, **3**, 211–29.

Schank, R.C. and Abelson, R. (1977) *Scripts, Plans, Goals and Understanding*, Lawrence Erlbaum, Hillsdale NJ.

Schneider, W. and Gupta, P. (1991) Attention, automaticity and priority learning, *13th Ann. Mtg. of the Cognitive Society*.

Searle, J. (1969) *Speech Acts*. Cambridge University Press, Cambridge.

Searle, J. (1980) Minds, brains and programs. *The behavioural and brain sciences* **3**, 417–57.

Shannon, C. (1950) Programming a computer for playing chess. *Philosophy Magazine*, **41**, 256–75.

Sharkey, N.E. (1989) A PDP learning approach to natural language understanding, in *Neural Computing Architectures*, (ed. I. Aleksander), MIT Press, Boston.

Shastri, L. and Feldman, J.A. Neural nets, routines and semantic networks, in *Advances in Cognitive Science* (ed. N.E. Sharkey), Ellis Horwood, Chichester.

Shepherd, R.N. and Metzler, J. (1971) Mental rotation of three-dimensional objects. *Science*, **171**, 701–3.

Simon, H.A. (1979) Information processing theory of human problem solving, in *Handbook of Learning and Cognitive Processes*, Vol. 5 (ed. W. Estes), Lawrence Erlbaum, Hillsdale NJ.

Skinner, B.F. (1974) *About Behaviourism*, New York Press, New York.

Smolensky, P. (1988) On the proper treatment of connectionism. *Behavioural and Brain Sciences*, **11**, 1–74.

Touretzky, D.S. (1986) BoltzCONS, reconciling connectionism with the recursive nature of stacks and trees. *Proc. 8th Annual Conf. of the Cognitive Science Society*. Lawrence Erlbaum, Hillsdale NJ.

Touretzky, D.S. (1987) Representing conceptual structures in a neural network. *Proc. IEEE First Annual International Conference on Neural Networks*, San Diego, Ca.

Touretzky, D.S. and Hinton, G.E. (1985) Symbols among neurons: details of a connectionist inference architecture. *Proc. International Joint Conference on Artificial Intelligence*.

Turing, A.M. (1936) On computable numbers with an application to the *Entscheidungs* problem. *Proc. London Mathematical Society*, series 2, **42**, 230–65.

Turing, A.M. (1950) Computing machinery and intelligence. *Mind*, **LIX**, **236**.

Von Neumann, J. (*et al.*) (1947) *Preliminary discussion of the logical design of an electronic computing instrument*. US Army Ordnance Report (1947).

Watson, J.B. (1919) *Psychology from the Standpoint of a Behaviourist*, Philadelphia Press, Philadelphia.

Waltz, D.L. (1975) Understanding line drawings of scenes with shadows, in *The Psychology of Computer Vision* (ed. P. Winston), McGraw-Hill, New York.

Weizenbaum, J. (1976) *Computer Power and Human Reason*, W.H. Freeman.

Wiener, N. (1948) *Cybernetics* or *Control and Communication in the Animal and the Machine*, MIT Press, Cambridge MA.

Winograd, T. (1972) *Understanding Natural Language*, Academic Press, New York.

Winograd, T. (1980) What does it mean to understand language? *Cognitive Science*, **4**, 209–41.

Winograd, T. and Flores, F. (1986) *Understanding Computers and Cognition*, Ablex, Norwood NJ.

Winston, P.H. (1975) *The Psychology of Computer Vision*, McGraw-Hill, New York.

Wittgenstein, L. (1981) *Zettel*, Blackwell, Oxford.

Index